THE SCIENCE OF LIFE

The

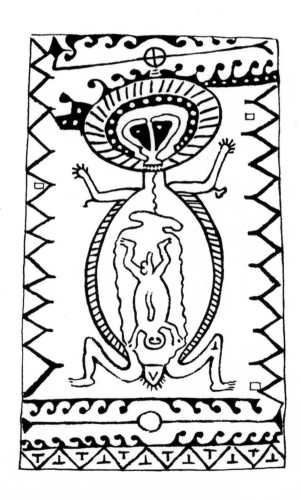

Science of Life

A PICTURE HISTORY OF BIOLOGY

GORDON RATTRAY TAYLOR

336 illustrations in photogravure
16 plates in full colour

THAMES AND HUDSON LONDON

FOR OLGA, WITH LOVE

By the same author
Economics for the Exasperated
Conditions of Happiness
Are Workers Human?
Sex in History
The Angel Makers
Eye on Research
The Biological Time Bomb
Abridgement
The Mothers, by Robert Briffault

© THAMES AND HUDSON LIMITED LONDON 1963
Illustrations printed by DuMont Presse Cologne Germany
Text printed by Ensslin-Druck Reutlingen Germany

PREFACE

It is 'highly dishonourable for a Reasonable Soul to live in so Divinely built a Mansion as the Body she resides in, altogether unacquainted with the exquisite structure of it,' declared Robert Boyle, and the dictum might be extended to cover the question of how that body arose, and thus the whole field of biological science.

Yet, although there are numerous clear and well-illustrated books on the history of the physical sciences, the history of the life sciences has been – as far as the general reader is concerned – almost entirely neglected. Singer's *A History of Biology,* a path-breaking work in its day, drops the story about 1900. Nordenskiöld's 600-page *The History of Biology* is too detailed for the general reader and stops around 1916. Neither pays any attention to the biochemical aspect, which in the present century has proved the most fertile of approaches. Still less do they hint at the development of physical methods in biology, which looks like being the central feature of the second half of this century.

It is to help in filling this gap that I have written the present work. I have taken my cue from Ceram, who described his *Picture History of Archaeology* as 'reality seen through a temperament'. I have attempted to bring out the broad sweep of progress in understanding processes and have ruthlessly omitted those who painstakingly accumulated detailed information without altering the general outlook. Personally, what I find interesting is the process by which knowledge advances. Why, for instance, did the mechanism by which inherited factors are recombined wait for a Mendel, when thousands of plant- and stock-breeders had been making crosses for a century or more? Accordingly, I have tried to spotlight crucial moments of intellectual insight and experimental observation, and to convey what manner of man it was who made the leap.

Nevertheless, though it was not my purpose to attempt completeness, there are omissions which I regret: de Tournefort, Hofmeister, Brown-Séquard are among the names which deserved a place. But strict conditions as to length and the number of pictures were imposed by the publishers. I was also disappointed not to be granted permission by the Librarian of the Royal collection of pictures to reproduce the 'coitus plate' of Leonardo da Vinci. For reasons explained in the text, I regard this plate as of unique importance in revealing the intellectual confusion of the time.

The task of acknowledging all the help I have received in writing the text, and still more, in obtaining the illustrations is really beyond my powers. Sir Hans Krebs wrote an account of his work on the citric acid cycle for me. Lord Middleton provided original sketches by John Ray for reproduction. Many scientists turned out their files to locate forgotten photographs for me. It would be invidious to mention names: the source of each picture is given in an appendix. I am deeply grateful to all of them, as I am to Professor C. H. Waddington, F. R. S., Dr Ian Campbell, Dr J. M. Mitchison, and Dr R. D. Keynes, F. R. S., who read portions of the manuscript, but who are not responsible for any errors that remain.

I also wish to thank the Librarian of the Musée d'Histoire Naturelle in Paris, and its Director, M. Roger Heim; Dr Haeberli and the Burger-bibliothek, Bern; Dr N. Mani and the Öffentliche Bibliothek der Univer-sität Basel; the Librarian of the Royal College of Surgeons and the Curator of the Hunterian Collection; the Librarian of the Linnaean Society in London; the Chief Librarian of the British Museum of Natural History; and, above all, the Librarian of the Wellcome Foundation, without whose co-operation I could hardly have done this book.

Valuable advice was received from the late Mr W. J. Bishop, the medical historian. I am also most grateful to Miss Ruth Rosenberg and Mr Stephen England of Messrs Thames and Hudson's editorial staff, who met my many awkward and time-consuming demands with unfailing patience and enthusiasm.

G. R. T.

London 1962

CONTENTS

*The picture on the title-page is taken from a carved and painted door in Dutch New Guinea,
and shows a primitive conception of the embryo. The placenta can be seen, but the artist's idea of
the umbilical cord is rudimentary.*

The leaves which fall *from this tree into the water become fish; those which fall upon the land become birds.*

THE FOUNDERS

Aristotle, Galen, da Vinci, Vesalius, Gesner

'THERE IS A TREE – not, it is true, common in France, but frequently observed in Scotland,' says a botanical work of 1609. 'From this tree leaves are falling; upon one side they strike the water and slowly turn into fishes, upon the other they strike the land and turn into birds.'

The science of living things, how they are formed and how they function, was not built up by filling a vacuum of ignorance, but by the gradual destruction of false and misleading beliefs, which the people of the Middle Ages regarded as satisfactory explanations. Obviously it was almost impossible to tackle the subtler problems of biology until the most obvious facts of life were recognized. Paracelsus, the great but erratic sixteenth-century doctor who was also one of the last alchemists, believed that it was quite possible to create a human being in the laboratory. He not only believed it, he was prepared to give you the formula, as follows.

'In order to accomplish it, you must proceed thus. Let the semen of a man putrefy by itself in a cucurbite . . . for forty days, or until at last it begins to live, move and be agitated. After this time it will be in some degree like a human being, but, nevertheless, transparent and without body. If now, after this, it be every day nourished and fed cautiously and prudently with the arcanum of human blood, and kept for forty weeks in the perpetual and equal heat of a venter equinus, it becomes, henceforth, a true and living infant, having all the members of a child that is born of a woman, but much smaller. This we call a homunculus; and it should afterwards be educated with the greatest care and zeal until it grows up and begins to display intelligence. Now this is one of the greatest secrets which God has revealed to mortal and fallible man.'

What strikes the modern mind as extraordinary here is not the traditional error of supposing some analogy between fermentation or putrefaction and conception, but the calm way in which Paracelsus announces it all as if it were a well-established fact within his own experience.

One is constantly struck by the similarity between the mediaeval attitude of mind and that found in certain forms of insanity today. There is the same

The Lamb of Tartary, *growing from a plant stalk, as shown by Duret (1605). Until such myths were exploded, no realistic classification of living forms was possible.*

inability to distinguish fantasy from reality, and to apply even the most obvious tests of plausibility. Until this attitude was replaced by a more realistic one, no development of science was possible. It changed in point of fact with the Renaissance. The anatomy of the body began to be accurately observed by surgeons and doctors. And from medicine sprang the sciences of life.

The word 'biology' was not coined until 1802, but if there is a moment at which biology began, it is perhaps in 1615, when William Harvey, the Court physician of Charles I, conceived the heart as a pump, circulating the blood. The idea that the body could be analysed in purely mechanical terms was one of the greatest milestones in man's intellectual history. Until then, life had been a quasi-magical phenomenon, which it was impious to expect to comprehend.

But, two thousand years before, the Greeks had glimpsed this truth, and it is with them that we must begin the story.

The first known dissection of the human body was performed about 500 B.C. by a Greek named Alcmaeon, who described the nerves of the eye, and the tube which runs from the mouth to the ear. Two thousand years later, this tube was rediscovered by Eustachi, a doctor and anatomist in

Rome, and is now called the Eustachian tube. Alcmaeon was also the founder of embryology, for he incubated eggs and studied the developing embryo.

The baked clay tablet seen below shows several sea creatures, and dates from this period. This was perhaps the first attempt at taxonomy, or classification. The Greeks, always insatiably curious, were naturally interested in fish, for they were a maritime people.

In a sense, the father of biology was Hippocrates, 'the father of medicine', for biology arose from medicine. He taught in the first known medical school, and saddled medicine with the theory of the four humours: black and yellow bile, blood, and phlegm. Men were melancholic, choleric, sanguine or phlegmatic according to which preponderated. 'One man's meat is another man's poison' is one of the many sayings which Hippocrates coined. He died in 357 B.C., aged 103.

About this time, the world's first botanist emerged in Theophrastos. He tried to find names for the parts of plants and clearly distinguished the different modes of development of the two kinds of plants – monocotyledons which put forth only a single leaf, and dicotyledons which put forth a pair. Theophrastos had been a pupil of Plato and of Aristotle. His *Enquiry into Plants* describes some 500 varieties.

PEERING INTO THE TRANSLUCENT WATERS of the Mediterranean, about 350 B.C., Aristotle, the former pupil of Plato and teacher of

Four fish and two shells *are shown on this rectangular plate of baked clay, the work of a Greek artist in South Italy in the fourth century* B.C. *This is perhaps one of the first attempts at taxonomy, or classification of living forms. The tablet is now in the Louvre, Paris.*

Alexander, studied the creatures of the sea. Among those he particularly observed were the cuttlefish, the electric eel, and the angler fish. He was especially struck by a shark-like fish, which he dissected to discover how it brought forth its young. Its eggs, he reported, passed into a womb and there were nourished through a navel-string running from a placental disc attached to the wall of the womb.

For 2200 years biologists dismissed this story of a fish which imitated a mammal as a myth or a forgery – until the great nineteenth-century biologist Johannes Mueller discovered that there *are* a few fish of shark character which do precisely this.

Aristotle also described the breeding habits of the catfish, as he observed them in the Greek river Achelous. His description was laughed at, since European catfish do not behave as he described, until in the mid-nineteenth century the Swiss naturalist Louis Agassiz, of Harvard, studying American catfish, found they behaved exactly as Aristotle had said. He therefore checked on the behaviour of the catfish in the River Achelous. They were still breeding in the manner Aristotle had described.

Aristotle was thus certainly one of the greatest working biologists of all time. He distinguished warm-blooded sea-creatures, such as whales, porpoises and dolphins, from the cold-blooded fishes, and some 520 species of animal are described in his surviving works.

The Paper Nautilus *(Argonauta argo) is here depicted using its tentacles as oars and its membrane as a sail, as Aristotle declared it did. The drawing, by the 16th-century naturalist Pierre Belon, is in his book on fishes (1551). The myth persisted to modern times, but actually the nautilus advances by ejecting a jet of water from a nozzle.*

Ironically enough, we do not possess a single word that Aristotle actually wrote. A part survives in translation, and some of what is attributed to him is certainly by other hands. From these fragments, we can see that he attempted to combine all that he himself had learned with data from other observers, and records from the past, into a systematic body of knowledge. These other sources he accepted quite uncritically, describing the crocodile, for instance, in the exact words of Herodotus, and accepting the latter's statement that its upper jaw is jointed in the lower. Elsewhere he says that a lion's bones are so hard they give off sparks when struck, like flints.

His physiology is scarcely removed from the principles of sympathetic magic. A man represents the warmer, more active element, a woman the colder, more passive element. Hence a cold north wind will favour the birth of girls.

On similar lines, Aristotle attempted to construct a comprehensive theoretical account of the functioning of living things. It contains many remarkable insights, and many grotesque errors. Owing to the veneration with which his works came to be regarded in the Middle Ages – at Oxford any don who taught other than according to Aristotle was subject to a fine – his views ultimately held up the growth of biological thought.

. His most useful contribution was to see that living forms could be arranged in a 'Ladder of Nature' which passed from inanimate matter through plants and crustaceans, egg-bearing creatures (reptiles, birds, fishes and amphibians) and mammals to man. This was the first statement of an idea which, in the eighteenth century, was to pave the way for the modern theory of evolution. Aristotle, indeed, enunciated a complete, though dogmatic, theory of the evolution of lower to higher forms, under the guidance of divine intelligence.

His most harmful contribution was his theory of the three souls, which not only dominated the biology of the Middle Ages, but was widely accepted in the sixteenth century. Seeing that plants can grow and reproduce, whereas animals can move and feel in addition, he postulated a 'vegetative soul' for plants, while animals also had an 'animal soul'. Man, who could think, had a 'rational soul' besides. By 'soul' he seems to have meant some miraculous animating principle: it was explaining the unknown by the still more unknown.

All this he dovetailed into an elaborate philosophical and cosmological theory of the universe: never before or since has so comprehensive an intellectual structure been attempted.

GALEN THE BRILLIANT was the last great biologist of antiquity, and his teachings, right and wrong, acquired almost divine force for the next 1500 years. Even today an aura hangs about him, and historians tend to underplay his unscientific thinking and ill-tempered polemics, and to emphasize his undoubtedly remarkable achievements.

The story goes that, discovering a skeleton one day, he was seized with the idea that living organisms were perfectly designed by an all-wise Creator.

Certainly, he took from Aristotle and Plato the idea of a divine intelligence revealed in nature, which was final and perfect. He scornfully denied the teaching of Epicurus and his pupil Asclepiades that organs develop with use and weaken with disuse – if that were so, he fatuously said, busy men would have four arms and lazy men but one. If it is asked why men do not have large ears, better adapted for hearing, like a donkey, it is because this would prevent them wearing hats.

Galen also made hysterical attacks on the atomic theory of Epicurus. His violent irascibility came, presumably, from his mother, who (he recalled) 'was constantly shouting at my father and quarrelling with him,' and who was so ill-tempered that she would sometimes bite the maids. Galen's name, which means calm or serene, must have been given him hopefully.

He was the son of an architect, who left him financially independent. It had been revealed to his father in a dream that Galen would become a doctor, and he accordingly studied for this profession.

At the age of 33 he emigrated from Pergamon to Rome, where within three years he became a highly successful doctor, and was before long appointed to be personal physician to the emperor. Before his death, he revisited his home town, and there wrote two autobiographies.

Galen's first job was that of doctor to the gladiators at Pergamon, north of Smyrna, in what is now Turkey. He noticed that an injury to the spine paralysed all parts of the body below that point, and realized that the muscles must therefore be controlled by the nerves running up the spinal canal. Dissecting a pig, he cut by chance the recurrent laryngeal nerve, and at once the pig, which had been squealing like murder, became silent, though continuing to struggle. Thus he proved that nerves control muscles. This famous experiment is depicted on the title page of the great Renaissance edition of his works, published in Venice in 1541, together with other famous experiments of his.

It was in fact in the field of neurophysiology that Galen made his most valuable contribution. The realization that the brain controlled the muscles was a big step forward – for Aristotle had concluded that the seat of intelligence lay in the chest, from which the voice comes. Galen described about 300 muscles, and showed that each muscle contracted in only one direction, causing only one kind of movement–contrary to previous belief. He showed that the nerves led to them, and supposed that they conveyed a 'force of contraction' to them.

Galen's conception of the circulatory system was wrong both anatomically and physiologically, and held up the progress of physiology for centuries.

His anatomical errors were mainly two: first, he thought the air passed from the lungs into the heart, where it met the blood, picked up impurities, and passed back to the lungs and out again. The lungs were merely bellows.

Second, he supposed the arterial and venous systems were distinct, and that the blood slowly ebbed and flowed in them like the tide.

He understood that the air must contain something needed by the body, and that the blood must pick it up. He guessed that this something was pneuma, or spirit, derived from the World Spirit. Pneuma, it was held, manifested in three forms: natural spirit, vital spirit, and animal spirit. Galen thought it was vital spirit which the air conveyed and which somehow purified the blood, restoring its crimson colour. (If for vital spirit we substitute oxygen, we see that he had an inkling of the truth.) Natural spirit, Galen thought, came from the food (here we should have to substitute energy) and reached the blood via the liver. Finally, when the blood reached the brain, it became charged with animal spirit (which we can equate with the electrical energy of nerve-impulses) which the nerves then distributed to the body. Galen made various attempts to detect the resulting concoction, without success.

Galen's picture failed to explain how the purified blood got into the body, so he postulated that blood passed from the right to the left heart by pores in the wall between them. No one could ever see the pores, which were presumed to be submicroscopic in size. It was 1500 years before anyone had the courage to deny that they existed. However, he did dispose of the idea that the arteries contain air.

Galen's experiment *on the pig, proving that nerves control muscles, is fancifully shown in this detail from the titlepage of the 1541 edition of his works. This was a long step forward, and could be called the birth of neurophysiology.*

A symbolic quartet *played by Aristotle, Galen, Plato and Hippocrates; mediaeval teachers thus represented the supposed harmony between their views. In reality, their teachings were often diametrically opposed.*

Strawberry plant, from a French herbal of about A.D. *550. The leaves are wrongly shown in groups of four and five, instead of in threes, and the 'runners' are too numerous, but it is a strawberry clearly enough.*

Galen's literary output was fantastic in quantity. By his own count, he wrote 256 treatises. The bulk perished in a fire in A.D. 192. Their strongly religious tone commended them to mediaeval theologians; moreover, Galen was a monotheist and spoke favourably of Christianity. He had even read some of the books of the Bible. It finally came to be believed that he had been converted to Christianity.

Galen's work (as he complained) was not much regarded in his own time: his religious bias and moralistic outpourings must have seemed unscientific to the older school, while his researches had no interest for the majority who were moving steadily towards mysticism. This injustice was more than rectified by posterity.

NOBODY HAS EVER explained satisfactorily why the outward-looking attitude of the Greeks was replaced by the inward-looking attitude of the whole area dominated by the Christian church. The Greeks were interested in what was new; in the millennium which we call the Dark Ages and the Middle Ages, men uncritically accepted what authority declared.

How uncritically, is shown by the two pages from herbals above. Both depict the strawberry. The first was drawn about A.D. 550, the second five hundred years later. It is obviously a copy of a copy of a copy. The 'runners' are now shown as thorns, and the plant is confused with the blackberry. Yet

Strawberry plant, *from a Rhenish herbal of about five centuries later. Evidently, the same drawing many times recopied. In the course of 500 years the 'runners' have become confused with thorns, and the plant looks more like a blackberry.*

the strawberry plant must have been well known to the very men who made these copies.

In like manner, the views of Galen, Aristotle, and even Pliny were copied and handed down, with increasing inaccuracy, as if divinely inspired, and without the slightest attempt to check them with the facts. Biology ceased to exist. Truth lay in books, and what was not in books was not knowledge. All problems could be solved by deduction from first principles. With this went an amazing credulity. Geese born from a tree, a lamb growing on a plant . . . Surely someone might have queried such reports? Even the vaguest knowledge of anatomy would suggest that men whose heads grew beneath their shoulders would present physiological difficulties.

The problems of biology were all solved. The origin of the species was accounted for by the Creation; Galen had explained physiology. The only problems were in embryology, where it was a matter of dispute at what point the soul entered the embryo. Aristotle was for the fifth day after conception but mediaevalists were for the third.

The principles of sympathetic magic were revived in the doctrine of signa-tures, which received its fullest statement as late as 1529, at the hands of the hyper-thyroid Paracelsus, the Luther of medicine, who should have known better. God has placed a mark on every plant to show the purpose for which

19

Herba luna   mandragora

The mandrake must not be touched *by human hand.*
Because it somewhat resembled the human form, it was
thought to be a medicine for all ills, on principles of
sympathetic magic. It was believed to shine in the dark,
and to shriek when plucked. Actually the mandrake is a
narcotic and an emetic.

he created it. A heart-shaped leaf is good for heart diseases, a leaf spotted
like the liver is good for liver complaints – which is why the liverwort
still bears this name.

The mandrake, which is forked and therefore looks like a man, is good
for all human ailments. At night it shines like a lamp. It must not be
touched: you must dig it up with an ivory spade, tie a rope to it, and tie the
free end to a hungry dog. Then offer the dog meat so that he pulls it up,
trying to get the meat.

A great trade in counterfeited mandrake developed, as Turner complained in his *Herball* in 1551. 'The rootes which are conterfited and made
like little puppettes and mammettes, which come to be sold in England in
boxes, with heir and such forme as a man hath, are nothyng else but folishe
feined trifles, and not naturall. For they are so trymmed of crafty theves to
mocke the poore people with all, and to rob them both of theyr wit and
theyr money.' He adds that the mandrake roots he has himself dug up do
not look like men at all.

At least twelve *distinct species of plant and flower can be identified in this detail from Botticelli's great painting 'Spring', executed in 1478. In the whole canvas, there are more than thirty varieties. This accurate observation of the world of nature, which came in with the Renaissance, was a precondition for the emergence of biology.*

SUDDENLY, a miracle occurred. Men began to look outwards again. It began in Italy. Botticelli's great canvas 'Spring' – painted in 1478 – contains at least thirty species of flowers, each quite recognizable. In painting thus he was turning aside from the manner of his master, Fra Lippo Lippi, who had died nine years before, and whose style is far less naturalistic.

Another man who observed the world minutely, and drew it accurately, was Leonardo da Vinci; he drew plants beautifully, and dissected more than thirty human bodies in order to improve his rendering of its form. This led him to an interest in anatomy: to resolve its mysteries he turned to comparative anatomy. His brilliant observations, which would certainly have advanced medicine and biology, were never published, and he was denounced by the Pope for his dissections. Dissection, long forbidden by the Church, was, however, gradually becoming re-established as a form of medical training, and in some cases was permitted under licence.

If Leonardo da Vinci had written up and published his notes, biology might have emerged from the dark ages about a century before it did. Most of what this remarkable man discovered was not revealed until the present century, when his notes were first published.

One of his anatomical drawings exhibits the best and the worst of his achievement. Brilliantly drawn, in its exact depiction of the mechanics of coitus it reveals Leonardo's training as an engineer, and his interest in the 'go' of things. But it shows, too, a second urethral canal, leading into the penis from the spine, by which the soul was supposed to be infused into the embryo. And in the woman, the epigastric vein is shown taking the menstrual blood to the breasts, where it is to form milk. The corrugations of the uterus reflect the odd mediaeval idea that it was divided into seven cells, for the seven days of creation. The diaphragm, Leonardo observes, repeating another mediaeval insight, serves to divide the spiritual parts of the body (meaning the heart, lungs etc.) from the material parts (meaning the stomach and intestines). Thus were the divine order and fitness demonstrated.

In making this drawing Leonardo was attempting to reconcile the teaching of Galen with the more accurate observation of the great Arab physician Avicenna. His comment on it is beautifully equivocal: 'I display to men the origin of their second – first, or perhaps second – cause of existence.'

Leonardo's anatomical drawings were at least a century ahead of their time, according to the great historian of biology, Charles Singer. His original interest in anatomy was to improve his painting of the human body, but he soon developed it further, and made acute comparative studies, such as that opposite. Here Leonardo shows that the hock of a horse is homologous not with the knee of a man, but with his ankle. The homologue to the human knee is the horse's stifle joint. The realization that parts which are analogous are not necessarily homologous (developed from biologically similar structures) arose again in the nineteenth century, nearly four hundred years later.

One of the earliest known illustrations of a dissection (early 14th century). Kidneys, heart, lungs and stomach (to very different scales) have been removed, and the dissector, knife in one hand and the liver in the other, is being rebuked by a physician.

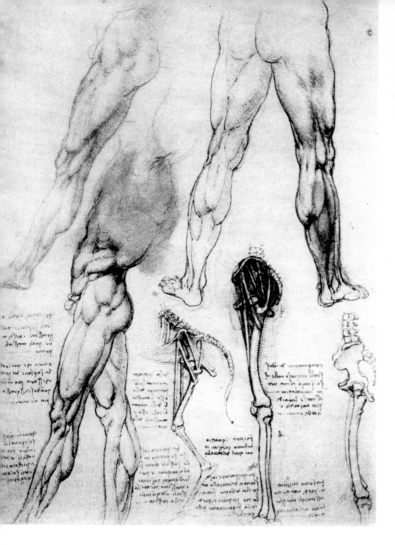

Leonardo's knowledge of anatomy, *gained through his own dissections, led him on to make acute comparative studies. Here he shows that a horse's hock is biologically similar not to the human knee but to the ankle.*

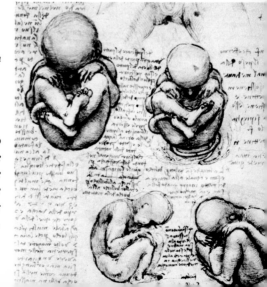

Leonardo's notebooks, *had they been written up and published, might have led biology out of the dark ages a century earlier. These sketches of the human foetus show the minuteness of the anatomist's observation as well as the artist's joy in pure form.*

IN 1542 A TRAIN OF MULES crossed the Alps to Basle carrying the blocks of a work which was to divide the study of anatomy into two epochs. With it went the author of the text, a 27-year-old Belgian named Vesalius. The illustrations by his friend Calcar, a pupil of Titian's, were so vivid that many thought that Titian himself must have cut them.

The work was the *De Humani Corporis Fabrica*; since its publication anatomy has been divided into the pre-Vesalian, the Vesalian and the post-Vesalian periods. Its author never produced anything comparable again.

Vesalius's father, grandfather and great-grandfather had been eminent in medicine. When he was a boy, no animal was safe from him: he dissected dogs, cats and rats. At Paris, he studied under Sylvius, a highly orthodox exponent of Galen, who asserted not only that Galen was infallible, but that any progress beyond him was impossible.

In vivid poses Vesalius depicted, in plates etched by Calcar, the knowledge gained in his dissections. Five years' work went into the 300 plates, which showed the nerves, veins and arteries as well as the muscles, skeleton and internal organs and the structure of the brain. These anatomical illustrations have never been surpassed; they ended many ancient errors.

Vesalius took his degree at Padua, doing so brilliantly that he was appointed professor the following day. He at once swept away the traditional system whereby a hired demonstrator did the dissection while the professor read his lecture. Under this system errors passed unnoticed by the professor, for if the demonstrator failed to show the organs he described, it was assumed simply that he was a bad demonstrator. Vesalius carried out all dissections himself, amid the applause of large numbers of enthusiastic students and doctors. He had already started work on an atlas of the body, for which Calcar did six plates. It was orthodox, showing the veins arising from the liver, as Galen had said, and the liver itself divided into five lobes. But it sold, and aroused the interest of a Swiss publishing house.

Vesalius saw his chance. His friend Calcar prepared 300 plates under his guidance, in five years of unremitting work. They were plates such as the world had never seen, sowhing the human body reconstituted in living

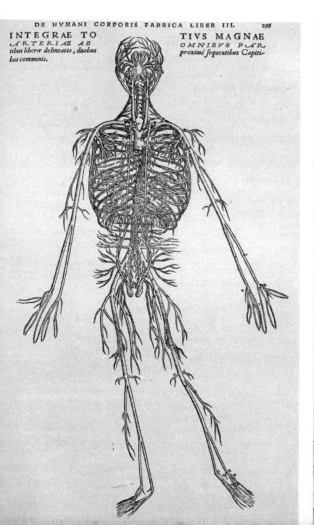

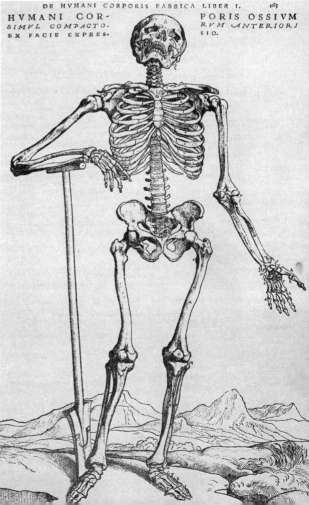

poses from the information Vesalius had gained. The venous system, the nerves, the muscles, the bones, the brain, all were displayed in plates of matchless beauty, accuracy and clarity. Uniquely, he succeeded in depicting the muscles, not stiffened in death, but with the normal degree of tone, as if seen through a transparent skin in a living body. Naturalists still learn from these superb pictures, even though they were drawn 400 years ago.

For the text, Vesalius provided no sober, pedantic catalogue but a verna͵ cular account which dealt with Galenical and other superstitions with violent scorn. Its publication caused a storm of fury. Vesalius showed that men have equal numbers of ribs, to the anger of the Church which claimed that, as God had taken one to make Eve, the number must be uneven. The doctors were equally annoyed. When Vesalius showed the thigh bone as straight, and not curved as Galen had taught, his old teacher Sylvius de͵ clared that the human body must have undergone changes since the time of Galen – no doubt the straight thigh bones were the result of the current absurd habit of wearing narrow trousers. Sylvius dismissed the whole work as 'a most verbose and false hodge͵podge', and those who praised it as 'two͵legged asses'.

Vesalius dealt firmly with the pores connecting, as Galen claimed, the right and left heart, saying that none of the pits in the dividing wall 'so far as the senses can perceive, penetrate from the right to the left ventricle. We wonder at the art of the Creator which causes blood to pass from right to left ventricle through invisible pores . . . Not long ago I would not have dared to turn aside even a hair's breadth from Galen. But it seems to me that the septum of the heart is as thick, dense and compact as the rest of the heart. I do not see, therefore, how even the smallest particle can be transferred from the right to the left ventricle through the septum.'

It was widely believed that the body contained an indestructible bone, which formed the nucleus on which, at the resurrection, a new body would be formed. Vesalius merely remarked that he would leave its existence to the theologians to prove, as it was not a matter of anatomy.

But the pressure brought against him finally became too great. In despair, he threw up his professorship and soon after took on the post of medical adviser to Charles V and to his armies, and later to Philip II. He wrote from Spain: 'I still live in hope that some time or other, by some good fortune I may once more be able to study that true Bible, as we count it, of the human body and of the nature of man.' His hope was not fulfilled: after twenty years of unproductive frustration, he died, aged 50, on the isle of Zante.

Vesalius prepared this skeleton (left) by request, when visiting Basle in 1546, and it is still at the University – the oldest biological preparation made with a scientific motive still in existence.

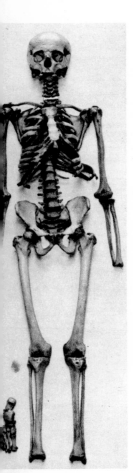

Still preserved at Basle University: skeleton presented by Vesalius in 1546.

Students climb the pillars *to see the young Belgian professor, Andreas Vesalius, dissect a human body in the anatomy theatre at Padua University — as depicted on the title page of the first edition of his great anatomical work 'De humani corporis fabrica', published in 1543. His arms — three weasels — are overhead.*

The first man *to introduce precise measurement into the study of physiological processes was the 17th-century Italian doctor Santorio Santorio, who studied the change in his weight before and after eating. He was in close touch with Galileo and Fabrizzi, his colleagues at the University of Padua.*

WEIGHING HIMSELF, before, during and after eating, Santorio Santorio, professor of medicine at Padua, found in the early years of the seventeenth century that the weight of his excreta was less than that of his food. He correctly inferred that he must be giving off matter in gaseous form, or, as he put it, as 'insensible perspiration'. He also weighed himself similarly after a variety of other activities.

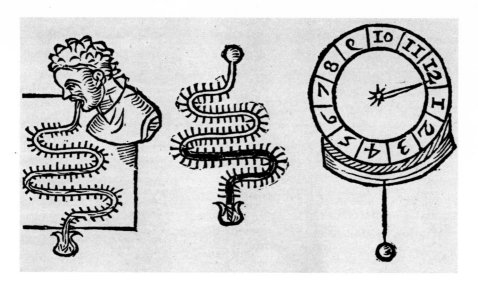

The first illustration *of a mouth thermometer appears in a book published in 1625 by the Italian doctor Santorio Santorio, but not until 1856 did anyone use it to draw a fever chart. The centre picture shows a thermometer, the bulb of which was held in the hand. On the right, a metronome-like device for taking the pulse.*

These were the first scientific studies in what today would be called 'basal metabolism'. They had little effect at the time, and it was not until about 1863–4 that metabolic studies were resumed, while 'insensible perspiration' was not studied again until 1926.

Santorio is famous as the first man to introduce instruments for precise measurement into medicine: he invented a device for taking the pulse rate by comparing it with a pendulum, and conceived the medical thermometer. Galileo had invented the alcohol-filled thermometer, but thought it was only a toy; Santorio saw its value for measuring fevers. These physiological instruments, too, were long neglected.

The word 'physiology' was first used in something like its modern sense in 1554, when the French doctor, Jean Fernel, republished an earlier book on the body in health as opposed to the body in illness, which he had originally called *On the Natural Part of Medicine*, under the title *Physiologia*. Previously it had meant the 'go' of nature in all its aspects, not simply in the biological. Fernel, a phenomenally successful doctor, who treated Diane de Poitiers, and was credited with having cured Catherine de'Medici's sterility, made a number of useful minor discoveries: notably that a man standing on his head can swallow food, a fact not rediscovered until the nineteenth century.

29

VIRTUALLY THE FIRST illustrated embryological work was prepared by Fabrizzi (known as 'of Aquapendente' to distinguish him from a German anatomist of the same period), and published in 1600. The drawings below (taken from another of his works) illustrate the development of the chick – not very accurately, but they are the first pictures ever made of the sequence of development. Fabrizzi has consequently been termed the 'father of embryology', but his text is more mediaeval than Renaissance, and debates such issues as how the contents of the egg got inside the shell.

Fabrizzi was a pupil of the great Fallopio, inventor of the condom and discoverer of the Fallopian tubes. Another of Fallopio's pupils was 'Coiter the Friesian', as he liked to call himself; he too gave a remarkable account of the development of the hen's egg – the first since Aristotle, save for some observations by Albertus Magnus – and also studied the development of the pig. But the field in which he is most remembered is that of comparative

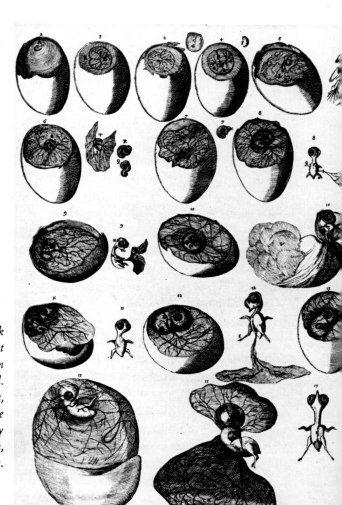

The first illustrations of the development of the chick and other creatures were made by the Italian anatomist Fabrizzi, and appeared in 1621. They were etched on copper plates in place of the woodcuts then usual. Fabrizzi, on becoming professor of anatomy at Padua, built an anatomy theatre at his own expense and made the school of anatomy outstanding. To it came many foreigners, including a young Englishman, William Harvey.

anatomy, on which he wrote the first books, describing a wide range of animal skeletons.

Soon after this, that extraordinary character, Sir Kenelm Digby, raised some of the basic issues of embryology, and started a controversy which lasted throughout the following century. He describes how Sir John Hey-don, Lieutenant of H. M. Ordnance, 'a generous and knowing gentleman', showed him how to incubate eggs, so that one could observe the develop-ment by breaking one open every hour. He describes the sequence very accurately, noting that the heart is formed first: its mode of working 'appears in the twinckling of the first red spot (which is the first change) in the egge.'

The question Digby raised was: is the adult contained with all its parts pre-formed in the egg, or is it put together from raw materials? These two doctrines are known, respectively, as preformation and epigenesis. Digby comes down firmly for epigenesis. Furthermore, he moves away from the mediaeval idea that some magical spirit animates development, and proposes to regard it as a physico-chemical process determined by its own nature. A bean, he argues, put in water, cannot choose but swell; swelling, it cannot help putting forth a root, and so on through the whole sequence. It is a strikingly modern view, and Digby has not received his due from historians.

His book, *Bodies and Souls,* evoked several replies, notably from Sir Nathaniel Highnore, who did not differ from him on the main issues, but put forward an atomistic theory which we shall find being taken up later by better-known writers, such as Buffon. The testicles, he claims, abstract 'spiritual atoms' from the blood, from which the embryo is created, by a process which he outlines in some splendid seventeenth-century prose: the atoms 'being in this Athanor cohabited and reposited into a tenacious matter, at last passe through infinite Meanders through certain vessels, in which it undergoes another digestion and pelicanising.'

Digby, still more brilliantly, struck at the semantic confusions of the me-diaeval attempt to explain everything by qualities and faculties. To explain the soporific character of a drug by its 'dormitive virtue' and the movement of the heart by its 'sphygmic quality' was, he said, 'the last refuge of ignorant men, who not knowing what to say, and yet presuming to say something, do often fall upon such expressions.'

The father of chemical embryology was Sir Thomas Browne, too often thought of only as a literary-minded doctor. His commonplace book, not published until 1836, reveals how in his 'elaboratory' near Norwich he treated eggs with oil, vinegar and other fluids to see what would happen. Remembering, no doubt, mediaeval ideas of the embryo being formed by a process analogous to cheese-making, he beat up rennet with white of eggs, and noted that it 'seems to perform nothing'.

31

The cheese theory, originally put forward by Aristotle, is recalled by the plate below, which illustrates the soul entering the womb, by a tube lowered from a divine rectangle (symbolic of permanence and solidity). The ten figures standing round hold vessels containing cheeses of various consistencies, which the text compares with the formation of different kinds of men, some soft and foolish, others hard and obdurate. It comes from the works of a strange abbess, 'St' Hildegard of Bingen, who wrote a series of extraordinary treatises, in which theology, mysticism, science and philosophy are combined in a curious medley. She died in 1179.

Aristotle's theory *that the formation of the embryo is similar to the curdling of milk into cheese is recalled in this picture from a 12th-century treatise. Ten figures holding cheeses watch a woman in labour, while the divine sperm descends, from a square symbolizing permanence, through a tube into her womb.*

COPIED AND RECOPIED from Greek and Latin originals – such as the list which Nero's army medico Dioscorides had drawn up – the herbals of the fifteenth century, even when the pictures were recognizable, had little relevance to the plants of northern Europe. Otto Brunfels, a Carthusian monk, decided to make a herbal of his own, and travelled up the Rhine observing the plants which actually existed.

The idea was almost impious. God had created certain species to people the earth, and so 'Dioscorides should serve as well at Wittenberg as Euclid'. If there were plants which did not seem to fit, they must be freaks.

By 1475, we find a book depicting for the first time such characteristically northern plants as the lily of the valley and ragged robin. By 1542, we find a really good illustrated herbal, in which the geographical range of each plant is indicated – that of Fuchs, one of the most remarkable of early botanists, for whom the Fuchsias are named.

PAPAVER.
Magfomen.

But by the sixteenth century, people were demanding more than alphabetical lists. New plants were pouring in from the explorers of the New World and the East: tobacco and maize, tea and rubber, chocolate and coffee, the potato and the tomato, quinine and cocaine, indigo and cotton. Enchanting new flowers – dahlia and zinnia, nasturtium and phlox – were arriving as cuttings, as seeds, as dried specimens, as living shrubs. What was wanted was a book in which each new specimen could be looked up and related to its European cousins – in short, what we now call a Flora.

Cordus was, perhaps, the first man to try to devise a classificatory system based on botanic principles. He died at 29, having accomplished an amazing amount, and has been unduly neglected by historians. He observed the nodules on plant-roots, which, as we now know, contain the bacteria which provide the plant with nitrogen. He discovered that ferns reproduce 'by means of the dust that is developed on the back of the leaves'.

Poppy *from the Herbal of Otto Brunfels (1530): realism and careful observation take the place of the unrecognizable mediaeval herbals.*

L'Obel, for whom the Lobelia is named, tried to classify by the shape of the leaf – in contrast to previous writers who classified simply by habit, distinguishing bushes from flowers, and trees from bushes. Cesalpino tried to derive principles of classification from the flower, though he did not realize that these were the sexual organs of plants. His *De Plantis* (1583) marks the divorce of botany from agriculture.

The one real achievement of this period, however, was the binomial (two-named) system of Bauhin, a Swiss doctor. This method of naming plants is still the basis of plant-naming today. The first name indicates the plant family or genus (pl. genera) to which the plant in question belongs. The second, or trivial name, distinguishes the various members of the family, i.e. the species. A similar system is also applied to animals: thus the lion is

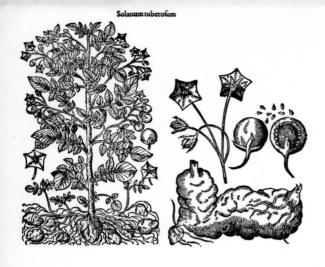

'Solanum tuberosum': *with two words only,
Bauhin captioned his picture of the potato plant in 1619.
The same two words still suffice for its botanical name.*

Felis leo, being a member of the cat family *Felidae,* and the tiger is *Felis tigris.*
Until the nineteenth century, species were thought to be fixed and definite,
created by God. Genera are grouped in families, families in orders, orders
in classes, classes in phyla or divisions. Thus vertebrates form a phylum,
mammals a class.

   Though Bauhin did not clearly grasp the distinction between genus and
species, he classified on the basis of natural similarity of form, in contrast
to Cesalpino's and L'Obel's more formal systems. Not until evolution was
understood could a fully rational natural classification emerge, and matters
rested in this impasse for another century.

   CONRAD GESNER, a myopic Swiss of vast learning, attempted to describe all known animals in his five-volume *Historia Animalium.* Where
the animals were well-known, like the greyhound, they are well represented;
those unfamiliar, like the camel, less well. He also included creatures he had
heard existed, like the basilisk. His representation of the whale was naturally

Modern zoology began *with Conrad Gesner,*
whose 'Historia Animalium' in five folio volumes was
published in Zurich between 1551 and 1587.
Though many of his pictures, such as the greyhounds
below, were well observed, some were fanciful,
depending on hearsay (the camel opposite),
and some, like the seven-headed monster above, the
crudest fables.

fanciful, but he laboured to obtain accurate pictures, and declared that his picture of the rhinoceros, an animal few Europeans had seen, was done by Dürer, no less. He was in correspondence with others who were specializing, like Moufet who wrote the first comprehensive account of insects, and Rondelet, who specialized in sea creatures. Rondelet's picture of a dissected sea-urchin is the first known dissection of an invertebrate.

An ill-paid doctor, Gesner wore himself out by hackwork, compiling dictionaries and publishing commentaries on classical authors. He was the first great encyclopaedist of zoology, as Brunfels, of Mainz, was the first of botany.

PLACING A HUMAN AND A BIRD SKELETON on the same page, and assigning the same letter to corresponding parts, Pierre Belon, a French naturalist (he introduced the cedar to France) laid the foundation stone of comparative anatomy, just about the same date as Gesner. This was a bold departure, for man was still regarded by the religious authorities as a different order of being from animals. Three hundred years passed before this view was firmly established.

Belon's friends made up a purse so that he might travel through Greece, Turkey, Syria and Egypt. He returned home with copious notes for his *Histoire des Oyseaux,* only to be killed by a thief while gathering herbs at night in the Bois de Boulogne, near Paris.

Comparative anatomy first appears *in the work of Pierre Belon (1517–1564). He compared skeletons of a man and a bird, indicating corresponding parts by corresponding letters – a bold departure in an age when the Church still regarded man as a different order of being from the animals.*

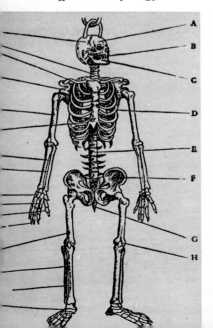
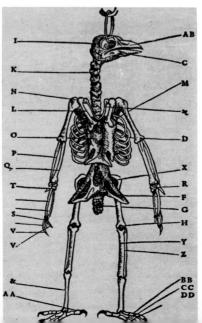

From the old physic gardens *came the great botanical collections such as that of Montpellier, near Paris. The famous Jardin des Plantes, in Paris, was founded in 1626.*

THE BOTANIC GARDEN at the great medical centre of Montpellier was started in 1593. There had been one at Padua from 1545; Pisa and Bologna followed, then Leyden and Leipzig. These started as physic gardens – collections of medicinal herbs – but gradually became botanical collections. Magnol, for whom the Magnolia was named, was an early director of the garden at Montpellier, and proposed, in the last decade of the seventeenth century, that plants should be grouped by families.

Padua was the earliest *of the botanic gardens of Europe, a centre for scientific collection, observation and classification.*

The Oxford Physic Garden was founded in 1621, and the Jardin des Plantes at Paris in 1626. The first gardener at Oxford was the patriarchal Bobart, who tagged his luxuriant beard with silver on feast days. This beard was the centre of a curious incident. A certain Mark Coleman, 'a melancholy, distracted man', who was a singer at Christ Church, one day, while walking in the physic garden, 'suddenly ran up to Bobart and caught hold of his beard, crying, "Help! Help!" upon which people coming in and enquiring of the outcrie, Coleman made reply that "Bobart hath eaten his horse and his tayle hung out of his mouth."'

The first gardener *at the Oxford Physic Garden (founded in 1621) was Bobart. His pet goat followed him at work – an inconvenient pet for a gardener, one would have thought.*

It was, in fine, a period of observation and classification. Men were looking about them once more and seeing what the world really contained. Until they had done so, effective generalization was impossible. Santorio stands almost alone in employing experimental methods to arrive at numerical measurements, as a means of investigating the workings of the body.

Actually, before such workings could be understood, a much more detailed understanding of anatomy was needed, and for this the microscope was invented at almost exactly the moment when Harvey took the first great step towards explaining the working of the body (although, ironically enough, Harvey himself never made use of the microscope). Together, these two events opened a new era in science.

2

THE ANATOMISTS

'THE MOVEMENTS OF THE HEART are known to God alone,' said Fracastoro, after Vesalius had destroyed the Galenic theory by showing that the supposed holes in the septum did not exist. It was the general opinion.

How did an Englishman, unsupported by a strong medical tradition and without important predecessors, solve the problem, and make the most significant contribution in a thousand years? It is now known that Harvey had arrived at a solution as early as 1615, when he was appointed Professor at the College of Physicians, for his lecture notes are still extant. But he dared not publish so radical a discovery, and it was not until 1628, when he was physician-in-ordinary to Charles 1, that he scribbled his *Exercitatio anatomica de motu cordis* and sent it off to Frankfort for publication. Even then his practice declined mightily, as he told Aubrey, and it was believed by the vulgar that he was crack-brained. Fortunately, it revived: Hobbes said he was perhaps the only man who had lived to see his teaching established in his own lifetime.

The method which Harvey employed was as important as the discovery itself. He applied the new teaching of Galileo to making a calculation of what the heart was achieving. He estimated the amount of blood ejected on each contraction as 2 fluid ounces. Beating 72 times a minute, the heart must therefore pump 8,640 fluid ounces, or three times the weight of the entire body, in an hour. This made Galen's notion of the continuous production of blood and its slow seeping into the tissues untenable. A relatively rapid circulation was the only reasonable explanation. This kind of reasoning was quite new.

By the experiment shown overleaf, Harvey proved that blood moves to the heart in some vessels, away from it in others, thus confirming his idea of a circulation. The valves had long been known, but the fact that some were disposed in one sense, the rest in the opposite sense, had not been realized.

The idea of a circulation was not wholly new. In a theological work published 75 years earlier, Servetus had thrown off the idea that the blood is

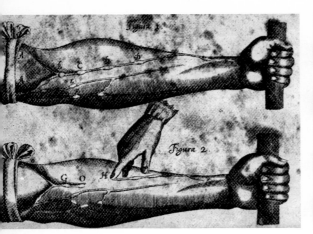
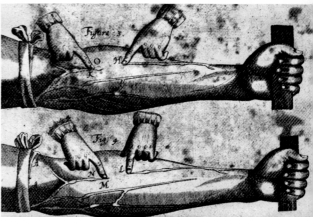

By this experiment Harvey proved the circulation of the blood, showing that in some vessels the blood moves towards the heart, in others away from it. The pressure of a fingertip demonstrates the valves, and proves that some are disposed in one direction, some in the other.

circulated through the lungs. Cesalpino had realized that venous blood moves towards the heart, but still thought of the movement of the blood as a gentle irrigation. Da Vinci had even made glass models of the heart, to study the blood flow through it, but this work lay unpublished.

Harvey's originality lay in substituting logical argument, based on measurement, for general speculation. His achievement was to establish the body as a machine, functioning by the same laws that applied to inanimate objects, instead of appealing to quasi-magical vitalistic forces. However, he remained completely puzzled about the origin of the blood and dissected eggs to observe when the blood-vessels appeared. 'What artificer,' he asked, 'can transform the two liquors [meaning, the yolk and white of the egg] into blood, when there is yet no liver in being?' It was to be another 200 years before Wolff demonstrated the blood-islets where the blood is formed, by a process the chemistry of which is still obscure.

Harvey devoted much effort to the problem of embryology, as we shall see in a later section. He also dissected more than 80 different species of animal at one time or another. What kind of man was he?

Harvey was described as 'not tall; but of the lowest stature, round faced, olivaster complexion; little eie, round, very black, full of spirit; his haire was black as a raven, but quite white 20 years before he dyed.' Thus Aubrey. 'He did delight to be in the darke and told me he could then best contemplate.' He therefore had 'caves made in the earth in which in summer time he delighted to meditate.' He was extremely fond of coffee. Aubrey

William Harvey, physician-in-ordinary to Charles I, who solved the problem of the circulation of the blood. For speculation he substituted logical argument based on measurement, and showed that in an hour the heart shifts three times the weight of the body.

adds: 'I remember he kept a pretty young wench to wayte on him, which I guesse he made use of for warmeth-sake, as King David did . . .'

Harvey was 'very cholerique; and in his young days wore a dagger, as the fashion then was . . . but this Doctor would be too apt to draw out his dagger upon every slight occasion.' Nevertheless, he was very generous, and in all his writings there is not one unkind remark.

He uttered many aphorisms, for instance: 'A blessing goes with marriage for love upon a strong impulse.' He was wont to say that man is but a great mischievous baboon.

As the King's physician, Harvey accompanied him in 1642 to the battle of Edgehill, where he calmly read a book until a shot falling nearby caused him to move. In his absence his lodgings in Whitehall Palace were looted, and all his papers – the notes on his dissections and in particular the manuscript of a book on insects on which he had worked for years – were destroyed, together with his personal belongings. He often said, of all his losses, no grief was so crucifying to him as the loss of these papers.

Precisely during the period in which Harvey worked, an instrument was devised which, in the hands of others, was to demonstrate the truth of Harvey's theory and to throw light on the development of the egg, on which he also spent so much time: to wit, the microscope. Yet Harvey, conservative as he was, never made use of this new-fangled device. It was left to an Italian, Marcello Malpighi, and to a Dutchman, Anthony van Leeuwenhoek, to demonstrate the circulation of the blood.

The mechanical view *of the body and its functioning is graphically represented in this plate from an eighteenth-century Jewish work*

MAN IS COMPARED with a house in this picture, dated 1707. The eyes are compared with look-out windows, the stomach with a kitchen, the kidneys with the water supply, while the cellar with its trapdoor resembles the intestinal tract and anus.

The idea that the functioning of the body could be explained in mechanical terms was well established by the beginning of the 18th century. This was primarily due to the Frenchman, René Descartes, who taught – particularly in his *Tractatus de homine*, 1662 – that all things in nature, including animals and men, are machines. He acknowledged no predecessor in this idea but Harvey. He denied the views that the hand of God could be inferred from the complex design of nature and that nature tended towards a predetermined end. However, aware as he was of the fate of Galileo, he

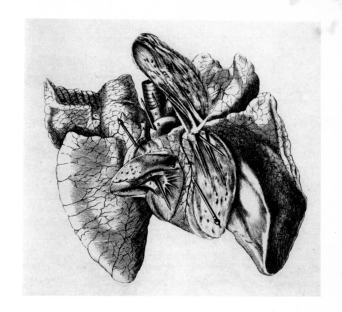

All things in nature, *said Descartes, including animals and men, are machines. This excellent drawing of the heart, from his 'Treatise on Man' (1662), has the diagrammatic clarity of a modern technical drawing.*

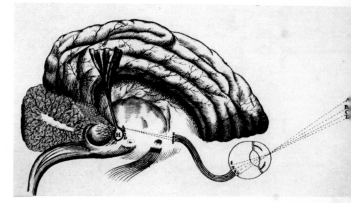

The perception of light *as figured by Descartes in his 'Treatise on Man' (1662): another illustration of his revolutionary thesis that all the functions of the body could be explained in purely mechanical terms.*

constantly reasserted the immortality of the soul. When Galileo was condemned, he withheld his book *Le Monde* from publication (it was published later in bowdlerized form) and he escaped the charge of heliocentrism (maintaining that the earth revolves round the sun, and not the reverse) by saying that all motion is relative.

To assert 'the clear and fundamental idea' that the physical world was sheer mechanism, against the stultifying but almost sacred 'forms' and 'qualities' of Aristotle's physics, was a brilliant, as well as a bold, intellectual leap. Huyghens, the mathematician and astronomer, said it was Descartes who had opened his eyes to science. Descartes, he considered, had not only exposed the failure of the old philosophy but had offered 'in its place causes which one could understand for all that exists in nature.'

'I think – therefore I am': *René Descartes set out to reconstruct all science. He held that all things in nature are machines, and acknowledged only Harvey as his equal.*

What sort of man was the genius – no less – who thus changed the face of science?

From his mother, Descartes inherited 'a dry cough and a pale complexion'. At the Jesuit college to which he was sent at the age of ten, he was excused work and allowed to lie in bed, where he thought with fierce concentration. Two years after graduating, he joined the army, rather surprisingly, and was sent to Breda, in Holland, on garrison duty. One day he saw a notice in Flemish challenging anyone to solve a certain mathematical problem; Descartes solved it. The following year he told a friend that he had devised 'an entirely new science . . . so that almost nothing will remain to be discovered in geometry'. It was to prove a powerful tool in the hands of Isaac Newton when Descartes published it, eighteen years later.

But the crucial step was to come soon after this, when Descartes was on duty at a remote village on the Danube. He spent a day shut up in the 'stove', or heated room, thinking, and came to two decisions: first, to doubt all organized knowledge; second, to reconstruct all science himself. The vast philosophical scheme which he subsequently constructed contained numerous errors, especially in matters of physiology, for he took as proved many erroneous beliefs. He saw the brain in Galenic terms as disseminating 'animal spirits' through tubes to the various parts of the body, causing them to do their work. But he held that this 'very subtle air, or rather, the very lively and pure flame' was produced in the heart by the blood. (Though he accepted Harvey's theory of circulation, he rejected the idea that the blood was propelled by contraction of the heart.) He did, however, as I shall describe later, put forward the idea of reflex action, which was to prove fruitful.

He died in Stockholm, in 1650, allegedly from a chill caught as a result of rising at 4 o'clock every morning to instruct the youthful Queen Christina. Sixteen years later, at the wish of his friends, his corpse was disinterred and sent to Paris, minus the right finger, which was appropriated by the French ambassador, who declared that he must have the finger which had written the words '*Cogito, ergo sum*'. Minus, also, as it turned out, the skull, which had been nobbled by a captain in the Swedish guards, who substituted another. The Cartesian cranium decorated the libraries of a series of Swedish collectors, until in 1809 it fell into the hands of the great Swedish chemist Berzelius, who offered it to Cuvier. Cuvier accepted it, on behalf of the Academy of Science, which received it back with '*déférence réligieuse*'.

Of all those who sought to apply the mechanist theories of Descartes none was more successful than Giovanni Borelli, a pupil of Galileo. He studied the movements of man and animals as problems of mechanics, using the principles evolved by Galileo, with such success that many were persuaded of the value of Descartes' physiology.

This idea was carried to its furthest extreme by an 18th-century doctor, de la Mettrie, who in 1748 published a widely-read essay, *L'homme machine*, or *Man a Machine*. La Mettrie had already angered the medical faculty in Paris by translating the works of the Dutch doctor Boerhaave, before he published his *L'Histoire naturelle de l'Ame – The Natural History of the Soul*. Accused of heresy, he fled to Holland and soon published anonymously *L'homme machine*. This work was too much even for the Dutch, and he had to go into hiding. He was rescued by Frederick II, who valued wit above religious orthodoxy.

His appointment as court lecturer only lasted three years, however, for in 1751 he demonstrated his theory that one should enjoy fleshly pleasures to the full by eating an enormous quantity of truffle pastry. He was immediately taken ill and died in agony. The religious declared with satisfaction that it was a judgment of God, and proved the falsity of his views.

Man as a machine: *John Mayow (1674) shows the muscles used in jumping.*

'HEREWITH an occhialino for examining minute things at a near distance. I hope that from it you will have as much use and joy as I . . . With infinite wonder I have examined very many minute creatures, among which the most horrible are the flea, the most beautiful ants and moths. With delight too have I seen how flies and other little animals can walk on mirrors and even upside down.'

Thus Galileo wrote to Cesi, a member of the group of wealthy amateur scientists who called themselves the Lynx-eyed Academy. Microscopes were fast becoming a popular toy. The compound microscope had appeared in Holland about 1590 and we find Galileo using it about 1610.

Cesi was delighted, and commissioned an artist to make drawings of what could be seen – notably of numerous plants which had hitherto been regarded by botanists as seedless, but which the microscope now revealed to be teeming with seeds. Such was the fine dust adhering to the back of fern fronds, which now appeared under the microscope 'as big as peppercorns'. He also commissioned a work on bees.

These first microscopes were extremely difficult to work with: the field of view was small, the image dark and distorted – the glass being uneven – and they were affected by chromatic aberration. Perhaps this is why, after the first surge of excitement, interest in them seemed to die down. Then suddenly there burst upon the world an epoch-making book, the *Micrographia* of Robert Hooke.

No portrait is known of Hooke, one of the most inventive and penetrating minds that ever lived. As a boy at Westminster School he absorbed the first six books of Euclid in a week and invented thirty ways of flying.

He devoted only two years to biology, and at the age of 29 he published his *Micrographia* (1665), the sixty plates of which record a number of

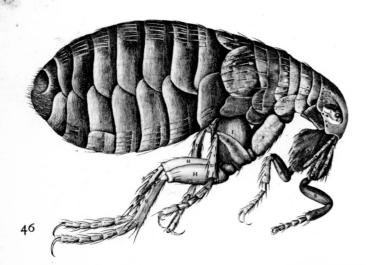

A flea eighteen inches long *is one of the beautifully detailed drawings in Robert Hooke's 'Micrographia'. Only someone who has examined such small creatures through one of the early microscopes can realize what an achievement this book represents.*

Clutching a human hair, *the head louse stares arrogantly out from the pages of 'Micrographia'. This is a detail from a drawing showing the whole insect.*

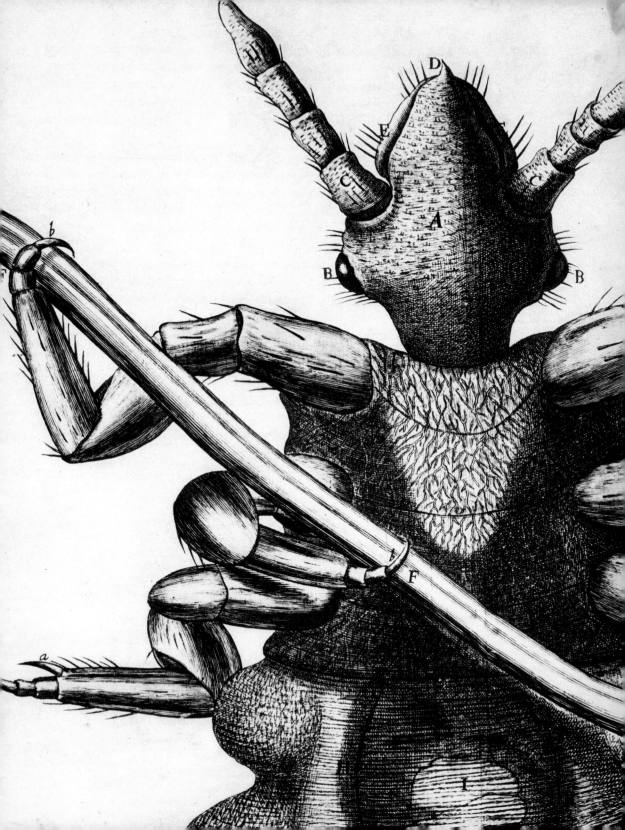

fundamental biological discoveries. He turned his lens on small creatures such as the flea, the louse and the silverfish, and drew them with extraordinary accuracy. Only someone who has examined such creatures through the primitive microscopes of the period, with low levels of light and colour fringes, will realize what an achievement these beautiful detailed drawings represent.

He looked at and recorded the sting of the nettle and the bee, at fungi and moulds, and at the compound eye of the fly. He described the structure of cork, and used the work 'cell' in its biological sense for the first time. He also examined inorganic objects – the point of a needle, the edge of a razor and the fragments of metal struck from steel by a flint. He was the first to depict exactly the metamorphosis of a gnat.

The *Micrographia* also includes astronomical observations. It describes the first wheel barometer, an alcohol thermometer, the first refractometer for liquids, and an indicating hygrometer. Pepys called it 'the most ingeniose book that ever I read in my life.'

Hooke's ingenuity was inexhaustible. He invented the clock-driven telescope and the universal joint. He was the first to observe the rotation of

Hooke's microscope made use of the reflected light of a small oil lamp, condensed through a glass globe filled with water and then again through a convex lens. The ball-and-socket joint enabled the instrument to be used horizontally as well, to examine specimens by transmitted light.

Reflected in the compound eye *of a fly we can see the window of Hooke's study, repeated over and over again, showing the precision of his drawing.*

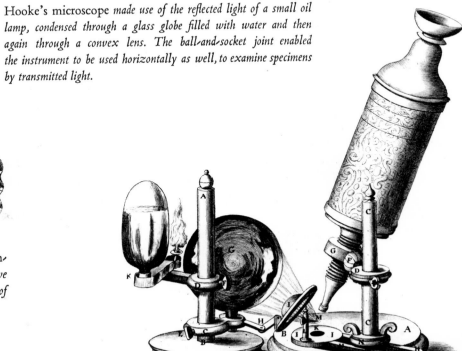

Jupiter. He was the first to propose as a zero temperature the freezing point of water, and he designed examples of most of the common meteorological instruments. He explained the circulation of the atmosphere, and pointed out that a rapid fall in barometric pressure presaged a storm. He did two experiments to show the likely origin of the craters on the moon: they exemplify the two theories still held, i. e. that they are due to volcanoes or to the impact of meteorites. He clearly put forward the mechanical theory of heat, made important contributions on elasticity, and lectured on earth-quakes and the origin of fossils.

In 1671 he tested himself in a chamber exhausted to three-quarters of nor-mal atmospheric pressure and reported pains in the ears and deafness. (He had previously invented the air pump.) He carried out experiments on skin grafting, artificial respiration, and blood transfusion.

His diary entries reveal the amazing, undiscriminating activity of his mind; and incidentally his fondness for coffee-house conversation.

'To Martins and Garaways Club; Ludowick, Aubrey, Wild. discoursed about Uni-versal Character, about preadamits and of Creation. about Insects. I mentioned all vegetables to be female. I told Wild and Aubrey of flying. Wild cold. Drank port.'

Again on New Year's Day they discussed crossing bogs, and walking on ice, and fire-eaters. Hooke told them a way of making thunder and light-ning in the theatre, and argued that there was water on the moon. Later the conversation touched on phosphorus and the propagation of plants.

Hooke was also an architect – he designed the monument to the Fire of London, often wrongly attributed to Sir Christopher Wren. No sooner was it built, than Hooke was busy making observations of the difference in air pressure between the bottom and the top. After the Great Fire he was called in to work with Wren on the redesigning of the City of London, and he produced a grid-iron plan, not unlike many American cities today, which was liked by the Common Council, but never carried out. With Wren he canalized the Fleet River, and designed a number of buildings, notably the headquarters of the Royal College of Physicians.

Wren and Hooke were firm friends – Wren was himself an early member of the Royal Society and performed a number of experiments – and Hooke was always hurrying to put his latest theory or newest invention before his friend.

'August 12, 1676, told Sir Chr. Wren my Invention of flying, air pump, and my anagram. He approved it.

Feb. 6, 1677. With Sir Chr. Wren at Childs told him of my mercuriall poysed clock and of the circular mercury clock.

Aug. 10, 1678, at Childs with Sir Chr. Wren, told him my designes of mapps, my equation of springs.'

Hooke's posthumous works alone total getting on for half a million words.

Hooke suffered from continual giddiness, indigestion, catarrh, insomnia and bad dreams. Hypochondriacally, he noted everything he ate and whether it agreed with him. ('Slept not soe well after eating Rice pudden.' 'Slept ill after cheese.')

The son of a clergyman, and brother of a grocer, he was simple and generous – he worked for thirty years without receiving his salary as Cutlerian lecturer from the Royal Society, without complaint. As a boy, he spent most of his time making mechanical devices: water-mills, clocks, and model ships. For a time he was apprenticed to the portrait painter, Lely, but the smell of paint made him sick, so he gave it up. At Oxford, his success in constructing the air-pump which Boyle needed brought him to the attention of the Royal Society, which appointed him Curator in 1662, and Secretary in 1667, a post which he held until 1682.

He was also irascible, and became involved in an unworthy feud with Newton. This seems to have dated from 1680, when Hooke approached Newton suggesting the inverse square law by which gravitation and light energy decrease with distance. Newton, who had perhaps already thought of this, failed to give Hooke any credit when he published on the subject. In consequence, Newton was obliged to wait until after Hooke's death in 1703 before being appointed President of the Royal Society.

Though Hooke was famous in his lifetime and for forty years after, he has since been generally underestimated – partly, perhaps, because of Newton's dislike of him. Extraordinary to relate, we not only have no portrait of Hooke, but we do not even know where he was buried.

'TIS MY WONT of a morning to rub my teeth with salt, and then swill out my mouth with water: and, often, after eating, to clean my back teeth with a toothpick, as well as rubbing them hard with a cloth: Yet notwithstanding, my teeth are not so cleaned thereby but what there sticketh a groweth between some of my front ones and my grinders . . . a little white matter, which is as thick as if 'twere batter . . . in the said matter there were very many little living animalcules, very prettily a-moving. The biggest sort had the shape of Fig. A: these had a very strong, swift motion, and shot through the water (or spittle) as a pike does through water. The second sort had the shape of Fig. B. These oft-times spun round like a top.'

'Living animalcules, *very prettily a-moving*'. Bacteria from his mouth, seen and drawn by Leeuwenhoek.

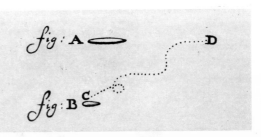

These words were written (originally in Dutch) by an unlettered linen-draper of Delft, by the name of Anthony van Leeuwenhoek. It is completely baffling, but the moving objects which he saw through his lens were certainly bacteria. He was the first person in the world ever to see them, and in fact it was 200 years before anyone else succeeded in doing so. How he managed it remains a complete mystery.

This tremendous discovery and others equally important – notably the discovery of spermatozoa in seminal fluid – were made, not with the new compound microscope, but with the single lens, known in principle for centuries, which van Leeuwenhoek brought to an undreamed-of pitch of perfection.

Equally odd is the fact that in a world teeming with lively amateur scientists, many of them equipped with microscopes or able to obtain them, it should have been an obscure tradesman who, with unhurried persistence, showed what the microscope could really achieve.

When van Leeuwenhoek showed his microscopes to a favoured visitor in 1685, he declined to reveal the best of them. And, as he never described his methods, the nature of these microscopes remains unknown. Those which we know of – and he left several hundred of them – consist of a glass bead, set in a hole in a brass plate, the object being adjusted before this lens on a movable pin, as seen below. Such a glass bead, being an almost spherical lens, provides powerful magnification when held close to the eye, at the cost of severe eye-strain.

Van Leeuwenhoek left behind him 419 lenses; some are of rock crystal. The most powerful of the instruments still extant magnified about 275 times. The unique feature of these lenses is that they are ground – Hooke and others used droplets of fused glass. A passing remark of van Leeuwenhoek's suggests that he had discovered the modern technique of viewing objects against a dark ground, which sometimes improves visibility. Hooke, seeking to solve the mystery of his achievement, tried putting the liquid under examination in fine glass tubes, which themselves acted as magnifiers, and found that this helped. Possibly van Leeuwenhoek did the same.

His technical skill was equalled by his persistence and objectivity. He looked repeatedly at anything he discovered before writing about it. 'In narrowly scrutinising 3 or 4 drops [of water] I may do such a deal of work that I put myself into a sweat,' he wrote. He was forty-one when the brilliant

With instruments like this van Leeuwenhoek showed what even a single lens could achieve. The lens itself – ground, not fused – was set into a hole in a three-inch-long rectangular plate of copper; the specimen would be held on the adjustable pin, and the whole apparatus held up to the eye.

Anatomy lesson by Cornelius van 's Gravesande, painted by Cornelis de Man at Delft in 1681. Leeuwenhoek is standing behind the lecturer, to his left.

young Regnier de Graaf (who was to die the same year, aged thirty-two) wrote to the Royal Society about van Leeuwenhoek's investigations, and thus inspired the long series of letters in which he recorded the many things he discovered.

Leeuwenhoek wandered over the field of nature with his lenses, recording without attempting to theorize. He correctly described the red blood cells (which he first saw in fishes) and which Malpighi had wrongly interpreted as fat globules. He gave clear accounts of the structure of the teeth, the skin and the crystalline lens of the eye. He showed that voluntary muscle was striped in appearance, and did useful work on the compound eye of insects. He was the first to note many of the single-celled water creatures known as Protozoa: the amoeba is a well-known example.

But the discovery which was to spark off more controversy than any other (as I describe in a later chapter) was his work on spermatozoa.

The matter was brought to his attention by a medical student, who had noted the sperm moving in the semen of a man treated for venereal disease. He seems to have regarded them as a product of the disease, and it was Leeuwenhoek who realized their true importance. Writing to the Secretary of the Royal Society he apologizes for discussing a subject which some may think distasteful, and explains that he obtained the material for his studies from the overplus of marital intercourse and without committing any sin. This material he found was 'crowded with an infinity of animals like tadpoles'. He was amazed at their number, which exceeded, he thought, the entire population of the earth, which he calculated at 13,000 millions. Soon afterwards he identified similar creatures in the milt of fishes, and in the semen of horses and other animals.

The immediate impact of the microscope was to fill men with a religious sense of awe. Thus Louis XIV's Court Physician, Pierre Boral, wrote, in introducing his collection of microscopic observations in 1656 – it was the first separate publication ever devoted to the microscope – of the microscope 'through which atoms become quasi-visible, and minute insects are changed into a colossal monster; with the aid of which countless parts are discovered in these living atoms; and, day after day, doors of the new physics are opened; so much so that God's Majesty becomes more illumined by these tiny Bodies than in gigantic ones, and their perplexing constitution convinces even the most godless, and leads them to the notion, the admiration and the veneration of their supreme Maker.'

Dr Henry Power was moved to put the same thought in verse, with somewhat erratic spelling, punctuation and capitalization:

Louis Joblot, 18th-century French microscopist, worked with direct, not reflected, light, holding the instrument to his eye like a telescope.

Of all th' Inuentions none there is Surpasses
the Noble Florentine's Dioptrick-glasses.
For what a better, fitter guift Could bee
In this world's Aged Luciosity
To Helpe our Blindnesse so as to deuize
a paire of new & Artificiall eyes,
By whose augmenting power wee now see more
then all the world Has euer donn Before.

Who can the old Phylosopher renounce
that sd a thousand Soules might dance at once.
Vpon a needles point, when wee see Here
as many in one dropp of Viniger.
This to our mind the a'theriall wisdome brings
how God is greatest in ye Least of things.

The microscope gave an immense new impetus to each of the main areas of biological enquiry. For there are, in essence, three questions to which the science of life addresses itself. The first is, how does the living organism function? This is the science of physiology, and this science arises from anatomy, for it is by studying the structure of the various organs that we come to understand their functioning. (Within the science of physiology is a major sub-section, neurophysiology; this is the study of how the more complex organisms are controlled and regulated.)

The second question is: how does the organism create new organisms to take its place? This study falls into two sections: generation and embryology. The third question is: how does the world come to be filled with precisely the array of organisms it is? This is the question which is answered by the theory of evolution, but before such a theory can be developed it is necessary to examine and classify the organisms that exist.

Finally, with one foot planted in each of the foregoing sections, is the question: why do organisms resemble their parents very consistently in the broad features (in the sense that a lion does not give birth to a man and still less to an amoeba) but much less so in details (such as eye colour)?

The microscope, by revealing the fine structure of organisms, showed that there was machinery enough in them to account for their behaviour, and sounded the death-knell of the semi-magical theories which sought to explain living processes in terms of nitro-aerial spirits and sensitive souls. It transformed, as I shall tell in the next section, man's knowledge of the generative process, and soon contributed to understanding the development of the embryo. And by revealing the unseen world of single-celled organisms and bacteria, extended the 'ladder of nature' downwards to the point at which the idea of an evolution from simple to complex (intuitively perceived by Aristotle) could be realistically entertained. More than two hundred years were to pass, however, before the microscope was improved to the point at which it would also disclose the mechanism of heredity.

IN 1672 TWO IMPORTANT PAPERS reached the Royal Society, reporting new advances in anatomy made with the aid of the microscope. The first, by a small margin, was from the pen of Nehemiah Grew, an English doctor, and was modestly called *The Anatomy of Vegetables Begun*. The plate opposite, which shows 'a gooseberry cut down', is from it. The second was entitled *Anatome plantarum* (the Anatomy of Plants), Part 1, and was from a professor of anatomy at Bologna named Marcello Malpighi. Between them, these two men launched microscopic anatomy – that is, the dissection of plant and animal material under the microscope.

Applying the microscope to every imaginable object which lay within his range, both plant and animal, Malpighi, a man of great drive and imagi-

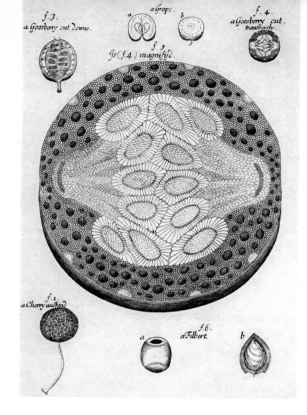

With the aid of the microscope *important advances in botany were made by Nehemiah Grew and Marcello Malpighi. Above (left) is a transverse section of a gooseberry from Grew's 'Anatomy of Vegetables' (1672), and (right) the title-page of Malpighi's 'Anatome Plantarum' (1672). Between them, they launched the study of microscopic anatomy.*

nation, tore into the subject like one possessed. So many-faceted was his work that I can only convey an impression of his achievement by tabulation.

He looked at the LUNGS and saw there the minute CAPILLARIES through which the blood flows, thus completing Harvey's work by showing how the blood gets from the arterial to the venous system.

He studied the METAMORPHOSIS of the larva into a butterfly.

He wrote a monograph on the TONGUE and its complex musculature.

He studied the SILK-WORM, in which he noted the tracheae or breathing tubes and excretory tubes, still called Malpighian tubes. It had been supposed that insects had no internal organs. His treatise on it was the first monograph on an invertebrate.

He hardened many organs by cooking them, and then inspected them. In this way he found the KIDNEY tubules, which are also still called Malpighian; the Malpighian follicular bodies in the SPLEEN; the pyramid cells in the CEREBRAL CORTEX; and also anatomized the LIVER.

He studied the development of the hen's EGG: some of his figures of the developing heart would serve for a modern text-book without much alteration. He was the first to describe such early developmental structures as the neural groove (the forerunner of the backbone) and the optic vesicle (the forerunner of the eye). Thus he put EMBRYOLOGY on a new footing.

He devoted a special work to PLANT GALLS, which had been thought to be spontaneous growths, and showed that each contains a grub.

Walking one day in a wood, Malpighi noticed the broken bough of a chestnut tree and observed that fine threads projected from the broken surfaces. With his hand-lens he saw that they had a spiral appearance. He was struck by their similarity to the breathing tubes which he had earlier discovered in insects and leaped to the conclusion that they likewise served for breathing.

This inspired him to an extensive study of plant anatomy, based on the idea that it would prove similar to animal anatomy. He discovered the main vessels – incidentally observing the pores or stomata through which breathing does take place, but failing to grasp their purpose – and made accurate drawings. In particular he studied the mode of germination of different plants, and the pattern of subsequent development, clearly distinguishing monocotyledons from dicotyledons. He studied root nodules (but remained baffled as to their purpose) and the relationship of the parasitic mistletoe to its host tree.

Though a brilliant observer, Malpighi was a dire writer and lecturer, and some of what he wrote is quite impossible to understand. But he was highly ingenious in devising techniques. Plant tissues are relatively easy to study microscopically, because the cellulose is comparatively opaque and the shape of the cells stands out, but animal tissues, when not obscured by blood, are highly transparent. Malpighi devised many methods of making animal tissues more visible, such as injecting them with wax.

His most important discovery, the existence of the capillaries, which he made in 1660, he achieved when he hit on the idea of injecting water into the pulmonary artery and saw it come out of the pulmonary vein. This had the effect of washing the blood out of the lung, making it more transparent, as a result of which the capillaries became visible.

Malpighi's contribution to embryology unfortunately did more harm than good. He believed that he had found the developing form of a chick in an egg which the hen had not incubated, and decided that the new organism is already present, preformed, in the unfertilized egg. (Actually, the egg he was studying had been incubated quite successfully by the hot Italian sun.) This error, as we shall see in a later chapter, dominated thinking on the subject for more than a century.

The vessels in the stems of plants, which Malpighi had seen, were discovered independently by Nehemiah Grew, an English country doctor, who drew them with three-dimensional solidity and in painstaking detail, as we see in the figure below.

Grew (who became secretary of the Royal Society five years after his paper was published) confined himself largely to the study of plants and, for the structures which he discovered, invented new terms distinct from those applying to the organs of the animals — unlike Malpighi who was always trying to stress the similarities between vegetables and animals.

Grew did however produce one remarkable work on animal anatomy, his *Comparative Anatomy of Stomachs and Guts* (1681). Incidentally, this was the first use of the expression 'comparative anatomy' in its current sense.

Between them, Malpighi and Grew advanced vegetable anatomy so greatly that more than a century passed before any significant addition to their work was made. And in general they bestowed on biology the idea that organisms had a highly specialized kind of structure: the idea of tissues was born, though the biological term was not coined for more than another century. Their contemporaries, however, failed to see the far-reaching nature of these discoveries, which struck them as merely 'curious'.

Malpighi maintained *that plant and animal anatomy were similar. His drawings were brilliant but his conclusions were mistaken on this point (left).*

The vessels in plant stems *were discovered independently by Grew. He drew them in painstaking detail and saw that plant and animal anatomy were quite distinct (right).*

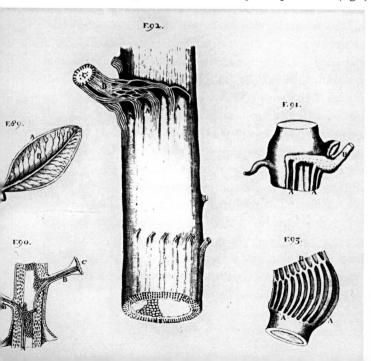

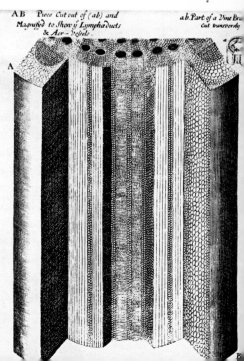

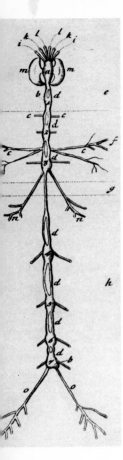

Dissecting the nervous system of the honey-bee demands a fantastic degree of delicate skill. This beautiful diagram is the work of Jan Swammerdam.

THE MAYFLY LARVA is only a quarter of an inch long. It was dissected by possibly the deftest anatomist who ever lived, the young, half-crazy Jan Swammerdam. In the centre can be seen the paired main nerve trunk, with a ganglion or nerve centre in each segment. The wavy lines on either side are the tracheae, discovered by Malpighi, tubes through which air is drawn, for insects have no lungs. The delicacy of touch required to make such a dissection passes all conception. Swammerdam discovered that the lining of the tracheae is cast when the creature moults, a phenomenon 'so consider-able that all humane understanding must stand amazed thereat'.

Swammerdam worked with the concentration of a madman, employing a variety of microscopes and the finest dissecting instruments, which he sharpened under the microscope, his practice being to start under the lower powers and proceed by stages to the higher. He made minutely accurate dissections of frogs, gnats, lice, tadpoles and above all the honey-bee, the nervous system of which is seen here. He even saw that the minute tracheae penetrate into the substance of the eye. Probably no other pioneer biologist left so little for others to discover in his chosen field. The great Dutch doctor Boerhaave describes how he could be found, bareheaded in the sun, working until the sweat ran into his eyes. When he was thirty-six, after five years' frantic work on the bee, his mental health worsened, and he came under the influence of the religious fanatic Antoinette Bourignon.

Pious before, he now 'resolved to addict my thoughts more to love the Creator of these things, than to admire him in his creatures'. Though he improved enough to publish his work on the mayfly in 1675 (to which Mlle Bourignon grudgingly agreed), he never revised it. The next five years were devoted almost entirely to religious exercises, and he died, completely unhinged, at the age of forty-three.

First one and then another Parisian anatomist acquired his papers, but lacked the energy to publish them. Finally, Boerhaave intervened and published them at his own expense in Dutch and Latin, beautifully illu-strated, in 1737–8, a century after the birth of the author. Even so, they were not out of date. It was probably Boerhaave who titled them *Biblia Naturae* (The Books of Nature), perhaps the finest work in the literature of zoology.

To list even the most important anatomical discoveries made by Swam-merdam would be tedious: but it is interesting that it has recently been realized that he also contributed to the physiology of muscle, inventing a form of plethysmograph, with which he proved that muscles do not increase in size when they contract. This disposed of the common idea that their contraction is caused by some 'nervous fluid' flowing into them.

His first book, on insects, which he classified according to their mode of development, laid the foundations of entomology.

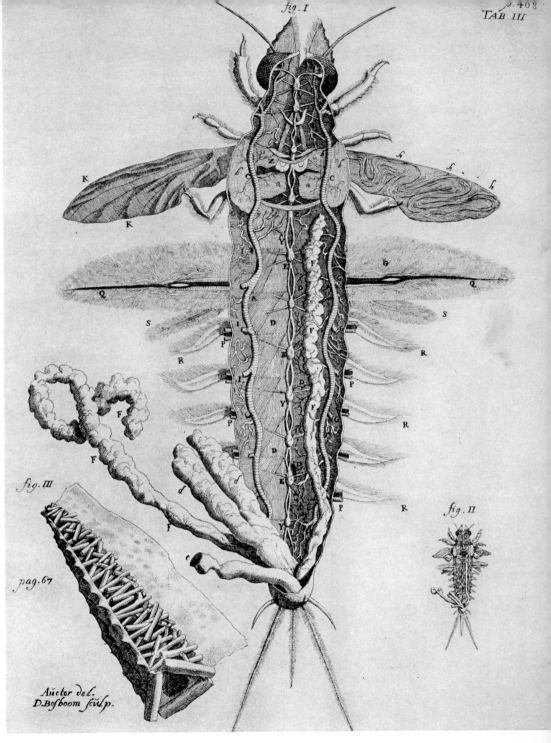

fig. I

K

K

Q

S

R

fig. III

F

F

F

d

d

e

pag. 67

Auctor del.
D. Boßboom sculp.

fig. II

Q

S

R

R

R

Only a quarter of an inch long, *the mayfly larva was minutely dissected by Jan Swammerdam, possibly the deftest anatomist who ever lived.*

WITH THIS DISSECTING MICROSCOPE, the Dutch lawyer Pieter Lyonet produced in 1740 dissections of the goat-moth caterpillar rivalling – perhaps even surpassing – those made by Swammerdam on the mayfly and the bee. As a refined anatomical examination it is still unapproached. It was, however, his only contribution to biology. Lyonet was a diplomat – a brilliant linguist, born at the Hague of French parents – who turned to biology as a hobby.

Much of the interest which inspired these incredibly painstaking dissections derived from the extraordinary metamorphoses which caterpillars, mayflies and such creatures make. One of the great controversies of the period was the question of whether the adult is preformed in the embryo, or whether it develops from undifferentiated raw materials. The phenomenon of metamorphosis promised an answer to this question, since on the preformation theory, one might expect to find a complete butterfly preformed in the larva. Hence when Swammerdam found such a butterfly in a larva which had reached the pupal state, he became a confirmed believer in preformation.

Accordingly, many of these metamorphosing creatures were dissected. It was not until the next century, however, that any real progress was made with the subject. John Vaughan Thompson, an English army surgeon who settled in Cork in 1816, showed that the common shore-crab passes through a series of changes as remarkable as those of insects. Later, he explored other crustaceans. Of him it was said, 'no great naturalist has ever written so little and that so good.'

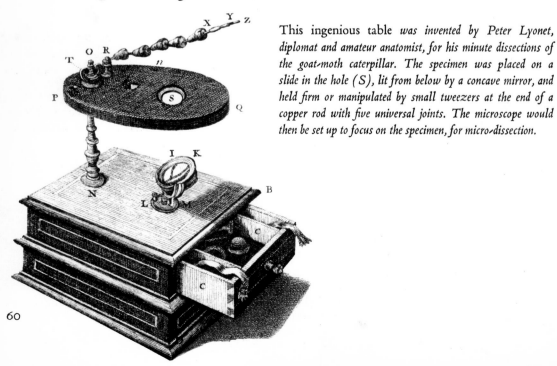

This ingenious table *was invented by Peter Lyonet, diplomat and amateur anatomist, for his minute dissections of the goat-moth caterpillar. The specimen was placed on a slide in the hole (S), lit from below by a concave mirror, and held firm or manipulated by small tweezers at the end of a copper rod with five universal joints. The microscope would then be set up to focus on the specimen, for micro-dissection.*

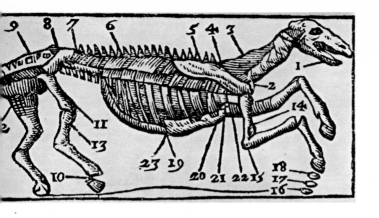

Caricatures like this *drawing of the skeleton of the horse by G. B. Ferrari (about 1560) were long accepted as adequate for teaching purposes.*

THIS CARICATURE was the best that 16th-century anatomists could do in representing the horse, until, as the century closed, an Italian senator, Carlo Ruini, produced his great work on the anatomy and diseases of the horse, from which the plate below is taken. (A tradition, probably inaccurate, attributes the plates to Titian.) This was the first comprehensive monograph on the anatomy of an animal.

A flood of such monographs followed, as the 17th century wore on, and animals of every type, from the slug to the chimpanzee and from the woodpecker to the whale, were solicitously dissected and their parts displayed with taste and skill. But the notion of comparison had still to be established.

First-hand observation *and superb drawing are seen in Carlo Ruini's great work on the horse (1598). This plate shows the superficial muscles.*

The tongue of a woodpecker *by Borelli (1681). He explained muscular movements in purely mechanical terms.*

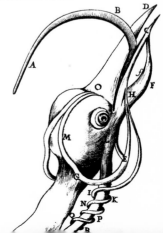

LOUIS XIV IS HERE SEEN visiting the French Academy of Science in 1671, five years after its foundation. With him is his chancellor Colbert, and between them Claude Perrault, the Academy's leading anatomist. Perrault had been a soldier and became one of the leading architects of his age, but he was also a skilled anatomist. The Academy was not a scientific society, as we know them today, but a laboratory for the practical examination and discussion of natural phenomena. Typically, it was divided into two groups, mathematicians and biologists. From the efforts of the latter, the whole modern development of comparative anatomy can be traced.

Their first venture was a short account of the lion and 'a large fish', written not in Latin but in French, as was all their work. Two years later they described the chameleon, dromedary, beaver, bear and gazelle. In the end, 49 species were described. Three of the plates from Perrault's works are reproduced below. Perrault died in 1688 of a disease contracted while dissecting a camel.

THE ANATOMICAL PREPARATIONS of Frederik Ruysch were famous all over Europe. He perfected the technique of injecting veins and other vessels with coloured substances, so as to reveal their course, and carried his activities to such a pitch that injection became known as 'the Ruyschian art'.

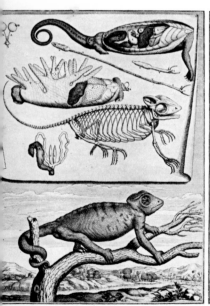
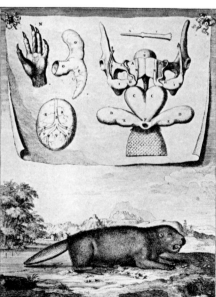

The French Academy of Science *was a working laboratory rather than an academy. Under the leadership of Claude Perrault, it produced detailed anatomical studies of such animals as the chameleon, the beaver, and the thresher shark with its curious spiral stomach.*

Royal patronage *was given to the Academy of Science. Here Louis XIV is seen, with his chancellor Colbert, visiting the Academy in 1671. Perrault stands behind and between them. Contrary to the practice of the time, the Academy's publications appeared in French, not Latin.*

The macabre ingenuity *of Ruysch's museum took the shape of arranging a collection of human and animal preparations into a group such as this, stiff with gothic symbolism. Ruysch, an intimate friend of Swammerdam, had learned from him how to inject coloured material into his specimens to show the intricate branching of the blood vessels.*

His preparations were arranged to produce a decorative effect, not to illustrate any biological principle. In the one shown above the pile of stones consists of renal calculi; an injected womb-coat provides a background, with trees consisting of ramifying vessels of various kinds. The prostrate skeleton clasps a mayfly, emblem of mortality; another plays upon a fiddle composed of arteries and other anatomical fragments. The broken column also signifies death.

Ruysch created the first anatomical museum at Amsterdam, some time before 1691. According to one visitor: 'All the bodies which he injected preserved the tone, the lustre and the freshness of youth. One would have taken them for living persons in profound repose.' It was 'a perfect necropolis, all the inhabitants of which were asleep and ready to speak as soon as they were awakened.' Ruysch disposed the corpses in attitudes of grief and equipped them with handkerchiefs of injected omentum. Suitably minatory signs such as *Ab utero ad tumulum* – from the womb to the tomb – were displayed in large type.

Peter the Great bought this macabre collection, which comprised some one thousand three hundred specimens, but when it arrived at St Petersburg it was found that the sailors had drunk all the brandy in which the corpses were preserved. Ruysch, although eighty, set out with undiminished vigour to create a new collection.

The eighteenth century's enthusiasm *for science and love of experiment are portrayed in Joseph Wright's painting of 1768, 'The Air Pump'. Subjecting a bird to a partial vacuum, the experimenter demonstrates its dependence on 'vital air'. Six years later, Priestley produced oxygen from mercuric oxide.*

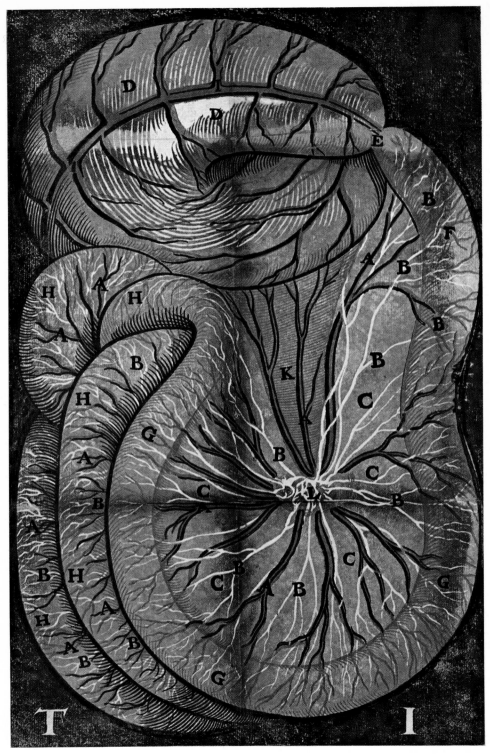

The first anatomical colour plate: *a dog's 'lacteal veins', from Aselli's 'De Lactibus', 1627.*

But grotesque as was Ruysch's museum of anatomy, Ruysch himself made an important discovery. Galen had taught that some parts of the body had no blood supply. Ruysch showed that every part was vascularized, and that even the blood vessels themselves had their tiny veins. As ever minuter threads came to view, as he improved his techniques, he became quite carried away and declared that the body consisted simply of a network of vessels, as Eristratos had supposed. Hunter was still teaching this erroneous theory at the end of the century.

Boerhaave, the most successful doctor of his day, whose advice was even sought from as far away as China, and who died a multimillionaire, relied heavily on Ruysch's preparations when he wrote his *Institutiones medicae,* a book which contained a section on physiology excellent by the standards of the day.

So famous did Ruysch become that, when Newton died, he was elected to fill the vacancy left by his death in the French Academy of Sciences.

THE FIRST ANATOMICAL ILLUSTRATIONS in colour appeared in a book by the Patavine doctor, Gasparo Aselli, published after his death by two friends. It appeared in 1627, two years before Harvey's treatise on the circulation, and reported the discovery of 'the lacteal veins'.

While vivisecting a dog which had just eaten a large meal, he found that the intestine was covered with white threads. Supposing them to be nerves, he casually cut some of them off, and was surprised to see a milky fluid ooze out. Actually, they were vessels which absorb the fat globules from the walls of the intestine (which have picked them up from ingested food) and convey it to the blood-stream. He called the vessels lacteals, because of the milky appearance of the fluid, which was known as chyle, a word we shall meet again.

Other workers soon discovered that the lacteals lead – not to the liver, as Aselli supposed – but to the thoracic duct (discovered 1647); and that a whole system of vessels, whose existence had been quite unsuspected, also drains into the thoracic duct. These vessels, the lymphatics – whose functions include dealing with invading bacteria as we now know – were explored by the Swedish student Olof Rudbeck, youngest but one of the eleven children of the imperious Bishop Rudbeckius.

So astonishing did people find the discovery of a whole new vascular system, quite unsuspected hitherto, that Rudbeck was commanded to demonstrate the vessels to the Queen – the famous Queen Christina – and was rewarded with a travel grant and a professorship. It was in truth an important discovery, which opened up the whole question of how the body deals with the food it takes in; and coming so soon after Harvey's it generated a feeling of exciting advance.

And in fact it was to prove only the first in a long series of anatomical discoveries about the human body made in the 17th century. Glands, ducts, bodies and follicles of every kind were discovered at intervals of a few years throughout the rest of the century. As the complexity of the structure of the living organism was gradually revealed, astonishment was succeeded by the feeling that a purely mechanical interpretation of its working was not as impossible as it had once seemed.

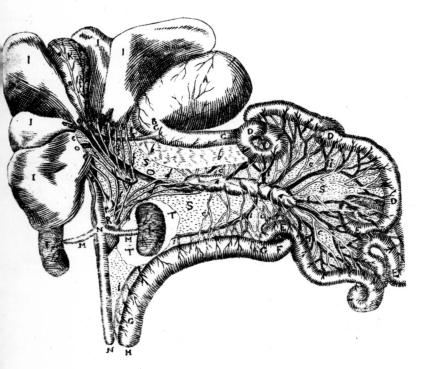

A wholly new and unsuspected *vascular system – the lacteals, draining into the thoracic duct – was discovered by Aselli: only one of a long series of anatomical discoveries in the 17th century. This diagram of the digestive system and the lacteals is by Olof Rudbeck (1653), who was commanded to demonstrate them to Queen Christina of Sweden.*

TO PASS from the higgledy-piggledy of Ole Worm's museum of 1665 to the orderly, though unsystematic Cabinet of Natural History of 1719 (opposite) is to pass from the Middle Ages to the age of reason. When twelve cartloads of rarities assembled by the two Tradescants arrived at the Ashmolean Museum in Oxford – 21 years after the death of the last of the Tradescants – it contained such items as 'a lacrymaticall Urne for Teares, a Nunnes Penitential Girdle of Haire, an orange gathered from a Tree that grew over Zebulon's tomb, a circumcision knife of stone, and a sample of the blood which rained on the Isle of Wight'. Just a century later, John Hunter, the English surgeon, was assembling his unique collection, in which all the items displayed the working out of a great philosophical scheme.

A haphazard collection of oddments, *monstrosities and genuine rarities, with no systematic arrangement – such was the 'museum' of Ole Worm, the 17th century Danish antiquarian. It was typical of what the later middle ages thought of as a museum.*

Orderly but still unsystematic, *this ideal conception (dated 1719) of what a 'natural history cabinet' should look like marks the difference between the middle ages and the age of reason. Preservation of specimens in alcohol was beginning to be understood.*

Very little blood can have been exchanged in the experimental transfusions of the 17th century. Since sheep's blood and human blood are not compatible, the two must have clotted in the transfusion tube, which may account for the patient's willingness to repeat the experience.

THE FIRST ILLUSTRATION of a blood transfusion appeared in 1685, but it was twenty years earlier that the first transfusion was performed, by the thirty-four-year-old Richard Lower at the suggestion of Sir Christopher Wren. He announced that he would exchange the blood 'of Old and Young, Sick and Healthy, Hot and Cold, Fierce and Fearful, Tame and Wild, Animals.' And when he did so, using a dog, there was great excitement, for it was thought that illness was due to humours in the blood, and the experiment seemed to offer a method of cure of universal application.

After his success with the dog, Lower repeated the experiment with 'a poor debauched man' and a sheep. The man, a Mr Anthony Coga, survived and said he was quite ready to undergo the experience again. Since the blood of sheep is not compatible with human blood, it is to be supposed that very little was actually exchanged, owing perhaps to coagulation.

Lower was one of the group of highly intelligent men who formed the 'Invisible College' which became the Royal Society. He had made his name performing skilled dissections of the brain for Dr Willis and drawing the plates for his *Cerebri Anatome,* the first attempt to establish the anatomy of the brain in any but the crudest manner. Soon after his blood transfusion, Lower showed that the heart is controlled by nerves: he ligatured the eighth cranial nerve, which we now call the vagus, and noted how the heart beat slackened.

But probably his most important experiment was one in which he blew air through the lungs of a suffocated dog, and observed that the blood, which had become dark, grew lighter again. He inferred that the blood absorbed air, and was in this way purified.

The plate below from Willis's *Cerebri Anatome* is said to have been drawn by Sir Christopher Wren, no inconsiderable experimenter, and one of the earliest members of the 'Invisible College'. At twenty-eight he was appointed Savilean Professor of Astronomy, but he also carried out many physiological experiments.

Robert Boyle, the fourteenth son of the Earl of Cork, had noted that birds and mice, placed in a chamber, died when the air was removed with the newly invented air-pump. He remarked: 'We may suppose that there is in the Air a little vital Quintessence . . . which serves to the refreshment and restauration of our vital Spirits,' and urged that someone should show this experimentally.

Lower was a Cornishman, and one of those who witnessed his experiments was another Cornishman, John Mayow. He observed that when antimony is burnt, it *gains* in weight. He inferred that it took up from the air a substance which he called nitro-aerial spirit – in other words, oxygen. The idea, and even the term 'nitro-aerial spirit', were not new, but Lower performed an entirely original experiment when he proved that an animal consumes something as it breathes. Taken together, Lower and Mayow's work explained the basic nature of respiration. It was extraordinary that another century was to pass before Scheele discovered, and Lavoisier named, oxygen; and before Priestley demonstrated its role in supporting life.

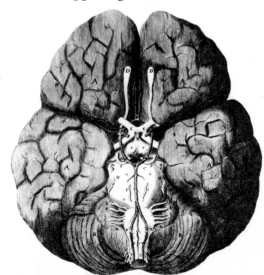

Sir Christopher Wren, *better known as an architect, was also skilled in anatomy, and was one of the earliest members of the 'Invisible College', which became the Royal Society. He is said to have drawn this plate showing a dissection of the brain, for Dr Willis's 'Cerebri Anatome', published in 1664.*

Collecting, sketching and recording, *John Ray and Francis Willughby amassed a vast amount of botanical and zoological material. Above, left, is a lily drawn by Ray; right, the francolin, by Willughby.*

DURING THE CIVIL WAR, a man might have been seen tramping the fields and woods round Cambridge. This was John Ray, the son of a blacksmith. In 1660, when he took his degree, he published a description of all the species of plant growing around Cambridge, the first exhaustive study of its kind. Soon after this he met the wealthy young Francis Willughby; a friendship sprang up between the oddly assorted pair, and they resolved to catalogue all living things. Willughby would do the animals, Ray the plants. They set off and travelled round the Continent together, returning with a vast collection of materials for their project, including, as Ray seriously recorded, a tame flea, which Willughby had bought in Venice. It was kept warm in a box lined with wool and fed once a day. 'It lived for three months by sucking blood from Willughby's hand but died of cold in the winter.'

Ray, who had been ordained as a clergyman, lost his living for refusing to subscribe to Charles II's Act of Uniformity, but Willughby made him his guest. Ray produced a catalogue of all the plants in Britain, the first Flora, or botanical handbook; it remained the pocket companion of every British botanist for generations. It was dedicated to Willughby.

Then Willughby died, at the early age of 37, leaving £60 a year for Ray's support. Ray struggled on in poverty, producing a book on birds, based on Willughby's material, a classification of plants, and finally his vast *General History of Plants* – 2,860 closely-set pages describing about 18,600 plants, with all that was known about them including their physiology, in 25 sections. The sketch of a lily opposite was prepared for the History.

Ray also produced works on fish and animals, as well as one asserting the true nature of fossils as the petrified remains of extinct species.

Ray's system of classification represented a considerable advance on what had gone before, being based on natural features, such as whether the animal had a two- or a four-chambered heart. In particular he clarified the idea of species as distinct from genus. The colour of an animal, he said, is not a specific character, for offspring may vary in colour from their parents. The specific characters are those which are transmitted, like having four toes, plumage, etc.

Ray had a surprisingly plastic conception of nature, for his day, and realized that there must be a reason why each species was as it was, in its adaptation to the environment. He even raised the question, why is it that birds stop laying eggs when they have laid enough – a matter which no one thought of investigating further until 1926.

He, rather than Grew, should perhaps also receive credit for being the first comparative anatomist, as he sent a long account of the anatomy of a porpoise to the Royal Society after dissecting one during a visit to Chester in 1671. Apart from his biological studies, he wrote books on folklore and on the classics, as well as many sermons.

Preliminaries to the Nuptials of Plants was the title, translated, of a small thesis which Linnaeus wrote in 1729 and dedicated to the learned Celsius.

Preliminary to the Nuptials of Plants – *a thesis by Linnaeus setting forth his doctrine of sexuality in plants – foreshadowed his great 'Systema Naturae', the system of classification that is still known by his name today. This title-page in his own hand is still preserved in his old university of Upsala.*

In it, in semi-poetic style, he sets forth the doctrine of sexuality in plants. The title continues: 'in which the physiology of them is explained, Sex shown, Method of Generation disclosed, and the True Analogy of Plants with Animals concluded, by Carolus Linnaeus.' Celsius was delighted and Rudbeck made him his protégé.

This was the prelude to the *Systema Naturae,* outlining the system of classification which made him famous. As originally published in 1737, the *Systema* covered only seven large pages, and included animals and minerals as well as plants. When the tenth edition appeared, in the heyday of his fame, it had swollen to 2,500 pages.

Linnaeus recognized that the stamens of flowers were not merely ornamental but were male sexual organs, and that the pistils were female organs. He proposed to classify plants by counting the number of each. All plants with one stamen would be called Monandria, those with two Diandria, and so on. Within each of these groups, those with one pistil would be Monogynia, those with two, Digynia, etc. The system did not work for flowerless plants, such as mosses, ferns, fungi, seaweeds and slime-moulds, and Linnaeus lumped them together as Cryptogamia, secret marriers. It was equally inadequate for those small organisms, such as amoebae, which are not obviously sexual, and these he lumped together as Chaos.

Nevertheless, the new system was an instant success. It had two great advantages. It could be applied by anyone who could count up to twenty, and, within its limits, it left no room for dispute. It provided a framework into which new plants could be effortlessly fitted, as they were discovered.

As originally propounded, it did not embody Bauhin's binomial system: this was only introduced by Linnaeus in his vastly expanded tenth edition, where he enlarged it to cover animals, and included man in his categories, inventing the unduly optimistic designation *Homo sapiens (Linn.).*

In it Linnaeus introduced the use of the astrological signs ♂ and ♀ to indicate male and female; he also used ☿ to indicate hermaphrodite.

The first condition of health and happiness, declared Linnaeus, is to be born to young and vigorous parents in the full flood of sexual ardour. This he considered to be his own case, but never was man more preoccupied with the ideas of sex and of death than this remarkable Swede who imposed on the world his sexual system of classification.

The Botanical Gardens *at Upsala were restored and enriched by Linnaeus when he returned from his botanical travels, world-famous, to become Professor of Medicine. The gardens are still maintained as a memorial to the ancient university's greatest son.*

'What do mortals more desire in this unsubstantial fleeting world than that ... when our feeble frame decays and after death becomes noisome, some ... remembrance of their names, however slight, should reach posterity and endure yet a few days?' Linnaeus wrote of himself in the third person (as did Caesar, for instance) and attempted no fewer than four autobiographies. He conferred the names of his friends on plant families – for instance the yellow *Rudbeckia*.

In his second year at Upsala University, where the neglected botanic garden contained but 200 plants, this country parson's son took over the botany lectures from the elderly Rudbeck, who was bored by the subject, and increased the attendance at the lectures from 80 to 400. Here he met a tall, silent Lapp, Paul Artedi, who practised alchemy and studied fishes. Linnaeus was fascinated by the ideas which Artedi propounded, and the strangely-assorted pair, in imitation of Ray and Willughby, decided to devise an universal scheme of classification; Artedi would do fishes, amphibians and insects; Linnaeus birds, flowers and minerals.

Lapland was at this time scientifically a *terra incognita*. Over a country almost the size of England and Scotland, 7,000 Lapps roamed with their vast herds of reindeer. Rudbeck had been there in 1695 but all his notes had been destroyed in the disastrous fire which razed the university of Upsala in 1702. Linnaeus conceived the idea of exploiting this opportunity, and, armed with a tiny grant, set off on the eve of his twenty-fifth birthday. He records what he took with him: it included one shirt, two pairs of false sleeves and two half shirts, a graduated octangular stick and a gauze cap to protect his face from the midges.

Five months later he returned, with very few specimens and heavily in debt, bearing a number of showy trophies, such as a Lapp outfit and a magic drum. His newspaper articles were a big success: if he had not much to report scientifically, he had learned the secret of Lapp love philtres, and vividly described his adventures: how he had ridden his horse across a torrent on a tree, and had been shot at by a Lapp as he clung to a cliff in search of specimens. He omitted to mention that he had not actually been to Lapland at all: he had penetrated to the source of the Lule river in Sweden, and then had returned to its mouth and made his way by the coast route to Åbo, a university town about five hundred miles from Lapland.

On his return he spent three ill-documented years, lecturing on assaying, writing about dietetics and, it would seem, formulating his theories, for he says that all his ideas were thought out before his twenty-eighth year.

Attired in his Lapp costume, with magic drum, Linnaeus called upon the pretty daughter of a local mining doctor, whom he had met in the Christmas festivities at Falun in 1734. Her name was Sara Lisa Moraea, and she consented to marry him. But her father declared that Linnaeus must show his ability to support a wife. Linnaeus therefore scribbled a thesis on ague, and set off, his luggage stuffed with MSS for the Dutch diploma mills. He went to the small town of Harderwijk, where the university (subsequently forced to close) granted degrees at cheap rates. After a stay of a week, and having defended his thesis, he left with a handsome medical degree.

Instead of returning home, however, despite a message that a friend was courting his Sara, he went to Leiden, where he scraped acquaintance with Gronovius, and so charmed him that he financed the publication of his *Systema Naturae*; to Amsterdam, where he persuaded Burman to support the publication of two more books; and to Hartekamp, where the wealthy Englishman, Clifford, supported him on a handsome scale while he produced a series of further works, including – believe it or not – a Flora of Lapland! Clifford was rewarded with a work called *Hortus Cliffortianus,* which he was permitted to publish with splendid illustrations at his own expense. In all, Linnaeus got fourteen works into print.

Fame arrived almost overnight. Visiting Paris, he was made a member of the Academy, and offered a pension if he would become French. Visiting England, he encountered heavier going with the aged Dillenius, the Germanic Professor of Botany at Oxford. After a brief and angry conversation, Dillenius stalked into his library saying: 'There goes a man who is bringing all Botany into confusion.' Later, however, Linnaeus succeeded in identifying a flower unknown to Dillenius, which so impressed the old man that he begged Linnaeus to remain at Oxford, and even offered to share his salary with him.

But now, four years after leaving Sweden, Linnaeus felt the time had come to return, marry his Sara, and set up in practice in Stockholm.

Linnaeus now became a nabob of science. Installed in a newly-created professorship of medicine at Upsala, he restored the botanical gardens, stocking them with thousands of specimens. He was made first president of the newly-created Swedish Academy of Sciences. The Royal Society and other foreign Academies of Science hastened to bestow membership upon him. The Swedish government knighted him.

Visitors came from all over the world. Lord Baltimore arrived to see him in a coach so large that the gateposts had to be taken down to admit it.

(Asked why he had not first paid a courtesy call on the King of Sweden, he answered with true 18th-century bottom, 'Why should I go to see the King of Sweden, when I have never even cared to look at my own monarch?')

It became the tradition that on May 21 each year – supposedly his birthday – Linnaeus would lead a botanical ramble, accompanied by his students and any visiting botanists. A party of up to two hundred would set out on these expeditions, accompanied by French horns and kettledrums, and wearing prescribed dress and equipment.

Linnaeus sent out his pupils – he called them his apostles – to every quarter of the globe, where many of them speedily met with disagreeable fates. Dr Bartsch died within a month of arriving in Surinam. Ternström died on his way out; Löfling soon after arriving in Venezuela. Hasselquist expired in Syria, Berlin as soon as he reached Guinea. Kahler was shipwrecked, Förskål perished, disguised as a Bedouin, in Arabia Felix. But Osbeck reached China, Kalm explored America, and Solander sailed with James Cook to New Zealand.

Botanical collection became an universal craze; it was the Linnaean age. Linnaeus' apostles led the van: Solander, who discovered the bread-fruit; Per Kalm, for whom the *Kalmia* is named, and Adam Kuhn, who gave his name to the *Kuhnia*. But amateurs too entered the game.

Natural history had suddenly become popular. Soon no country house

In reindeer-skin tunic, *with native drum and magic amulet, Linnaeus looks the complete Lapp. But his journey in fact only took him to the source of the Lule River in the far north of Sweden.*

was complete without the splendidly illustrated *Histoire Naturelle* of Buffon, and by the end of the century moralists were bewailing the interest of young ladies in matters so obviously sexual.

A trade in specimens sprang up, with clearing houses in the big cities. Thus the brothers Verraux of Paris specialized in rare birds. Artists hastened to supply those who could not afford the real thing, or wished to identify their specimens. Gould's vast series of bird illustrations in 25 volumes is a case in point.

Not merely flowers and birds, but eggs, butterflies and even shells inspired the collectors' instinct. Hugh Cuming, a wealthy British collector, cruised the world in his private yacht, seeking unusual shells, many of which he subsequently sold for a hundred pounds apiece or more. One day, he came across a reef in the Pacific on which there were eight magnificent shells, complete with their inhabitants, of a kind never seen before. In ecstasies, he named them 'Glory of the Sea', and added them to his collection. A hurricane then obliterated the reef, and none has ever been found again.

Linnaeus sent his 'apostles' to the far corners of the earth, in the golden age of botanical collection. Many of them met their deaths on hazardous collecting trips. This old Danish print gives an impression of the dangers and hardships encountered by the botanists of the 'Linnaean age'.

3

THE ENCYCLOPAEDISTS

Buffon, Réaumur, von Haller

FIFTY-FIVE YEARS IN PRODUCTION, issued in forty-four volumes, the *Histoire Naturelle* of Georges Buffon was to be found in every house of consequence in the eighteenth century, in England as in France. This titanic work – it was finished years after Buffon's death by an assistant – contained hundreds of beautifully hand-coloured plates, and was typical of one side of 18th-century biology, as was Buffon himself. In its encyclopaedic range, as in the many shrewd observations within it, it reflected the attempt of the 18th century to order its thoughts. Scientifically, it was superficial: animals were described in sentimental manner – the lion was brave, the horse was man's noblest discovery, and so on. (But there were excellent anatomical appendices by Buffon's assistant, Daubenton.)

Elegant in all things, Buffon was accustomed to rise precisely at six, to dress with care in full Court costume, with orders, and to stand at his work table, writing steadily, for eight hours a day. After studying law, and inheriting a fortune, he had interested Louis xv in supporting science, and at the age of thirty-four had been made the Keeper of the Jardin du Roi, which was to become, after the Revolution, the Muséum d'Histoire Naturelle. He had already translated works by Newton and Stephen Hales, the clergyman-physiologist, into French.

His brilliant and lucid style ensured success for the *Histoire*. In an age of phrase-makers, he was '*roi des phrasiers*': 'genius is an infinite capacity for taking pains', '*le style c'est l'homme même*', 'the purpose of philosophy is not to understand the why but the how of things'. These *mots* are his. He also said: 'I have learned botany three times, and all the same I have forgotten it.'

An indictment of fourteen points was brought against Buffon for the views at which he hinted in his *History of the Earth*. Suppose, he said, that the earth were far more than 6,000 years old; that it had been stricken off the sun by a passing comet, in an incandescent form; that it had cooled through a period of volcanic activity and mountain upheavals; that tropical animals had once roamed through regions now cold; and that finally modern fauna and man had appeared. Suppose further 'that man and monkey have a common origin . . . that each family among the animals has come from only one animal . . .' One could say, he sardonically remarked, 'that the monkey is of the family of man, that it is a degenerated man . . .'

But no, he added, we know from revelation that every animal came from God's hand as it is, and that the origin of the earth from the sun is but a theoretical possibility.

Despite this precaution, the pressure brought by the Church against him was so great that he was obliged to recant. In the next volume of his *Histoire Naturelle* he wrote: 'I declare that I had no intention of contradicting the Scriptures, that I believe most firmly all therein stated about the Creation . . . I abandon everything in my book respecting the formation of the earth, and in general all that may be contrary to the narrative of Moses.' The next year he was elected to the Academy without a canvass, and married an heiress.

Buffon, always the centre of attention, is seen here at a meeting of scientists at the Jardin du Roi. The scene is an imaginative reconstruction by Eugene Fichel, painted in 1872.

Almost incredibly, even the atheist Voltaire joined with the church in condemning Buffon's theory. The shells on the tops of mountains, to which Buffon had pointed as proof of mountain upheaval, had been left there by pilgrims, Voltaire said. The bones of fishes had been left by picnickers.

Nevertheless, Buffon became a titan.

Rousseau kissed the threshold before entering the château at Montbard where Buffon worked. Cuvier regarded him as a god. Mirabeau thought he was the greatest man of the century. Even Voltaire said he was a second Archimedes. (Buffon himself said there had only been five really great men: Newton, Bacon, Leibniz, Montesquieu and himself.)

Buffon has often been decried as a dilettante; yet he started trains of thought which persisted long after his death. Cuvier adopted many of his ideas, and he influenced many of whom I have not yet written – Erasmus Darwin and Lamarck, Goethe and St Hilaire, even Bichat.

He denied that plants and animals had been created by a single fiat of the deity. He also denied that the species were fixed and distinct, holding that they graded into one another. Remarkably, he stressed that there was no fundamental difference between plants and animals. He maintained that men, too, were physically similar, even if physically different. These were views of the highest originality and cleared the ground for a theory of evolution. He also offered a scientifically plausible account of generation, to which we shall come in the next chapter. Buffon was thus a mechanist in a far wider sense than Borelli, and saw the whole of nature as causally related.

Not only a biologist, he was the founder of anthropology, describing man with the same detachment as he had described animals, and making longevity studies on calculations of probability.

Buffon's reputation declined before the work of Spallanzani (which I am about to describe) disproved Buffon's theory of how new life is created. And the vast scheme of the *Histoire Naturelle* gradually overwhelmed him. Buffon toiled on despairingly into old age. There were always more species to be described. 'These endless water birds,' he moaned, 'with their sad cries, and about which it is impossible to find anything to say.'

After his death, the revolutionary mob broke open his tomb, pulled down his statue, and scattered his bones to the wind. His son was guillotined.

If Buffon, in his glory, represents one aspect of the 18th century, the Comte F. A. L. de Réaumur represents the other. In accordance with the rule that scientists tend to study the animals, or the problems, which they most resemble, or the problems which most preoccupy them, de Réaumur studied ants and other insects. Between the two men no love was lost. Buffon grandly said that a bee should occupy no more room in a naturalist's head than it does in nature. Réaumur criticized the *Histoire Naturelle* as inaccurate and pompous.

Réaumur was a man of wealth and his interests were wide. He kept a pet kite with the aid of which he opened up the physiology of digestion. The kite is a bird which vomits up indigestible foods. Réaumur had the idea of training his pet to swallow small open-ended metal tubes containing sponges. When the bird brought them up, the sponges were soaked with gastric juice, and Réaumur then showed that the juice softened meat. 'When I put some of the juice from the buzzard's stomach on my tongue, it tasted salt rather than bitter, although the bones . . . on which the fluid had acted, had not a salt but a bitter taste,' he recorded, about 1752.

Unfortunately, the bird died in the course of his observations, and he was obliged to continue his experiments upon less obliging animals, such as ducks and chickens, from whom the sponge had to be withdrawn by a thread.

The forty-four titanic volumes *of Buffon's 'Histoire Naturelle' represent the attempts of the Age of Enlighten-ment to order its thoughts and classify its knowledge. Above, the Urubu, a South American vulture, shows the meticulously careful hand-colouring of this great work's hundreds of plates.*

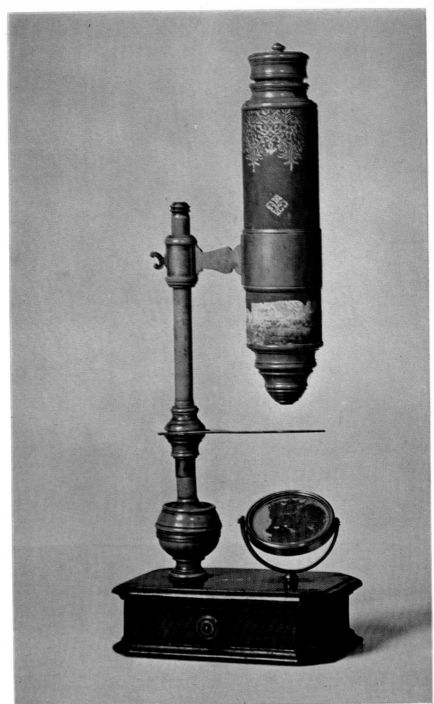

Decoratively tooled, but crude in design, Spallanzani's microscope can still be seen at the Wellcome Historical Medical Museum, London. Focussing must have been by relatively coarse manual adjustment of the eyepiece.

The Comte de Réaumur, *one of the most wide-ranging minds of the 18th century, worked on the physiology of digestion (with the aid of a pet kite), wrote a 6-volume survey of the insect world, and devised the thermo-metric scale that still bears his name.*

Prior to this, he had placed bits of meat in the tubes, and found, when they were regurgitated, that the meat, though partly digested, was neither putrefied nor minced up. Thus he proved that digestion was not, as had been commonly supposed, a simple process of trituration or of putrefaction.

De Réaumur also worked on a wide range of other biological subjects, as diverse as the locomotion of starfish, marine phosphorescence, the effect of heat on insect development, regeneration in crustaceans, artificial incubation, and bees. His magnum opus was a monumental 6-volume survey of the insect world, with 5,000 illustrations, containing countless important original observations, which appeared between 1734 and 1742.

He also contributed to metallurgy, invented 'Réaumur's porcelain', and the thermometric scale (on which the boiling point of water is 80°) which still bears his name.

THE ABBE SPALLANZANI had a passion for travel, and visited many parts of the Mediterranean. In particular he made a detailed geological survey of the two Sicilies, and closely studied the volcanoes. Overleaf he is seen, after a difficult climb, at the summit of Mt Etna, with two guides, who relax as Spallanzani sketches the scene.

By what strange means Spallanzani became an abbé remains a mystery. But the post gave him time for an industrious and fruitful career in science. At the university, where he was studying law, his talent for science was so marked that Vallisnieri, a professor of medicine, persuaded his father to let him switch from law to science.

With the versatility which was so characteristic of the 18th century, he made contributions in meteorology, topography and geology, as well as in physiology, embryology and other biological fields. He was the discoverer of artificial insemination, at a time when it was not even known that the seminal fluid was essential to conception.

He was also the discoverer of the fact that bats can avoid stretched wires even in a dark room, or when their eyes are covered – though the explanation, that they emit high-frequency sound pulses and detect the echoes, did not come until 1920.

In a famous series of experiments, he disproved Buffon's theory of the existence of 'organic molecules' and the Abbé Needham's belief in the spontaneous generation of living organisms: this I shall discuss more fully later.

When Réaumur attempted to dissolve meat in gastric juice, it did not occur to him that it should be kept at the same temperature as within the body, and the meat was only softened. Spallanzani, now using a vomiting crow, extended these experiments, discovering that after seven hours most kinds of food are completely dissolved and learning many other facts.

Finally, Spallanzani experimented on himself, in order to show that human digestion was similar to that of animals. After pondering the fact that children often swallow objects, such as plum-stones, without harm, Spallanzani forced himself one morning, on rising, to swallow a linen bag containing 52 grains of masticated bread. On emerging, 23 hours later, it contained no bread, though the bag was undamaged. Subsequently, he swallowed wooden spheres and metal tubes with ends closed by gauze, containing various foods. He attempted in vain to vomit these up, commenting sadly that his scientific curiosity could not conquer his repugnance.

The English surgeon, Hunter, condemned his work in rough terms, because he had said that digestion does not take place below the temperature of the body – whereas Hunter had found, in dissecting certain corpses, that a part of the stomach had become digested by the juices within it. (The implicit question, why the stomachs of all animals are not digested during life, should have shown him that the problem is not as simple as it seems.)

Still more than Hunter, Voltaire heaped scorn upon him. Spallanzani remained courteous to his critics, and was in fact most judicious in his generalizations. He died of apoplexy on 11th February 1799.

'Sweating and breathless' *after clambering over great shifting blocks of lava,*
the Abbé Spallanzani surveys the crater of Etna, his two guides beside him.
The Abbé estimated the circumference at $1^1/_2$ *miles. The figures on the crater's rim*
are disproportionately large, but 'the painter conceived he might be permitted
this licence, as, had he attempted to observe the rules of proportion,
these figures would have been scarcely discernible.'

'IN THE SCIENCES, England appears to be second to none... in the study of nature, in brilliant experiments, and in all spheres involving geometry and the nature of living creatures, they excel all previous epochs and all other countries today.'

Such was the impression formed by the young von Haller when he visited England in 1727.

In von Haller, Switzerland produced one of the greatest figures in scientific history: a man of fantastic erudition, vastly productive and an investigator of genius. He was equally eminent as an anatomist, physiologist, botanist, medical historian and poet. Von Haller listed what he considered his important works, to the number of 49, including two encyclopaedias, four treatises on anatomy, twelve on physiology, seven on botany, five on bibliography, one book of poems, two theological works and four historical novels.

At nine years old, he wrote Latin verse, studied Chaldaean, composed a Greek and Hebrew dictionary, wrote brief biographies of more than 3,000 people and produced some promising poems. He gained his doctorate at nineteen.

He published his first poems at twenty-six – they were received with rapture – and at twenty-nine was so famous that he was called to be professor at the new university of Göttingen. Here he set up botanic gardens and conducted countless researches in anatomy and physiology, and in bibliography. His published papers number about 1,300. He made Göttingen the finest centre of physiological research in Europe. Such was his reputation that when pirates seized a ship containing a box of books addressed to him, they immediately forwarded it to him.

The plates in von Haller's atlas of the blood vessels, of which this is one, constituted a milestone in anatomical illustration, and provided a counterpart to the plates of bones and muscles in the Albinus folio (1747). Von Haller made himself a master of techniques for injecting blood vessels with substances which would reveal their course, and cleared up many obscure points.

His greatest contribution, however, was the notion of irritability: certain tissues have the power, he realized, of responding to stimuli. In a series of 567 experiments, of which he performed 190 himself, he developed this point, establishing that pain was dependent on the nerves. Obvious as this now seems to us, it was in fact an important step, for it was the first time that a specific function had been shown to be related to a specific tissue.

For more than a century physiologists kept going back to von Haller's *Elementa Physiologiae*, a work of completely modern character, describing body structure and function systematically, and containing many discoveries

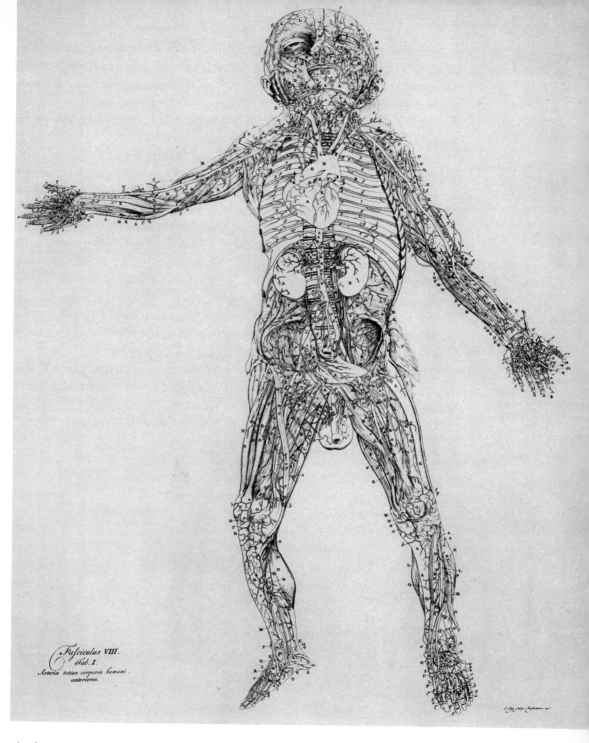

The fantastic erudition *of von Haller is well represented in his 'Atlas of the Blood Vessels', from which this is* taken. *He mastered the technique of injecting blood vessels with substances which would reveal their course.*

subsequently forgotten and rediscovered, e.g. the role of bile in digestion, and the theory that heart-beats originate in the heart-muscle itself. Magendie, the 19th-century physiologist, once complained that often 'after I had finished the work, I found the whole discovery in Haller. I was greatly provoked, I cursed more than once this wretched book where everything was to be found . . .'

He threw light on the action of the digestive juices, the formation of bone, the mechanism of respiration, and much besides, and with a simple microscope observed thrombosis – blood clotting within a vein – 120 years before its formal discovery by Zehn.

To the amazement of all Europe, at forty-nine von Haller, refusing posts at Oxford, Berlin and elsewhere, returned to Berne to become manager of a near-by saltworks, and to be Town Administrator and Doorman.

This extraordinary man had been a sickly, rickety child, whose mother died when he was very young. All his life, his constitution was weakly but he was driven by a relentless ambition and self-discipline. He was a pietist Protestant, deeply conservative, critical of others, humourless and resentful of any opposition to authority. (His *bête noire* was Rousseau.) It has been said that he 'thought as a rationalist, but believed as a Christian'. In old age, he was troubled increasingly by religious scruples, and sought surcease in the Bible and in toil. He died in 1777.

One of the last great polymaths *of the 18th century, von Haller was anatomist, physiologist, botanist, historian, theologian, poet and artist. Here he is seen painting in the Alps.*

The ventilation of Newgate prison *by means of this windmill was Hales' contribution to the prevention of gaol fever – actually caused by bacterial infection, not by 'bad air'.*

THE WINDMILL in Newgate Prison, seen in this print, drove ventilators devised by the Rev. Stephen Hales, a Twickenham parson. Hales had designed them for use in naval ships, but the Admiralty laughed at the idea. He got them installed in slaving vessels, where they so greatly reduced the death-rate among the overcrowded slaves, that the Admiralty finally adopted them. Hales got them installed at Newgate in the belief that 'gaol fever' was caused by 'bad air' – though it is really caused by lice-borne bacteria. But Hales, of course, had no knowledge of micro-organisms.

Hales was seventy-five and full of honour when he turned to the study of ventilation. In 1718, when he was forty-one, he was made an FRS for having performed a crucial series of experiments on the circulation of the blood, the first significant contribution to be made since Harvey's more than half a century before. He was in fact the first man to measure the pressure of the blood. Borelli had estimated blood pressure at 135,000 lb., and had argued that the swelling of a muscle on contraction was due to the blood, under this terrific pressure, dilating its fibres. It was to test this erroneous thesis that Hales undertook his experiments. He describes his crucial experiment thus:

'In December I caused a mare to be tied down alive on her back; she was 14 hands high, and about 14 years of age ... having laid open the left crural artery about three inches from her belly, I inserted into it a brass pipe whose bore was $^1/_6$ of an inch in diameter; and to that, by means of another brass pipe which was fitly adapted to it, I fixed a glass tube of nearly the same diameter, which was 9 feet in length; then untying the ligature on the artery, the blood rose in the tube 8 feet 3 inches perpendicular above the level of the left ventricle of the heart ...'

It occurred to Hales that possibly the blood pressure had built up to an abnormal level during the time the artery was ligatured. He therefore devised a way of taking the blood pressure while the blood was actually flowing.

From such experiments he established many new facts, such as that blood pressure is roughly proportional to the size of the animal, and that the pulse

Fig. 19.

S.G.

The first measurement of root pressure – the osmotic force that raises sap in a plant – was performed by Stephen Hales. In the experiment figured here, he fixed glass tubes in the cut stems of a vine – a method suggested by his earlier experiments on blood pressure.

is more rapid in smaller animals than large. He also attempted to study the speed of blood flow, clotting and other problems.

For seven years Hales despaired of finding a way to extend these enquiries to plants. One day, desiring to stop the bleeding of an old vine stem, he tied a bit of bladder over it. A day or two later, he noticed that the force of the sap had distended the bladder. By fixing a glass tube to the cut stem of a vine, and sealing it with beeswax and turpentine, he became the first man to measure 'root pressure' – the osmotic force which raises sap in the plant before the leaves are formed.

Many botanists supposed that sap circulated in plants like blood in animals, rising in the older, central wood, and falling in the newer layers beneath the bark. Hales, by boring lateral holes into the branch of a dwarf golden pippin apple tree, showed that a branch can imbibe water from either end.

The oak beams of Hales's church at Twickenham were hung with garlands in honour of young women of the parish who had died virgins, and Hales made sex offenders do public penance in a manner already almost obsolete. Mild-mannered Hales, painting the posts along the footpath white to help benighted passers-by, belongs to the age when science and religion could still go hand-in-hand. He avoided preferment in the Church lest it interfere with his studies, and it was he who advised housewives to put an inverted tea-cup in their apple-pie to support the crust and prevent it from becoming soggy.

When Sachs came to write the first great account of the physiology of plants in 1865, he had to go back to Hales to find results of an accuracy comparable with his own. In the century which separated Hales's death from the work of Sachs, the main features of how plants and animals respire became clear.

IN 1774 AN UNITARIAN MINISTER named Joseph Priestley heated mercuric oxide with a burning glass – which produced a more intense heat than any flame available to him – and produced a gas which he found caused a candle to burn more brightly than in air. In March 1775 he had the idea of seeing whether it was breathable. Placing a mouse under a bell-jar filled with the gas, he found it lived for half an hour, whereas it would have survived for only a quarter of an hour in air. Encouraged by this, he cautiously inhaled it himself. 'The feeling of it to my lungs was not sensibly different from that of air,' he commented, 'but I fancied that my breast felt peculiarly light and easy for some time afterwards. Who can tell but that, in time, this pure air may become a fashionable article in luxury? Hitherto only two mice and myself have had the privilege of breathing it.'

The gas, of course, was oxygen – though this name for it was invented later by the French chemist Lavoisier, whom Priestley told of his experiments. The discovery of oxygen soon led to the first understanding of the processes by which animals and plants breathe.

Lavoisier made these experiments quantitative. He shut up animals and weighed how much air they breathed, showing that oxygen is absorbed in the lungs and carbon dioxide given off in exchange.

A mouse placed in a bell-jar *by Joseph Priestley was the first creature privileged to breathe pure oxygen. 'Who can tell,' wrote Priestley, 'but that, in time, this pure air may become a fashionable article in luxury?'*

As a Dissenter, Priestley was denied access to British universities. He was a fearless advocate of civil and religious liberty, writing many pamphlets on these subjects. Such feeling was aroused that Lord Shelburne, for whom he worked as librarian and intellectual companion, felt obliged to terminate the appointment, though he gave him an annuity.

Priestley took on a ministry in Birmingham, and continued to write. When he wrote of scientific enquiry 'blowing up the old building of error and superstition' he was nicknamed 'Gunpowder Priestley', and the rumour was spread that he planned to blow up the churches.

He was playing backgammon at home in 1791 when a friend brought news that an angry mob had already set his chapel on fire and was on its way to destroy his house. It is now known that this mob was incited by the authorities of the established church. Priestley fled with his family, while the mob destroyed his apparatus and scattered his books to the wind. Subse-quently, he emigrated to the United States of America.

*'The Priestley politican or the political priest':
a contemporary cartoon shows Priestley, the
defender of civil and religious liberties, as an
incendiary tub-thumper.*

In the same year, a French popular tribunal sent Lavoisier to the guil-lotine. Lavoisier had been unconcerned about the effect of the revolution on himself, saying he could always get a job as a chemist. He counted without the cynicism of the tribunal, which accused him of the fantastic charge of watering the army's tobacco, and rejected a plea that he be spared as a scientist who had honoured France with the crass comment: 'The revolution has no need of scientists.'

Also a protégé of the Earl of Shelburne was a Dutch doctor, Jan Ingen-housz. Shelburne, 'the most good natured man in the world', gave him a room at Bowood Park. Ingenhousz was a skilled inoculator, and had been recommended as the man to inoculate Queen Maria Teresa. However his main interest was plants. Intrigued by Priestley's experiments, he demon-strated, four years later, that the leaves of green plants, under the influence of sunlight, also produce oxygen – but that at night they produce 'a kind of air' fatal to animal life, which in a confined space will extinguish a flame.

Here was a mystery: the production of 'pure air' in daytime and 'polluted air' at night. This was a milestone in the discovery of the mechanism of plant respiration, but it was to be many years before its significance was appreciated.

De Saussure, a Swiss chemist and physicist, held the chair of geology – he introduced the term – in Geneva and worked on vegetable physiology. (He also initiated the modern interest in mountaineering, climbing Mont Blanc in 1787.) Taking advantage of the new quantitative methods devised by Lavoisier, he went far beyond Ingenhousz or any of his contemporaries, enclosing plants and parts of plants in measured quantities of air, weighed and analysed, exposing them to different conditions, and investigating the changes. He found, to the general amazement, that it is from the air, not from the soil, that the plant derives most of its nourishment. The water and carbon dioxide are just what the plant requires.

De Saussure also realized that certain minerals were essential, and determined what they were by analysing the ashes of burnt plants.

The green colouring matter, chlorophyll, he wrongly thought unimpor-tant, owing to the fact that some plants lack it. It was another Frenchman, Dutrochet, who found that only cells containing chlorophyll can take up carbon dioxide. But not until 1865 did Sachs, a German botanist, show how the chlorophyll is contained in special bodies, and that starch appears in them following the absorption of carbon dioxide. But how does the carbon dioxide get in? By the beautifully simple device of coating parts of leaves with a film of wax, thus blocking the small pores by which carbon dioxide enters, Sachs showed in 1894 that this was indeed the mode of entry, for starch only developed in the uncoated parts.

WITH THE DEVICE known as Knight's wheel, another English country gentleman, Thomas Knight, attacked the second great problem of plant physiology – how plants move. Malpighi and Ray had observed the periodic movements of plants, the bending of shoots towards the light, the shrinking of mimosa, the way roots turn down towards the earth. But, like many later writers, they attributed these movements to a mysterious 'vital force'.

The first man to give a purely mechanical explanation of such movements was Knight. Rotating seedlings on the wheel, he found the roots now turned outwards, along the lines of centrifugal force. He concluded that an alteration in the position of the sap was the cause. He accounted for the curling of tendrils in much the same way. But he was totally baffled by the way in which some leaves turn at right angles to the sun. These movements could only be accounted for, he argued, by some 'vehicle of irritation'. Yet, he added, 'I am wholly unable to trace the existence of anything like sensation or intellect in plants.'

The term 'tropisms' was not coined for such movements until 1868.

Knight, whose object was the improvement of agriculture, also tackled the third great problem of plant physiology: the process by which plants are fertilized. His book on the subject, which argued that interbreeding between the male and female elements in the same flower – 'plant incest' – would lead to infertility (which is untrue), attracted great attention.

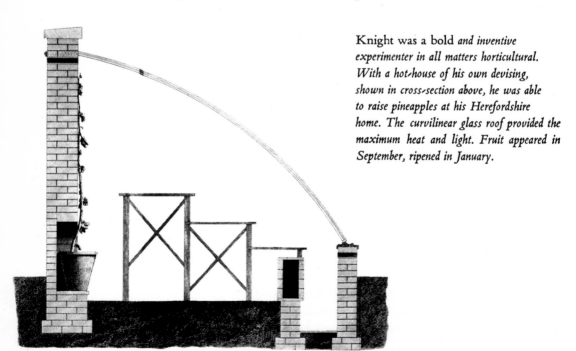

Knight was a bold *and inventive experimenter in all matters horticultural. With a hot-house of his own devising, shown in cross-section above, he was able to raise pineapples at his Herefordshire home. The curvilinear glass roof provided the maximum heat and light. Fruit appeared in September, ripened in January.*

John Hunter, *Surgeon General to the Army. After Sir Joshua Reynolds.*

'THEY WANTED TO MAKE AN OLD WOMAN OF ME,' said Hunter of his relatives' attempts to improve his education, 'or that I should stuff Latin and Greek at the University: but these schemes I cracked like so many vermin as they came before me.' He left Oxford after two months.

His style remained rough, and when he set up as a lecturer he had to calm his nerves with a draught of laudanum before each lecture. A sample of his mode of expression: 'The bullet went into the man's belly, and hit his guts such a damn thump that they mortified.'

Some time after qualifying as a doctor, he joined the army and went to Belle Isle, where he whiled the time away with experiments. He tested whether fishes could hear, by firing a gun above the water, and showed that food in the stomach of a hibernating lizard remained undigested.

He became, eventually, an eminent surgeon: in 1789 he was made Surgeon Extraordinary to the King, and later Surgeon General to the Army. His achievement was to make surgery, which had been solely an operative science, into a physiological science. Typical of the experiments by which he did this was that in which he tied a cord round the arteries supplying the half-grown antlers of a deer. They became cold, but a week later, he noticed that they were warm again – for other blood vessels had increased in size to take up the load. On the strength of this, he decided to tie off the artery in a patient suffering from a defective artery in the leg. His fellow⸗

surgeons were horrified, believing the patient would lose his leg from gangrene, but, just as in the case of the deer, a subsidiary circulation developed.

In another heroic experiment, Hunter inoculated himself with pus from a patient who had gonorrhea, to discover whether it had the same cause as syphilis. The patient must have had both, for Hunter developed both, and was led to conclude that it had.

He wrote four great books, one of them the first thoroughly scientific work on the teeth in English, another on the nature of inflammation. To achieve all this and maintain his practice, he worked eighteen or nineteen hours a day, in the intervals of repeated heart attacks, one of which killed him.

But his supreme service to biology was his unique collection, which took much of his time and all of his money. With the building he erected for it in Leicester Square, it cost him £70,000.

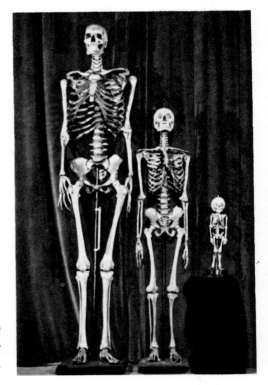

approximatly
1mm. = 1 inch
IN SCALE OF
PICTURES.
O'BRIEN'S SKELETON
STANDING 7FT 7 INCH.

Over seven foot tall, *the skeleton of the Irish giant O'Brien, in the Hunterian Museum, stands beside skeletons of a normal man and a pygmy.*

The Irish giant, O'Brien, or Byrne, hearing that Hunter coveted his body, ordered that it be placed in a lead coffin and sunk at sea. But Hunter, it is said, bribed the watchers and obtained the body at a cost of £500, which he had to borrow for the purpose.

The Hunterian Museum *as it appeared in 1830. O'Brien's skeleton can be seen on the right. It was Hunter's brilliantly original conception to arrange the collection, not as a 'cabinet of curiosities', but as an instructive, scientifically ordered display. Much of the collection was destroyed in the air raids on London during the last war.*

Byrne claimed to be 8 feet 4 inches, but his skeleton, as it stands in the Hunterian Collection today, is a mere 7 feet 7 inches. The Collection contained 13,682 specimens, including 1,000 complete organisms. (Many were destroyed by a bomb during the last war.) It also contained pictures and illustrations, including paintings by George Stubbs, and Hunter had his own draughtsmen and a printing press.

Whenever he had saved ten guineas, he would purchase something for his collection with it. But it was no random assortment: the exhibits displayed various complete series of ideas, showing the structure and activities of plants and animals in various phases of life. This was Hunter's brilliant conception – to turn the museum from a 'cabinet of curiosities' into a scientifically ordered and instructive display. Every object had its logical place, and was necessary to the scheme.

In his will Hunter proposed that this unique collection be sold to the nation at a nominal sum, but the government refused it. 'What! Buy preparations!' exclaimed Pitt, the Prime Minister, 'Why, I have not money enough to buy gunpowder!' Hunter's servant, Clift, living on seven shillings a week, kept the collection intact until the government changed its mind, and he became its curator until his death in 1849.

A little gentleman, with a deal of business on his hands –

Hunter's servant *Clift* loyally kept the Hunterian collection intact after his master's death, until it was bought by the nation. He eked out his tiny income by helping with the specimens for Sir Charles Bell's lectures, as is shown in this irreverent sketch by his son.

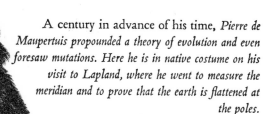

A century in advance of his time, *Pierre de Maupertuis propounded a theory of evolution and even foresaw mutations. Here he is in native costume on his visit to Lapland, where he went to measure the meridian and to prove that the earth is flattened at the poles.*

WHILE WE ARE STILL in the 18th century, I must mention a man who, though he was born at the end of the 17th century and died in 1759, I place at the end of the chapter, because he originated ideas so greatly in advance of his age that his thought belongs rather to the century which follows than his own.

Born far, far in advance of his time, Pierre de Maupertuis – here seen in Lapland, where he went to measure the meridian – anticipated all the main teachings of Mendel, Darwin and de Vries. That is to say, he produced a coherent theory of evolution, provided it with an adequate genetic basis, and even foresaw mutation – all this a century or more before the official proponents of these ideas.

In addition, this soldier-mathematician enunciated the Principle of Least Action, usually credited to the mathematicians Euler, Lagrange, or Hamilton, according to national preference. In biology this principle implies that the internal milieu of the body will tend to remain stable – a principle only formally enunciated a century later by Claude Bernard.

Maupertuis was the first man on the Continent to expound the ideas of Newton; and he undertook his Lapland expedition to prove that the earth was flattened at the poles, as Newton's theory required. In the course of the expedition, he fell in love with a Lapp girl whom he brought back to Paris.

The arrival in Paris at this time of a 'white negro' and the occurrence of a case of hexadactyly (six fingers) dramatized the whole question of physical inheritance and turned Maupertuis' thoughts from physics to genetics. He engaged in the large-scale interbreeding of animals, in the hope of producing a new species, for he totally rejected the idea of fixity of species, and spoke in a strikingly modern way of animals adapting to their environment.

'Chance, one might say, turned out a vast number of individuals. A small proportion of these were organized in such a manner that the animals' organs could satisfy their needs. A much greater number showed neither adaptation nor order; these last have all perished . . . Thus the species which we see today are but a small part of all those that a blind destiny has produced.' Thus he flouted the authorities, much more directly than had Buffon, rejecting not merely fixity of species, but the whole conception of a divine plan in nature. These bold words he published under the name of 'Dr Baumann'.

In the 18th century the idea of the Ladder of Nature was being modified. Whereas, to the mediaeval mind, the order of nature had been fixed, and to attempt to improve one's position in it betrayed the sin of pride, in the Age of Reason the idea was current that the ladder could be climbed. Man was perfectible and could hope to become an angel. Animals, by implication, might expect one day to become men. The background of ideas against which a theory of evolution could be propounded was being sketched out.

The idea of missing links between man and apes was already common,

ANTHROPOMORPHA

TROGLODYTA *Bontii*   2. *LUCIFER Aldrovandi*   3. *SATYRUS Tulpii*   4. *PYGMÆUS Edwardi*

and some are seen (left) in a work of 1760. When the chimpanzee and orang utan were discovered, they were widely regarded as candidates for this role, and enormous interest was aroused. But before we can come to the first theories of evolution, we must look at some other aspects of 18th-century biology, and complete our account of Maupertuis.

By a fantastic piece of insight, Maupertuis foresaw that heredity must be due to particles derived from both father and mother; and that similar particles have an affinity which makes them pair; and that in each pair, the particles from either father or mother may dominate; so that a trait may be inherited from ancestors through parents who do not possess it. When I come to describe what we have learned about genetics in the last hundred years, we shall see how precisely correct he was.

More than this, he saw that new particles might arise, and result in new species, if their effects were advantageous. From this he derived the central concept of the mechanism of evolution. 'Could not one explain by that means,' he said, and these are pregnant words, 'how from two individuals alone the multiplication of the most dissimilar species could have followed?'

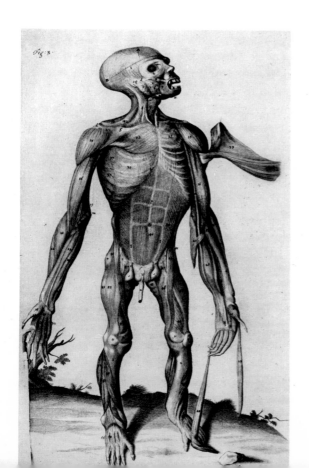

The idea of missing links *was very much in the air towards the end of the 18th century. The 'Anthropomorpha' (opposite) of Hoppius, a pupil of Linnaeus, put forward various candidates for the part – an engaging jumble of hearsay and legend. A long step nearer to zoological realism, Tyson's dissection of the muscles of a chimpanzee (or, as he put it, 'of the fore-part of the body of a pygmie') is part of a comparative study of man and apes. 'The Pygmie more resembles a Man than Apes and Monkeys do; but where it differs, there it is like the Ape-kind.'*

Maupertuis' ideas aroused no response: and Voltaire poured ridicule on him until his death in 1759.

People had, of course, been familiar with the idea of improving breeds of animals from time immemorial. The crucial advance was to realize that there were circumstances in which modifications of the breed could become so marked that a new species was created. This, it cannot be too strongly emphasized, was the key idea which made a theory of evolution possible.

But for the modification of species to take effect, clearly long periods of time were needed. Thus any theory of evolution controverted the theological view in several ways: it denied that the Creator personally devised all the species in a single act of creation; it was inconsistent with the whole concept of a fixed order of nature, in which every being had its assigned place; it was inconsistent with the theory of plenitude; and it required much more time than was allowed by the orthodox view – that the history of the world went back only 6,000 years. Conflict with the Church was inevitable.

Although geology was not established as a reputable science until the surprisingly late date of the end of the 18th century (James Hutton, 1726–1797, may be regarded as its founder), people had begun to think in terms of a long cosmic evolution, and only the very orthodox believed in a world history of a mere 6,000 years.

What was a much more active issue was the question of fossils: for if the bones of vanished species were admitted, then clearly the principle of plenitude was incorrect. And, from admitting that species could vanish, it was a small step to supposing that they could also appear. And this clashed unambiguously with the received theory of creation.

Fossils, of course, had been observed from early times, and even in the 16th century da Vinci and others proposed their true origin. The Church replied that they were due to such causes as a 'lapidific air' or a 'tumultous movement of terrestrial exhalations'. When, around the beginning of the 17th century, the scientific view was restated, the theological faculty of Paris burned the offending books, and banished their authors.

These drawings of 'insectiform stones' were the undoing of the geologist Beringer. So committed was he to the view (derived from Avicenna) that fossils were 'stones of a peculiar sort, hidden by the Author of Nature for

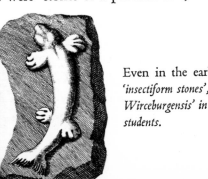

Even in the early days *of geology, fakes abounded. These* 'insectiform stones', *figured in Beringer's* 'Lithographiae Wirceburgensis' *in 1726, were devised by some irreverent students.*

his own pleasure', that some of his sceptical students decided to test his faith. They baked a variety of 'fossils' from clay, representing imaginary creatures, birds on their nests, and even representations of the sun and moon, and buried them where Beringer would find them. Convinced that he had come upon unimpeachable evidence, he published in 1726 these plates of his discoveries, despite warnings that they were fakes. Only when a 'fossil' turned up bearing his own name was his faith in their divine origin shattered. He spent his fortune trying to buy up all copies of his book, and died of chagrin.

In 1726, Scheuchzer exhibited the bones here shown as those of a man, a 'human witness' drowned in the Flood. This, he calculated, had taken place exactly 4,032 years previously. The discovery was hailed with joy; Scheuchzer prepared a magnificently illustrated Bible (from which the plate is taken). The bones were those of an ichthyosaurus.

A 'human witness', *drowned in the Flood: a fossil ichthyosaurus was published by Scheuchzer, in 1726, as a true specimen of prediluvian man whose death had taken place in the year 2306 B.C.*

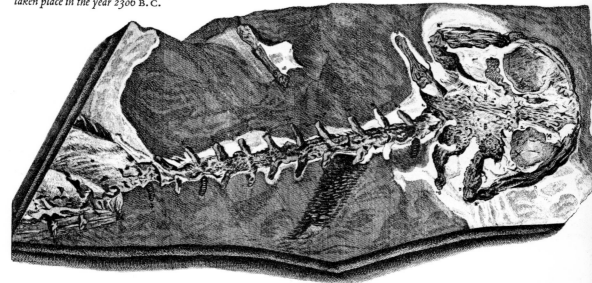

Calmet, the learned Benedictine, believed that the mastodon's bones exhibited by the French surgeon, Mazurier, in 1613 were those of King Teutoboccus, and valuable proof of the existence of giants. Increase Mather took the same line in the United States. In France such bones were hung up in churches as proofs of the deluge, and Henrion was inspired to calculate the size of our primitive ancestors. Adam, he worked out, was 123 feet 9 inches in height; Eve 118 feet 9 inches.

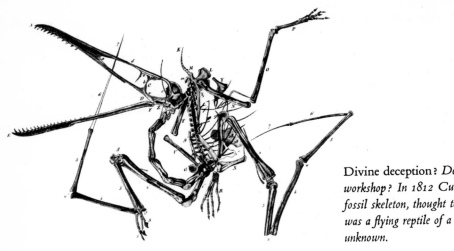

Divine deception? *Detritus of the Creator's workshop? In 1812 Cuvier showed that this fossil skeleton, thought to be that of a bird, was a flying reptile of a sort previously unknown.*

Earlier it had been claimed that fossils were models and abandoned projects of the Creator, the detritus of his workshop. But the numbers of fossils which could not thus be explained away increased rapidly. This fossil skeleton was found in 1788 and at first regarded as that of a bird: in 1812 Cuvier showed that it was a flying reptile of a sort previously unknown, and named it Pterodactyl. Chateaubriand was driven to write his *Genius of Christianity* – once thought a work of greatness, now merely ridiculous – in which he claimed that God had organized 'a general deception', in which everything was created with an illusory appearance of having had a previous existence. Even the previous year's birds' nests had been placed in the trees by the Creator, despite the fact that there had been no previous year, nor any birds to inhabit them. This proved the perfection and harmony of nature.

When geologists began to account for the structure of the earth's surface in terms of the slow deposition of sediments, the cooling of volcanic fires, and the gradual heaving and crumbling of these strata, the orthodox view became even harder to maintain. The poet Cowper complained, with what he thought was crushing irony, of those who

> Drill and bore
> The solid earth, and from the strata there
> Extract a register, by which we learn
> That He who made it, and revealed its date
> To Moses, was mistaken in its age!

Small wonder that geology was soon declared 'not a subject of lawful enquiry', and 'dangerous and disreputable'.

4

THE CONTROVERSIALISTS

Harvey, Buffon, Spallanzani, Pasteur

HARVEY, DISSECTING THE DEER in King Charles's forests – his privilege as King's physician – once found in the uterus of a doe, a foetus 'the magnitude of a peasecod . . . complete in all its members.' He showed this 'pretty spectacle to our late King and Queen. It did swim, trim and perfect, in such a kinde of white, most transparent and crystalline moysture (as if it had been treasured up in some most clear glassie receptacle) about the bignesse of a pigeon's egge, and was invested with its proper coat.' The King was much delighted.

But how did the foetus get there? The principle was fairly simple and today it is common knowledge. But two hundred years were to pass before the process was grasped. The difficulties were twofold. First, the fact that mammals produce eggs was unknown: mammalian eggs are microscopic in size. Moreover, Aristotle had taught that the foetus developed from a 'coagulum' of menstrual blood, the coagulation being brought about by the male semen. Secondly, it was still held that animals could be spontaneously generated, magically arising from dung and urine.

Harvey, with singular insight, dismissed both these errors. Perceiving the similarity between the development of animal foetuses, such as those of the deer, and the development of eggs, he boldly generalized: all animals come from eggs. The title page of his work on the generation of animals (which he published with hesitation knowing its incompleteness) shows Zeus liberating living beings from the egg, and bears the words: *ex ovo omnia* – all things from the egg. These words sounded the death-knell of medieval theories of spontaneous generation.

Harvey's attitude was neatly put by Llewellyn, who translated his works into English from the Latin in which they were written. Harvey holds, he said –

> That both the Hen and Housewife are so matcht
> That her Son born, is only her Son hatcht;
> That when her Teeming hopes have prosp'rous bin,
> Yet to conceive, is but to lay, within.

'Ex ovo omnia' – all things come from the egg – is the bold statement on the title-page of Harvey's book on the generation of animals. Out of the egg in the hand of Zeus come not only insect, bird, fish, reptile, amphibian and spider, but also mammal and man.

Gulielmus Harveus
de
Generatione Animalium.

Drawings of the ovarian follicles *by the Dutch scientist Regnier de Graaf. He compared them with the eggs of birds, but of course the human eggs are microscopically small.*

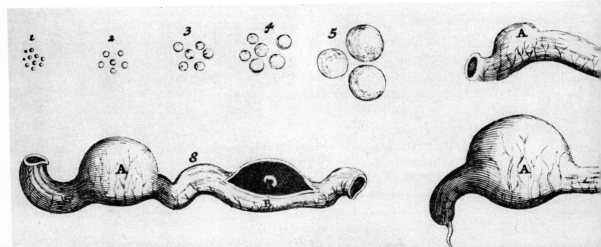

Seventeen years later, his views received apparent confirmation when the brilliant young Dutch scientist Regnier de Graaf, after making a comparative study of the ovaries of mammals and birds, came to the conclusion that the small lumps or follicles, which Vesalius and others had seen in mammalian ovaries, corresponded to the eggs found in bird ovaries, and that they pass thence into the uterus to develop in a similar way.

De Graaf drew these follicles – but he was wrong. In fact they are blastocysts, or cells from which eggs develop: the eggs themselves are microscopically small. When de Graaf opened the follicles he could see only fluid within. Perhaps if he had not died at the age of thirtytwo, he might have discovered his error. The follicles are known as Graafian follicles to this day; and the word ovary was suggested by him.

Harvey, who died in 1657 and never knew of this apparent confirmation of his view, also made a second great advance in this field. He destroyed the Aristotelian theory of the coagulum in a brilliant series of experiments at Hampton Court, which he described in 1653.

In front of the King, he dissected a newlymated deer, and showed that, far from there being a coagulated mass in the uterus, there was apparently nothing at all. The huntsmen, standing curiously round, began to debate furiously and claimed that the deer must be late conceiving that year, owing to the drought. When they realized that the rutting time was past, they eventually had to believe the evidence of their own eyes. 'But all the King's Physitians persisted stiffly, that it could no waies be, that a conception should go forward unless the males seed did remain in the womb, and that there should be nothing at all residing in the Uterus after a fruitfull and effectuall Coition . . .'

In order to prove the point, the King therefore ordered an experiment using, as we should now say, control animals. A dozen mated does were to be separated from the bucks and locked up in the Course near Hampton

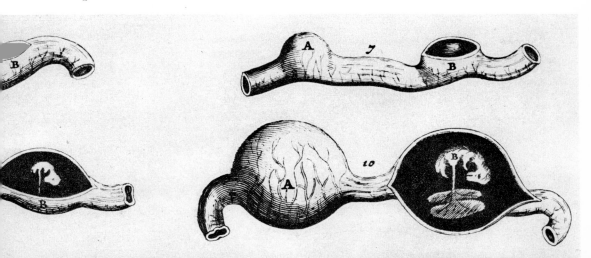

Court. Some of these Harvey dissected, showing that there was no seed in their uteri, while the rest proceeded to fawn at the normal time.

But as to what caused conception, Harvey had no idea. The fact that the semen apparently lay latent for some time before anything developed seemed to him to resemble the latent period in the development of many diseases. Doubtfully, he fell back on the theory of an *'aura seminalis'*, 'a kind of contagious property' in the semen. He confessed himself 'at a stand' about the action of the seed.

The semen, of course, he conceived as a simple liquid, for, while the mammalian egg had not been discovered, neither had the sperm. Leeuwenhoek's famous letter to Oldenbourg did not come until 1676, nineteen years after Harvey's death. When it did, Harvey's dictum was cast in doubt.

Parasites? Fertilizing agents? Anti-coagulators? What was the function of the 'infinity of animals like tadpoles' which Leeuwenhoek's beads of glass had revealed within the seminal fluid of man and beast?

The discovery aroused intense interest – even alarm. Other body fluids, such as saliva and chyle, were hastily investigated. 'Sir' John Hill said they were animals. Buffon said they were not animals but 'living molecules' and increased in number and size after leaving the body. Some followers of Leeuwenhoek declared that they comprised two sorts of animals, which copulated and multiplied. Linnaeus looked and said they were inert. That they developed into men seemed incredible. Vallisnieri thought they served to stir up the seminal fluid, to prevent it coagulating. Were they even the agent of fertilization? The wastage seemed absurd. Were thousands of millions of living things to be produced that a single new creature might be born? Du Cerf observed that they were few or absent in the semen of elderly and sterile men.

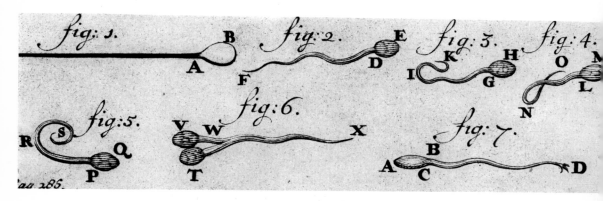

'An infinity of animals like tadpoles': *spermatozoa as seen by Leeuwenhoek through his magnifying glass beads. Those in figs. 1 and 7 are human, the rest from sheep.*

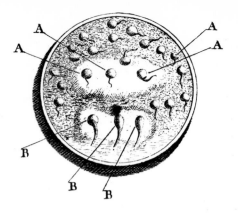

Pollen grains *of Auricula, drawn by Grew. With a low-powered glass he observed that they were 'perfect Globes or Globulets'.*

It was Spallanzani, the Italian abbé, who tried filtering the seminal fluid, and artificially inseminating with it a frog, a tortoise and a bitch – thus proving that sperm were essential to fertilization. However, this did not convince him that they alone were necessary, and he continued to regard the fluid as the vitalizing part. Nevertheless, this demonstration disposed finally of the magical *'aura seminalis'* which Harvey had felt obliged to accept. Meanwhile, the methods by which flowering plants reproduce were becoming clearer.

Both being 'contrivances of the same Wisdom', plants and animals must present some similarity of structure. Such was the argument advanced by Nehemiah Grew. He drew the pollen grains of various plants (which he called globulets) for his great *Anatomy of Plants* (1682) and guessed that flowers were the sexual organs of plants, as did his acquaintance the Sedleian professor, Sir Thomas Millington.

But it was R. J. Camerarius, professor of medicine in Tubingen, who won himself a niche in the history of biology by proving the point conclusively. By experiments on a variety of plants, he showed that if the male organs are removed in time, no fruit will develop; while if pollen is dusted on the pistils of the female flowers, fruit is certain to form. He published his results in *A Letter on the Sex of Plants* in 1694. The mode of fertilization of non-flowering plants remained, however, a mystery.

During the 18th century, following several descriptions of pollinations, various botanists succeeded in fertilizing plants of one species with the pollen of another, thus launching the practice of hybridization.

The work of Camerarius was carried further by two contrasting Germans: Koelreuter, the director of the Karlsruhe Botanical Gardens, and C. C. Sprengel, the eccentric rector of Spandau (near Berlin). Koelreuter perceived the role of the wind in pollinating plants, and perceived that where wind could not be the agent – as in the case of mistletoe – birds or insects must be the agents. He proved that in the case of mistletoe it is birds which effect dispersal.

Sprengel was removed from his post as rector for neglecting his religious duties in favour of biology. He lived, poor and solitary, universally regarded

as a crank, writing a book on the sex of plants which is a work of near-genius: *The Secret of Nature discovered in the Structure of Flowers* (1797). In it, he describes, among many other things, how certain plants cannot fertilize themselves, since stamen and pistil ripen at different times (dichogamy). Believing that God had made all things for a purpose (or, as we say today, for every structure a function) he sought a function for every structure. Thus he discovered, for instance, how a flower's nectaries are protected from the rain.

He made many far-reaching observations, but his great achievement was to carry botany beyond mere classification and collecting. He lived in an age and a country in which such detailed research was still despised: the Romantic philosophers were in their hey-day. It was Darwin who rescued him from oblivion, finding support for the theory of natural selection in the mutual interdependence of flower and insect.

THE DISSECTION of a virgin bitch, above, is being carried out under the eye of Buffon and his friend, the English priest, John Needham, and Daubenton, Buffon's hard-working assistant.

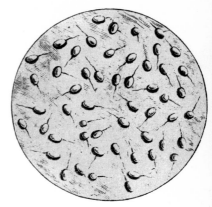

Dissecting a virgin bitch, *Buffon declared that spermatozoa had been found in the ovary. How he could have made such a glaring mistake has never been explained. Buffon is shown at the end of the table, talking to the Abbé Needham and watching the surgeon, while Daubenton looks into the microscope. The actual dissection is left to a youthful assistant.*

Buffon's 'proof' was in these figures of 'spermatic animalculae' from (upper right) the semen of a dog, and the ovaries of a bitch.

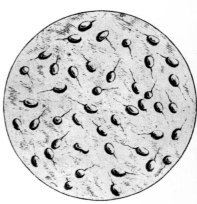

Buffon and Needham expected to find sperm in the ovaries of the bitch, and by some extraordinary piece of mis-management, believed that they had succeeded. The ovaries, they said, were sperm-making organs.

Buffon had elaborated a theory of the origin of life according to which the atmosphere was full of minute living particles. It was an idea which harked back to the medieval theory of sperm dropping from the stars. To the extent that the air is full of invisible bacteria, he was right, and his theory thus gave a correct explanation of the appearance of decay. But it could also be used to account for spontaneous generation. Moreover, he believed that the body collected these living particles which then appeared as sperm. Thus he could account for sexual generation at the same time: it was a kind of specialized spontaneous generation – an ingenious attempt to cover all the facts. Cooke embroidered this idea by suggesting that the sperm, if unsuccessful, returned to the atmosphere where they hibernated until required again.

'Sir' John Hill, the witty quack physician, mockingly advised the Royal Society that he had invented a machine for trapping these aerial animalcules, in an essay entitled *Lucina sine Concubitu* (1750).

'After much Exercise of my invention I contrived a wonderful cylindrical, caloptrical, rotundo-concavo-convex Machine (whereof a very exact Print will speedily be published for the Satisfaction of the Curious, designed by Mr H–y–n, and engraved by Mr V–rtu), which, being hermetically sealed at one End, and electrified according to the nicest Laws of Electricity, I erected in a convenient Attitude to the West, as a kind of Trap to inter-cept the floating Animalcules in that prolific quarter of the Heavens. The Event an-swered my Expectation; and when I had caught a sufficient number of these small original unexpanded Minims of Existence, I spread them out carefully like Silk-worm's Eggs upon White-paper, and then applying my best Microscope, plainly discerned them to be little Men and Women, exact in all their Lineaments and Limbs, and ready to offer themselves little Candidates for Life, whenever they should happen to be imbibed with Air or Nutriment, and conveyed down into the Vessels of Generation.'

He often, he added, looked at them through his glass and said to himself, 'This little reptile may be an Alexander, that a Faustina, another a Tully.'

'Sir' John's claim to have discovered minute human beings within the motes was a side-swipe at the theory of preformation, which was designed to explain the development which followed upon fertilization.

Almost the first man to look at the developing embryo with the aid of the microscope was Marcello Malpighi, whose acquaintance we have already made in discussing the microscope. Studying the first hours of development of the chick, he saw the appearance of the first blood vessels; he saw the neural groove hump itself mysteriously up; he saw the two bulbs from which eyes would later develop swell into being, and saw the tissue segment into paired somites, the forerunners of the backbone. His book describing these wonders earned him the title of 'father of embryology'.

Malpighi's work gave birth to one of the most protracted contro-versies of the 18th century. How does the embryo develop? Malpighi con-cluded that the process was not the assembly of a machine, but rather a gradual unfolding of what was already there, like a Japanese paper flower placed in water – the view known as preformationism. Today we know that epigenesis – or differentiation from a material which is, to start with, uniform – is in fact the process involved. At the time, preformation seemed much more plausible.

It also had important theological implications. For if in the first egg there was implicit all subsequent eggs, then original sin could be explained and the curse on Adam and Eve justified. Swammerdam, that 'mystical micro-scopist', finding a perfectly-formed butterfly within a chrysalis, took the idea up, as did Malebranche. In 1684, Zypaeus reported that he had seen minute embryos in unfertilized eggs. De Graaf's supposed discovery of the mam-malian egg seemed to confirm the idea. But when spermatozoa were dis-covered some thought that is was here that one ought to look for the origin of the embryo.

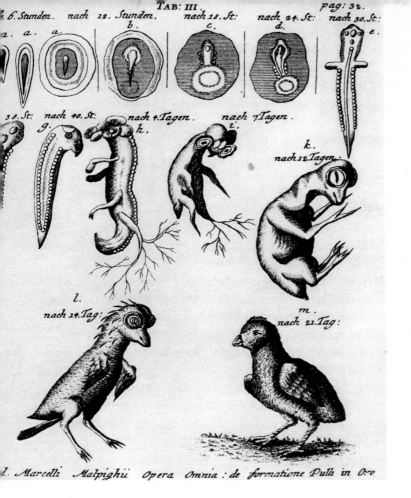

l. Marcelli Malpighii Opera Omnia : de formatione Pulli in Ovo

The father of embryology *was Marcello Malpighi, who studied under the microscope the development of the chick embryo (1672). He was a preformationist, holding that the process involved in the growth of the embryo was merely the unfolding and revealing of something that was already there, infinitely small, from the beginning.*

By the eye of faith, complete miniature human beings – termed 'homunculi' could be seen within Leeuwenhoek's newly-discovered spermatozoa. Leeuwenhoek himself denied being able to see them, though he supported preformationism. But Gauthier d'Agoty, more renowned as a colour-printer than as an anatomist, claimed to have seen a miniature donkey, cock and horse in the seed of the appropriate animals. However, Dalenpetius' claim to have seen a homunculus take off its coat was intended as a joke.

Leeuwenhoek's discovery thus split the preformationists into two camps: the ovists, who believed the preformed adult was enshrined in the egg, and the animalculists, or spermists, who preferred to believe the spermatozoa were the more important. This was a return to the theory of Aeschylus: the parent is the male, the mother 'is only the nurse of the young life that is sown within her'. In 1805, Good, speaking of the past fifty years, could write: 'Every naturalist and indeed every man who pretended to the smallest portion of medical science, was convinced that his children were no more

Minute human beings *visible within spermatozoa – to the eye of faith.*

related, in point of actual generation, to his own wife, than they were to his neighbours.' By 1768 to doubt preformationism was treated as atheism.

However, there were some who perceived the illogic of this. Needham felt that the occasional emergence of defective or monstrous infants looked more like an error of assembly than an unfolding, and Maupertuis considered that both parents must contribute, since offspring sometimes resemble one, sometimes another. Hybridization is also hard to explain on a preformationist view.

Charles Bonnet gilded the lily of preformation by the specific claim that within the first female of every species were contained the germs of all subsequent offspring, each generation within the previous one, like a nest of Chinese boxes. This doctrine was known as encapsulation or emboîtement. When the last box had been opened, the human race would cease to be.

Bonnet, fervent Catholic as he was, raised this fantastic doctrine to the rank of a dogma. It was, he said, 'a triumph of the sensual over the rational imagination'. At the same time he strongly opposed spontaneous generation.

Bonnet is chiefly known for his elaborate speculations, produced when a disease of the eyes prevented him from doing further experimental work. Pages of effusions about angels intersperse his scientific writings, which are couched in a polemic, fervently Christian tone, but which contain many good ideas and shrewd observations. But it is for his work on aphids, earthworms, and other small creatures, and for his studies of the metamorphosis of insects, that he is chiefly remembered.

In 1759, the 21-year-old Caspar Friedrich Wolff published observations which eventually re-established the idea of epigenesis, although his ideas did not gain acceptance until many years after his death in 1794. The preformationists had thought it a waste of time to study the embryos of animals and plants, since all could be seen more clearly in the adult. Wolff looked through his microscope at plant embryos and perceived that the rudiments of flowers are indistinguishable from the rudiments of leaves. Turning to the developing chick, he showed that the intestines develop from apparently homogeneous tissue. He also discovered the 'Wolffian body' or 'primitive kidney' which

The fantastic doctrine *of Charles Bonnet — here seen in his study dictating a letter — was that the first female of every species contained, like a nest of Chinese boxes, the preformed germ of every subsequent generation.*

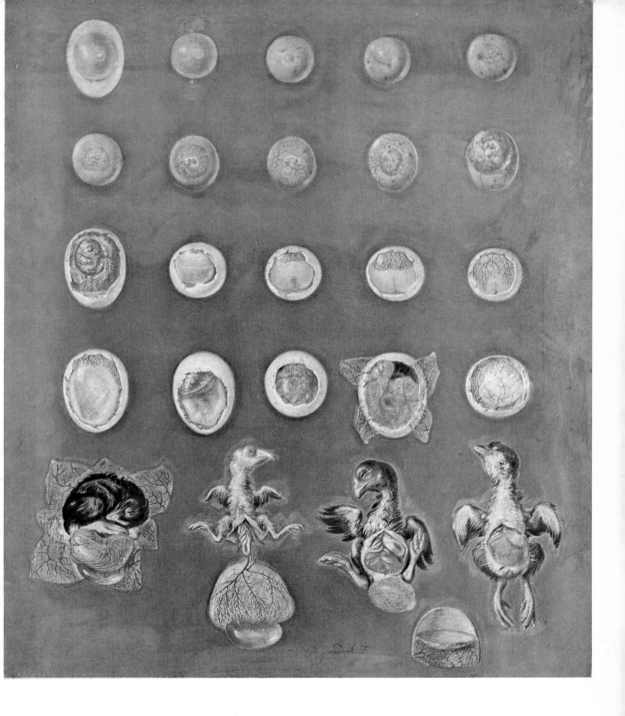

The incubation of the chick *as depicted by John Hunter. The Hunterian Collection (now in the care of the Royal College of Surgeons, London) was the first museum on modern lines, organized to display complete series of ideas rather than a random collection of curiosities.*

This embryo, *which never dwelt in any womb, was drawn from life in a glass of water into which semen had fallen. The date was about 1750, the artist Gauthier d'Agoty, colour printer and anatomist. The embryo is seen in its true size at A, and magnified at B.*

(except in certain fish) vanishes in the adult. He reported his findings in his doctoral thesis, which he dedicated to the great von Haller. Haller, however, favoured preformation and paid little attention.

Wolff also emphasized the similarity between plants and animals, to the point of absurdity, comparing the plant's vessels to the animal's arteries and so on. Yet this led him to a second observation of basic importance: both plants and animals are composed of cells (he called them ampullae). Like his other discovery, this too was neglected. His works were not translated into German until 1812, eighteen years after his death. His defect was that of too extensive theorizing from philosophical premises. He sought facts only to prove his theories.

Redi could not understand *how the egg which gave rise to the 'worm' could have got into the cherry, or how insects could emerge from plant galls.*

HOW DID THE FLY get into the cherry? The problem baffled Francesco Redi, the Italian poet, antiquary, doctor and naturalist who in 1668 sought to destroy the second great obstacle, the belief in spontaneous generation.

By this date, few still believed in the spontaneous generation of complex animals such as vertebrates, but the idea that flies were generated by urine, or decaying matter, seemed very plausible. Redi was the first to bring experimental evidence against this view. He took a snake, some fish, and a slice of veal and placed them in four sealed jars, with similar samples in open jars as controls. (The veal was not just a touch of Renaissance magnificence, but reflected the specific belief, held by van Helmont and others, that veal engendered flies.)

The first batch of material did not decay, the second did. Redi concluded: 'Thus the flesh of dead animals cannot engender worms unless the eggs of the living be deposited therein.' Galileo had appeared before the Inquisition for his heretical beliefs when Redi was a boy, so he must have been aware of the risk he was running: nevertheless, he firmly nailed his colours to the mast. 'I shall express my belief that the Earth, after having brought forth the first plants and animals by order of the Supreme and Omnipotent Creator, has never since produced any kind of plants or animals, either perfect or imperfect; and everything which we know in past or present time she had produced, came solely . . . from seeds of the plants or animals themselves, which thus, through means of their own preserve their species.'

Francesco Redi, *scientist and poet in the Renaissance tradition*

Nevertheless, Redi was disturbed to find cherry flies emerging from cherries and insects from plant galls. He spent the rest of his life investigating this apparent exception to his rule, without solving the mystery. It was not until 1700 – three years after Redi's death – that Vallisnieri showed how the larvae originate from eggs deposited in the plants previously.

A splendid Baroque figure, Redi deserves a biographical aside. His dithyrambic poem *Bacchus in Tuscany* was translated into English by Leigh Hunt in 1825. It has a fine contemporary ring.

> Dearest, if one's vital tide
> Ran not with the grape's beside
> What would life be (short of Cupid)?
> Much too short, and far too stupid.

He was an active figure in the Accademia del Cimento, where he urged that 'all their efforts be concentrated upon experimentation, upon the creation of standards of measurement and exact methods of research.' Prior to his studies of alleged spontaneous generation, he had studied snakes and snake-bite. He showed that the 'serpent stones' or 'mad stones', then widely traded as a preservative against snake-bite, were useless, and observed that snake venom has no effect if taken internally; it must be introduced under the skin.

Harvey, despite his declaration *'Omnia ex ovo'*, several times uses language consistent with a belief in spontaneous generation, and though he declares that all beings arise from a *'primordium'*, nowhere positively denies that such a *'primordium'* could arise spontaneously. It is to Redi, therefore, that the credit for first denying this error unambiguously must go.

In 1748, Needham, in conjunction with Buffon, had repeated Redi's experiment in a more refined manner, but with the contrary intention. He boiled mutton broth and placed it in a sealed jar. He used especial care in sealing the jar because he did not want anyone to say, if living organisms appeared, that they had been brought in by the air. After a few days the flask was opened and found to be swarming with multitudes of organisms. He repeated this with other animal and vegetable matter, with similar results. Spontaneous generation, he concluded, had been proved.

Spallanzani, hearing of this experiment, perceived however that if the living organisms were themselves so minute, their spores or eggs must be invisible under the microscope, so that Needham's experiment was not conclusive. He therefore boiled infusions of various seeds for half an hour, only to find that microscopic organisms developed within a few days. He next tried excluding air. One batch of flasks he sealed with a blow-pipe and then brought to the boiling point, the other he left open. The first batch developed only a few extremely small organisms, the second batch swarmed with them. So he extended the period of boiling from a few minutes to half an hour or more. Result: no organisms.

Unfortunately it is impossible to prove a negative. Some objectors argued that the air had been spoiled for the support of life by heating. (In the 19th century Schwann returned to the attack, using heated air which he showed would support respiration.) The subject was not finally settled until Pasteur attacked it in the 1850's.

In the meantime a French chef named Appert profited from Spallanzani's work by inventing the canning of food, about 1810.

'TWO RATHER CURIOUS FACTS in natural history [wrote Buffon to the Vice President of the Royal Society in 1741] have been discovered – the first is the reproduction of plant lice, which takes place like that of plants in that the louse produces young from itself without any copulation; the second concerns an animal called "polipe" which attaches itself to duckweed; on being cut in two the upper part of it regenerates a tail, and the lower a head, so that from a single animal it makes of itself two . . .' These two discoveries – the first made by Bonnet, the second by his cousin Trembley – which were in reality exceptions to the normal rule, greatly added to the difficulty of recognizing the basic rule of sexual generation.

Trembley was at the time tutor to the two sons of Count Bentinck, at Sorgvliet in Holland, and in the print below we see him fishing for pond creatures which he used as food for the hydra, which he was studying. Antoine and Jean Bentinck can be seen examining specimens which he has already caught and put in a jar, while one of his collecting instruments leans against a tree. Trembley was not yet thirty.

Fishing for pond creatures to feed the hydra which he was studying: Abraham Trembley with his pupils, the sons of Count Bentinck.

Jars containing hydra *are ranged in the window of Trembley's study at Sorgvliet. Jean and Antoine Bentinck watch as he turns a hydra inside out.*

Bonnet was only twenty when he proved the reality of parthenogenesis. Van Leeuwenhoek and others had found young aphids within the bodies of plant lice, but hesitated to infer anything so improbable as parthenogenesis. Réaumur suggested to Bonnet that he repeat the experiment. Taking a newly-born aphis, Bonnet watched it almost unceasingly for twelve days as it passed through its moults. At last, with red-rimmed eyes, at 7.30 p.m. on the 1st June 1740, he saw a young one born from it. The Academy wished the experiment repeated. Bonnet, with fanatic determination, now watched ten successive generations of lice being born without male intervention, ruining his eyesight in the process.

When Trembley first saw the curious green organisms we now call hydra, he thought they were plants, growing parasitically on other plants. He was puzzled to observe the arms twist and turn apparently of their own motion, but thought it must be due to currents caused by swimming creatures. He was doubly surprised, when he moved the jar, to see the arms vanish and the creature retract into a ball. Finally, he spotted some of the creatures walking and was convinced that they were animals. Having solved this question, he turned his attention elsewhere.

But a month later he found all the hydra gathered on the sunny side of the jar, and began to wonder whether perhaps they were plants after all. This led to the idea of trying to settle the point by making a graft. He therefore, as a first step, cut one in half. He was not too surprised to see the head regenerate a tail, for he knew that lizards could do as much. But on the ninth day after making the division, he was astonished to see three little points developing on the front end of the tail section, just where the arms would be in an undamaged polyp. With great excitement, he watched all day, until they were so big there was no room for doubt. The next day two more arms appeared, and then three more.

His bafflement increased when he found that the hydra multiplied by budding. He sent a consignment of the strange creatures to Réaumur, who named them polypes, from the similarity of their arms to those of octopi. The following spring, Trembley finally saw hydra feeding: they were animals for sure.

The curious method of progression of hydra, like that of looping cater-pillars, is seen here, as drawn by Lyonet, together with the apparatus Trem-bley devised to observe these creatures. Trembley found he could make many-headed monsters, like those on the right, by grafting.

It is difficult to grasp the sense of utter amazement Trembley's discovery caused. Some declared that they would not believe the facts, even if they saw

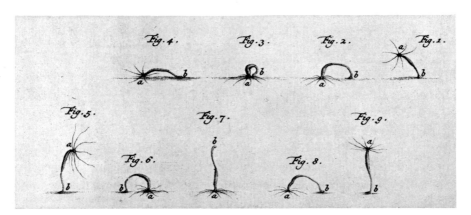

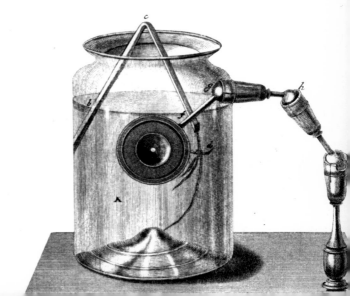

Hydra monsters produced artificially are shown in the margin: the middle one has no fewer than seven heads, produced by slitting lengthwise down the trunk. Above, Lyonet's drawing of the caterpillar-like way the hydra moves. Right, a humble jam jar and a magnifying glass on a jointed arm were all that Trembley needed to observe these creatures.

them with their own eyes. 'Apparently,' wrote Trembley to Réaumur, 'these gentlemen have some cherished system that they are frightened of disturbing'. In Paris, 'polipes' were second only to the War of the Austrian Succession as a topic of conversation. Ambassadors carried the news from Court to Court. Trembley was made an FRS and was awarded the Copley medal in the same year.

A creature which could be cut in two indefinitely! It recalled the fables of the Greeks, and was uncomfortably like the alchemical notion of palin-genesis, the regeneration of plants and animals by grafting together the dis-membered parts. Moreover, hydra multiplied itself by budding – so that development from an egg was clearly not the unique method of reproduction. The whole theoretical position as regards fertilization was thrown into confusion.

Finally, as if this were not enough, here was Bonnet proving that aphids could propagate from eggs alone, without sperm or other male contribution. The ovists were cock-a-hoop. Preformation seemed to be confirmed. Epi-genesis was thrown into the discard. Hence, too, the theory of emboîtement.

Trembley worked for eight more years on hydra. Through Bentinck's father, the newly-made Earl of Portland, he received some diplomatic employment and eventually was granted a pension by George III.

It was Trembley who drew the first picture of cell division ever made (op-posite). It shows the diatom Synedra dividing, and appears in a manuscript letter which Trembley wrote to Bentinck. Trembley did not know, of course, that Synedra could be regarded as a single cell. Nor had anyone thought to class together all single-celled creatures as Protozoa. Trembley's discovery of their mode of reproduction provided the basis for such a step. Synedra (seen attached to a water-weed, above right) was Trembley's dis-covery, which he recorded only in a book of religious advice for children. He made many other minor discoveries, the significance of some of which was not clear at the time. But most of all he changed the climate of thought: and for this he has been called 'the father of experimental zoology'.

He wrote: 'In order to extend our knowledge of natural history, we ought to direct our efforts to the discovery of the greatest possible number of facts. If we knew all the facts contained in nature, we should possess the explanation of them – we should see the Whole that they combine to produce . . . Nature should be explained by nature, not by our own views; for these are too limited to encompass such a great object in its whole extent.'

In a letter to his patron *Bentinck, Trembley sketched the diatom* Synedra *dividing into two. This was the first sketch ever made of cell division.*

sur les quelles ils sont fixés différens angles. Ils sont
différent quelques fois seuls, et d'autres réunis en
un groupe c. Nous avons souvent souhai-
té de savoir ce qu'étoient ces corps. Nous
b avions à peu près décidé, que c'étoit des
animaux. Nous avions même en quelques soupçons sur leur manière de multiplier.

Je suis parvenu à leur voir faire deux sortes de mouve-
mens. Je leur ai vu varier l'angles qu'ils forment avec
le corps sur le quel ils reposent. Je les ai vu nager et
venir se reposer sur un brin d'herbe.

Il faut considérer cet animal comme un tuiau à peu
près cylindrique. Sa transparence permet de distinguer
facilement l'intérieur, le vuide du tuiau. Voici comment
il multiplie. Suivés en un tel que a placé de façon
a qu'il vous sera facile de le reconnoître, et que vous
laissés toujours au foier d'une lentille du microscope, au moien d'un porte loupe. Ce corps a pré-

sente distinctement le vuide dont j'ai parlé. Quelque tem
b après, en l'observant de nouveau, vous trouverés qu'il
s'est formé au milieu dans toute sa longueur, une lign
a de a en b. Continués à l'observer de tems en tems
vous trouverés que la ligne a b devient plus remarquable
tout le corps paroit s'élargir un peu. Vous vous apperce-
vrés ensuite que la ligne a b est au fond d'une sorte
de rainure. Bientôt après les deux portions du corps
que cette ligne forme, paroissent s'arondir; et enfin
                                      paroit
vous trouvés, que ce corps unique est actuellement deux
corps, qui se touchent immédiatement dans toute
leur longueur c d. Ces deux corps s'éloignent
ensuite l'un de l'autre. Ils commencent à s'éloi-
gner par le bout supérieur, et très ordinairement
ils restent auprès l'un de l'autre, et se touchent
encore par le bout inférieur, tel que e f. Ces deux corps
e au bout de quelque tems se partagent de nouve
Cette opération est fort longue. Il faut bien près
f de 24 heures pour qu'elle soit complette.

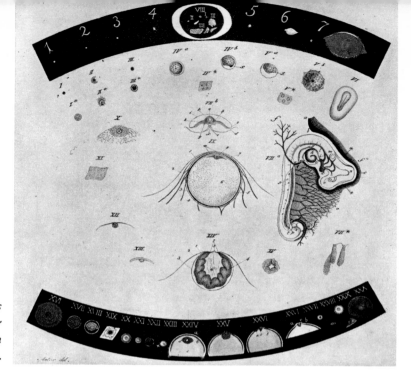

With these figures *in his 'Epistola' of 1827, von Baer illustrated his successful search for the mammalian egg.*

'LED BY CURIOSITY I opened one of the follicles and took up the minute object on the point of my knife, finding that I could see it very distinctly and that it was surrounded by mucus. When I placed it under the microscope I was utterly astonished, for I saw an ovule just as I had already seen them in the tubes, and so clearly that a blind man could hardly deny it.'

In these words, Karl Ernst von Baer, an Estonian who had become a professor at Königsberg, announced his discovery of the genuine mammalian egg. The date was 1827 – 159 years after de Graaf had believed himself to have made the discovery. In 1797 Cruikshank had seen eggs in the Fallopian tubes of rabbits, three days after coitus, but had been unable to find anything in the first few days.

As von Baer told the story in his *Autobiography,* at the end of his life, he saw the blastocysts in 1826, and, inspired with the idea that they might contain eggs, told his colleague Burdach that he needed an unmated bitch. Burdach had just been given one as a pet, but immediately volunteered to sacrifice it for science. Dissecting it, von Baer noticed a yellowish blob in a Graafian follicle, which proved to be an egg. But in a work written at the time he tells a different story. He says that he lacked the resolution to search for the egg, and it was while comparing the ovaries of a number of different animals, that he chanced to notice – with unaided eyes – the yellowish spot which the microscope disclosed to be an ovulum. The borrowing of Burdach's bitch came much later. The discovery was an accident.

It might be thought that the process of fertilization would now at last have become clear. In fact it took just over fifty years more to establish the crucial fact that only a single sperm fertilizes an egg. The establishment of the parallel process in plants was not achieved much faster. Finally, the idea of spontaneous generation had to be dismissed.

ANIMALS

1824 Prevost and Dumas showed that it was the sperm and not the seminal fluid which was essential – thus concluding the experiment that Spallanzani had attempted.

1843 Martin Barry found fertilized eggs in the Fallopian tubes of a mated rabbit, but no one believed him.

1852 George Newport, studying frogs, saw the spermatozoa penetrate the gelatinous envelopes and become embedded in the internal wall. None appeared in the yolk.

1868 Charles Darwin, citing Newport, stressed that several male elements were needed to effect fertilization.

1879 Herman Fol, studying starfish, saw that it was only a single sperm which entered the egg.

PLANTS

1823 Amici, using his newly-invented reflecting microscope, saw an isolated pollen grain put forth a pollen tube.

1823 Amici, in the living plant, found an ovary into which a pollen tube had entered.

1837 Schleiden confirmed the existence of the tube, but asserted that it was the tube itself which became the embryo of the new plant. When Amici protested, he abused him roundly.

1846 Amici, working persistently to redeem his point of view, succeeded in showing that, in orchids, an egg cell is already present before the tube arrives, and it is this which develops into an embryo.

1849 Hofmeister confirmed this in a variety of flowering plants. But the nature of the stimulus exerted remained mysterious.

1856 Pringsheim actually saw a spermatozoon enter the egg-cell of Oedogonium.

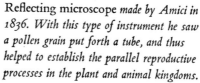

Reflecting microscope made by Amici in 1836. With this type of instrument he saw a pollen grain put forth a tube, and thus helped to establish the parallel reproductive processes in the plant and animal kingdoms.

121

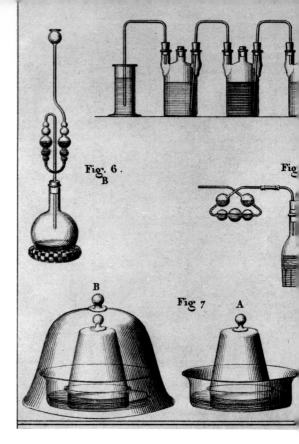

The Catholic doctor Pouchet devised complex methods of purifying air, hoping to demonstrate at least the possibility of spontaneous generation.

ABOUT 1859 AN ELDERLY FRENCHMAN could have been found trying to gather flasks of pure air on the tops of mountains. This was Felix Archimède Pouchet, a devoted Catholic doctor who fought a gallant rear-guard action in support of spontaneous generation. He had been stimulated to this effort by the work of the young Pasteur on fermentation.

Pasteur, who had recently been appointed to his first professorship in the industrial town of Lille, had been approached by a local manufacturer of alcohol from sugar-beet who was having trouble with the fermentation process by which the sugar is converted to alcohol. Pasteur, looking at the wort through the microscope, saw that in the healthy wort countless globular objects were present, while in unhealthy wort there were instead long threads. Boldly opposing the view of the great chemist, Liebig, that fermentation was a product of the death of organic material, Pasteur declared it was caused by minute living organisms.

Pouchet, who felt that spontaneous generation was 'a philosophical necessity', thought he saw his chance. Perhaps these minute organisms were

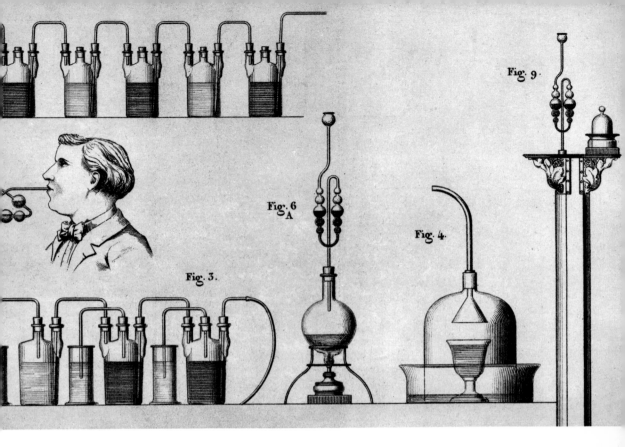

Fig. 9.

Fig. 6
A

Fig. 4.

Fig. 3.

actually generated by the chemical changes occurring. Life had to start some⁄where, why not here? Pouchet tried to controvert Pasteur's experiments. He tried to show that are there no organisms scattered in the air. Pasteur filtered air through gun⁄cotton and proved they were. When Pasteur reported that the organisms were killed by boiling, Pouchet asked why boiled milk turns sour. Pouchet sought to show that the organisms could not survive being dried. If Pasteur were right, the air should be solid with germs.

News of the controversy spread. The antagonists were invited to de⁄monstrate their experiments before the Academy of Science.

With the flasks shown overleaf, Pasteur proved that micro⁄organisms are indeed the agents of putrefaction. Organic material placed in the flask after boiling does not decay – for bacteria entering by the long neck are deposited on the walls of the curved tube. If the neck is snipped off, decay starts forth⁄with.

But this does not prove that the organisms never originate spontaneously: a negative cannot be proved. No dramatic victory finally established Pasteur's view. The success of aseptic methods – Lister's scheme was inspired by his seeing Pasteur's flasks – was one factor. Another was a series of elegant experiments in confirmation of Pasteur by Tyndall at the Royal Institution. Finally the work of Koch and Ehrlich on bacteria made the character of these micro-organisms clear. Spontaneous generation ceased to be heard of. In short, two hundred years elapsed from the discovery of spermatozoa and the declaration of Harvey, before the bare mechanics of fertilization were fully understood. (Many details, such as why only one sperm can enter an egg, remain a mystery to this day.) What happens within the egg after fertilization is another story.

Pasteur replied *with these curved-neck flasks. Boiled broth put in the flask does not decay, since bacteria entering the tube are deposited on its walls. As soon as the neck is snipped off, bacteria enter and the broth decomposes.*

THE EXPLORER NATURALISTS

Banks, von Humboldt, Bartram

'NO PEOPLE EVER WENT TO SEA BETTER FITTED OUT for the purpose of Natural History. They have got a fine library of Natural History; they have all sorts of machines for catching and preserving insects; all kinds of nets; trawls; drags and hooks for coral fishing; they have even a curious contrivance of a telescope, by which put into the water, you can see the bottom at a great depth, when it is clear. They have many cases of bottles with ground stoppers of several sizes, to preserve animals in spirits. They have the several sorts of salts to surround the seeds; and wax, both beeswax and that of Myrica; besides there are many people whose sole business it is to attend them for this very purpose. They have two painters and draughtsmen, several volunteers who have a tolerable notion of Natural History; in short, Solander assured me this expedition would cost Mr Banks £10,000.' Thus John Ellis, FRS, much impressed, in a letter to Linnaeus.

And who was Mr Banks?

A young man of wealth, he undertook a voyage to Labrador and New-foundland, almost as soon as he had left the university. In 1778, at the age of thirty-five, he was elected President of the Royal Society, and became a statesman of biology. It was he who got Bligh appointed to the *Bounty,* for the purpose of conveying a cargo of live bread-fruit trees to the West Indies.

His hobby was recording the weights of his visitors, himself, his sister and others in his household, including his dog, Mab. Thus it is that we know that John Hunter weighed a mere 10 stone 12½ lb., while Banks himself finally reached 17 stone 2 lb., a figure he queried incredulously. Alone of the entries, Mab's remained constant at 10 lb.

Banks was a shrewd patron. When the government decided to send Matthew Flinders to explore the area south of New Guinea in 1801, Banks gave the job of naturalist to the expedition to a young man who had left Edinburgh without a degree: Robert Brown. He did so well that, after he had returned from the expedition, Banks appointed him his librarian, and he became famous as the discoverer of the general existence of nuclei

There was no one quite like Sir Joseph Banks. *The wealthy patron of science is seen above in a painting by William Parry, seated by the window of his library. With him are Solander, his Swedish librarian-botanist, and Omai, the native boy he brought back from Tahiti.*

Strange new animals *found in Australia by the Flinders expedition in 1801 were drawn in exquisite detail by the expedition's artist, Ferdinand Bauer. Below is his drawing of that curious survival, the duck-billed platypus.*

Disaster struck *the Flinders expedition on its homeward voyage in 1803. Eight hundred miles from Port Jackson, it was wrecked on a sandbank, losing precious plant collections and drawings. Leaving the crew in sailcloth tents, Flinders and a few picked men rowed back to Port Jackson for help.*

The first drawing *of that nursery favourite the koala bear was made by Ferdinand Bauer on the uncharted shores of Terra Australis. This is one of the 2,000 sketches that escaped disaster.*

in plant cells, and of 'Brownian movement'. Banks also found an outstanding artist for the Flinders expedition in Ferdinand Bauer, an Austrian botanical artist.

Pushing south from New Guinea, Flinders came across an uncharted shore, on which he landed. He named this supposed island Terra Australis, or Australia, and set out to sail round it. Unwittingly, he had discovered a continent. Fortunately he allowed his botanist and illustrator freely ashore.

Brown and Bauer found themselves in a paradise of weird animals and plants unknown to science. The Linnaean scheme of classification was quite unable to cope with them. They rose to the opportunity magnificently. Though damp cockled his drawing paper, Bauer made many thousands of drawings. Brown collected 7,750 dried specimens. Unfortunately, many were to be lost, when the expedition was wrecked on a sandbank near a coral reef. By the greatest luck, Brown and Bauer had remained behind to work on their collections: 2,000 sketches and nearly 4,000 dried plants escaped the catastrophe.

Sir Joseph Banks conceived the idea of making the gardens at Kew into a great botanical centre and exchange for the British Empire – a place from which specimens of every kind could be drawn for research and where the possibility of acclimatizing new-found species could be tested.

It was Banks, too, who persuaded Franz Bauer, the brother of Ferdinand, to settle down at Kew in 1790. Here he painted flowers and investigated their structure for some fifty years.

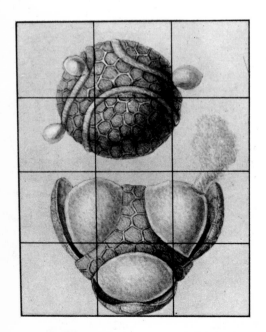

The two Bauers *raised the art of botanical illustration nearer perfection than ever before or since. Ferdinand, the traveller, was the better at animals; Franz, the stay-at-home, was unsurpassed at flowers – whether in microscopic detail, as with the pollen grains of the passion flower (left), or in the large, as in his startling water-colour (opposite) of the fabled mandrake, from John Sibthorp's 'Flora Graeca' (compare the version on p. 20).*

Atropa Mandragora.

The belted kingfisher, *from Audubon's epoch-making 'Birds of America'. Audubon broke new ground with his natural, almost snapshot-like posing and his vivid, economical suggestion of habitat and food habits.*

South America offered another rich treasure-trove. A world record was set by Alexander von Humboldt's climb to 18,096 feet on Chimborazo. (It stood until 1848, when Hooker reached 19,000 feet in Sikkim.) Accompanied by Bonpland and Montufar, a native *mestizo,* he staggered on through cloud and snow, bleeding from the gums and suffering from mountain sickness, until stopped by an impassable crevasse. On this sketch of the summit, he has entered the names of innumerable plants at the relative heights at which he found them, carefully noting the last cryptogam at 16,920 feet. (This is the class that includes ferns, mosses and lichens.)

For his subject was: how the plant is influenced by climate, or as we now say, plant geography. He distinguished sixteen landscapes as determining the range of plant-types. From studies such as these came the idea of 'plant associations'. Humboldt noticed that certain plants are usually found in association with others, because soil or climate suit both. Such plants may

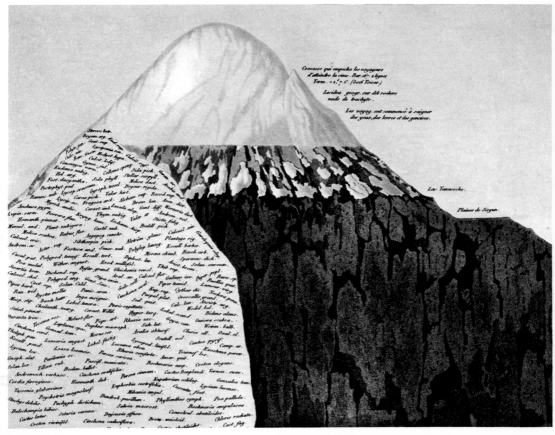

Bleeding from the gums *and suffering from mountain sickness, Humboldt staggered to 18,096 feet on Chimborazo, noting on this sketch the names of plants and the heights at which they grew.*

A rich harvest *of scientific discovery was reaped by Humboldt and Bonpland in South America. Here Humboldt is handing a sextant to his native helper while Bonpland, a dead condor beside him, writes up his notes.*

also compete, and a change in the prevalence of one may cause changes in the prevalence of others – as we see when a wood is thinned and, later, bushes spring up to take advantage of the greater intensity of light. These studies of the interrelationships of species have become, in the present century, the subject known as ecology.

Von Humboldt had been fired with the idea of travel by Georg Forster, who sailed with Cook, and when his mother died in 1796 leaving him private means, he spent three years in preliminary study, and then set off and travelled for five years (1799–1804) throughout Central and South America. These journeys yielded a rich scientific harvest. It took one assistant 22 years to describe the 3,000 species of plants he discovered, while the publication of his *Voyages aux régions équinoctiales* in 30 volumes, written jointly with Bonpland, swallowed up his fortune.

Humboldt raised geography to a science. In addition to his work on plants, he made studies of terrestrial magnetism, and of volcanoes, and he created climatology, even inventing the system of isothermal lines which still appear in our weather charts. Besides this, he made studies – many of them on himself – on the influence of electricity on muscles and nerves. He was undoubtedly one of the greatest personalities in the entire range of science. Darwin said his whole career was the result of reading von Humboldt's *Personal Narrative*.

Two almost forgotten naturalist-explorers of this age were Spix and von Martius, who penetrated the Brazilian jungle in 1819.

Spix, the zoologist, died of a tropical fever a few years later, but von Martius, the botanist, lived to produce his titanic *Flora Brasiliensis,* which surveyed the entire plant population of Brazil, a work almost without parallel. 'The name Martius will be remembered with honour as long as men know the name of palm-tree,' said von Humboldt.

Meanwhile, the biological exploration of North America was also being attempted. The first American-born naturalist was Thomas Bartram, and Linnaeus called him 'the greatest *natural* botanist in the world.' He started as a ploughman; he tells how he once pulled a daisy apart, and suddenly wondered how it came to be made. He became a professional collector of specimens, to meet the English demand for curiosities from the USA. Gradually his fame spread, as English botanists heard of his discoveries.

Bartram's most treasured discovery was a 100-mile-long flower-filled valley, the location of which he would never disclose. In it he found such treasures hitherto undreamed of as the silverbell tree, the trillium, and the calycanthus, 'whose dark-red blossoms have the fragrance of sun-parched strawberries.' It was in fact the Shenandoah Valley.

After him came other naturalists, such as Michaux, a Frenchman who wrote the first American *Sylva,* or catalogue of trees, and Alexander Wilson, a Scot, who classified the birds. There was also the famous Audubon.

Flower *of the Franklinia tree, discovered by Bartram and never found again in the wild.*

These trees were young *when Christ was born. Spix and von Martius found them in the primeval forests of Brazil, and their nine Indian porters could only stretch halfway round them.*

Europe had gasped when Audebert illustrated Viellot's book on birds, minutely gilding each feather by hand. But Audubon was something else again. His brilliant use of three-quarter views, spontaneous posing, and skilful suggestion of habitat and food habits contrasted with the formality of Audebert, as with the woodenness of Alexander Wilson's drawings.

An odd figure presented itself at Audubon's grocery store, in or about the year 1815. 'He wore an exceedingly remarkable attire' – a worn yellow coat, a waistcoat with enormous pockets, buttoned up to the chin, and tight pantaloons. Lank black hair hung down to his shoulders and his beard was long. But, said Audubon, 'his forehead was broad and prominent, indicating a mind of strong power . . . and as he directed the conversation to the natural sciences, I listened to him with great delight.'

This was Constantine Rafinesque, the son of a Frenchman working in Constantinople, married to a German woman born in Greece. He had no formal education, but had a passion for biology, and proposed to do for fish what Wilson had done for birds.

New species were a passion with Rafinesque. He announced them with such uncritical enthusiasm that the *American Journal of Science* ended by banning his contributions. Audubon once pulled his leg by showing him drawings of two fish he pretended to have seen in the river. Rafinesque published their descriptions under the names of Pogotoma and Pilodictis, and these fictitious species puzzled ichthyologists for years. Nevertheless he did describe ninety new species, from the Ohio River.

In 1819 he obtained a professorship at a minor college, and created himself a PhD a few years afterwards. But his actions became so strange that he was forced to resign, aged forty-three. Now reduced to poverty, he kept himself alive for another fourteen years on salt pork and corn bread, scribbling poems, devising an aquatic railway and a steam plough, and inventing a remedy for consumption and a new banking system.

Dotty as he was, he had one miraculous insight, neglected at the time and even today scarcely known. In his *Herbarium Rafinesquianum* (1836), he said: 'The truth is that Species, and perhaps Genera also, are formed in organized beings by gradual deviations of shapes, forms and organs, taking place in the lapse of time. There is a tendency to deviations and mutations through plants and animals by gradual steps at remote irregular periods . . . Every variety is a deviation which becomes a Species as soon as it is permanent, by reproduction. . . . It is not impossible to ascertain the primitive Species that have produced all the actual.' And he added: 'This view of the subject will settle botany and zoology in a new way . . .'

Peattie calls him 'the only United States Naturalist who could be called a Titan.'

6

THE EVOLUTIONISTS

Cuvier, Lamarck, the Darwins

WHEN MRS SCHIMMELPENNINCK WAS A CHILD, she saw a sulky drive up to the door; it was worn and bespattered with mud. Lashed on at the back was a container of hay and a pair of oars. In front was a receptacle for writing materials, which also held a fork, knife and spoon. On one side of the vehicle there was a pile of books as high as the window; on the other a hamper containing fruit and sweetmeats, cream and sugar. A skylight illuminated the interior.

Out of this whimsical vehicle climbed a massive figure, the head almost buried in the shoulders, and crowned with a scratch wig, tied up in a little bobtail behind. This was the irascible, benevolent Dr Erasmus Darwin, the grandfather of Charles Darwin, a true English eccentric and surely one of the most original-minded men in the history of science.

He had made many inventions: a speaking machine capable of saying 'Papa' and 'Mamma', a rotary pump, a device for writing in manifold, and a new kind of W.C.

He was no dry-as-dust. Not only did he have an extraordinary fondness for food, but we are told by a contemporary: 'In his youth Dr D. was fond of sacrificing to both Bacchus and Venus, but he soon discovered that he could not continue his devotions to both these deities without destroying his health and constitution. He therefore resolved to relinquish Bacchus, but his affection for Venus was retained to the last period of his life.' In addition to two marriages and eleven legitimate children, he also fathered the Misses Parker illegitimately.

In addition to these multifarious activities, he enunciated, in quite detailed form, a theory of evolution. As if this were not enough, he chose to express it in three long books in poetic form, one of which, *The Botanic Garden,* was described by Horace Walpole as 'sublime ... divine', and more recently as 'the best bad poem in the English language'.

In these extraordinary poems he proposes the idea that all living things are descended from a common ancestor, and this ancestor is a 'living filament' endowed with irritability. 'Shall we conjecture,' he asks, 'that one and the same kind of living filament has been the cause of all organic life? I suppose this living filament to be endowed with the capability of being excited into actions by various kinds of stimulus.' He describes how the myriads of living things moved from the oceans on to shelving shores or rocky steps, until tall oaks, lions, eagles and even men arose.

He even faced the question of how the first forms of life originated, and proposed an answer not unlike that which would be given today. There is an extraordinary hint of the modern conception of long-chain molecules being assembled in lines, under the influence of enzymes:

> ATTRACTION next, as earth or air subsides
> The ponderous atoms from the light divides
> Approaching parts with quick embrace combines
> Swells into spheres and lengthens into lines.
> Last, as fine goads the gluten-threads excite
> Cords grapple cords, and webs with webs unite.
>
> Hence without parent by spontaneous birth
> Rose the first specks of animated earth . . .

This last couplet has been taken as indicating a belief in spontaneous generation – but, in this sense of a single lucky concurrence of molecules billions of years ago, this is the view of the probable origin of life which has been adopted today (see p. 347).

Erasmus Darwin also faced the question of *how* this modification of the primitive form into more elaborate and diverse forms could have taken place. He gave the first clear statement of the idea, hinted at by Buffon, that the effects of use and disuse of an organ or capacity could be inherited. He did not, however, foresee the idea of natural selection, and considered the struggle for existence only as a force limiting numbers. Four years later Malthus picked up this idea and based on it his theory of over-population; the following year was born Charles Darwin; nine years were to pass before Lamarck began to expound the idea of the inheritance of acquired characteristics. Another of Darwin's grandsons, Francis Galton, later developed his grandfather's ideas of breeding and invented the study of genetics. Neither of his grandsons acknowledged their debt to him.

Darwin held up his first work, *The Botanic Garden,* for twelve years, thinking it would have an adverse effect on his practice, which it did. Three years after publication of Part I (which followed Part II) his *Zoonomia* was published, and soon placed on the Index of prohibited books by the Catholic church.

A DISCHARGED LIEUTENANT, become literary hack, was at the age of fifty made professor of botany in Paris, and attained lasting fame, despite his lack of scientific training. This was Jean Baptiste Pierre Antoine de Monet, better known to history as the Chevalier de Lamarck (1744–1829).

In the same year that Erasmus Darwin's third work, *The Temple of Nature*, was published, Lamarck brought out his *Researches on the Organisation of Living Bodies*, in which he put forward a theory of the development of life, in which, like Darwin, he asserted that acquired characteristics could be inherited. Though ridiculed at the time, this theory has been proved a bone of contention, offering as it does the only alternative to natural selection as an explanation of the evolutionary process. After Charles Darwin's work had made the subject of universal interest, Haeckel, looking for the intellectual origins of the idea, traced them to Lamarck, so that this view is often called Lamarckism. This has made Lamarck considerably more famous in death than he was in life.

Lamarck declared that it was possible to place all living beings in a series, beginning with the lowest and ending with the highest, the steps being marked by increasing complexity of organization. This was only the idea of the Ladder of Nature re-asserted, but he applied it systematically. Thus he was able to distinguish the Radiata (such as starfish) from the polyps, in that the Radiata, even though sexless and eyeless, possess organs of generation, while the polyps possess no organs at all.

Then he explained these differences in equipment by the radical assertion that they had been produced by the environment. It was not, he declared, the animal's bodily construction which dictated its habits, but its 'habits and manner of life and the conditions in which its ancestors lived that have in the course of time fashioned its bodily form, its organs, and its qualities.' In proof of this he pointed out that moles have lost their sight from living underground, swimming birds have acquired webbed feet, while waders have acquired long necks and legs from stretching.

A source of wonder *to the Parisians of the time; this giraffe was presented to the Museum of Natural History in 1827. Lamarck found it a perfect example of bodily construction shaped by habit and environment.*

Lamarck went further and asserted that if the left eye of children were put out at birth, and such children interbred, eventually a one-eyed race would result; an assertion which led to a great many useless experiments involving the mutilation of rats and other animals later in the century. But not only such specific acts, but environment generally could effect such change. These claims drew down on his timid head the wrath of the great Cuvier.

'ONE OF THE MOST magnificent-looking men he had ever met, and one of the least agreeable' – such was the verdict of an American historian on Georges Cuvier (1769–1832), known as the Dictator of Biology.

The son of an impoverished army officer, Cuvier was brought up in the quasi-military discipline of the immensely strict Karlschule, from which Schiller ran away in terror. Sent as a tutor to Normandy, he dissected starfish and molluscs – a group of organisms neglected by Linnaeus – and sent drawings of them to Geoffroy St Hilaire, the newly appointed professor of zoology at the Academy of Sciences. St Hilaire was so impressed that Cuvier was summoned to Paris and immediately given the chair of anatomy, even though he had never dissected a human body. There was irony in this, since Cuvier later publicly demolished St Hilaire's theories.

Cuvier's immense energy, power of organization and attention to detail recommended him to Napoleon, who was just the same age. Napoleon

The Chevalier de Lamarck, whose *theory of the inheritance of acquired characteristics offered the only alternative to natural selection as an explanation of evolution.*

Georges Cuvier, *founder of modern comparative zoology. He was the first to include fossils in a scheme of animal classification.*

made him Inspector General for education. It was said of him in this role that he reformed a school as soon as he had inspected it.

Cuvier is known as 'the founder of modern comparative zoology' not because he adduced new facts, but because he introduced a new way of looking at the structure of living organisms, one which created an entirely new view of the connection of causes in nature, both in respect of the construction of individual organisms, and also in the relationship between different species of animal.

His brilliant insight was that the organs of an animal are functionally interrelated. Thus, for instance, a carnivore must have claws and teeth; it must have good eyes and the power of swift movement; it must have an intestine capable of digesting meat, and so forth. Vicq d'Azyr had made the point: Cuvier worked it out in detail. To develop a system of classification based on this idea became one of his life-objects.

Cuvier's second original idea was to apply himself to the systematic study of fossils. Taking the Paris area, rich in fossil remains, he noted where each fossil was found, and all the fossil types associated with it.

He then applied his correlation theory to reconstructing the original creatures. It was said that he could reconstruct a complete animal from a single bone.

Weighty, patient, thick-skinned himself, he was especially interested in pachyderms, studying hippopotami and rhinoceri and their extinct ancestors, as well as elephants. Typical of his achievements was his showing that the Indian elephant is nearer to the mammoth than to the African elephant – previously they had been classed as one species. He reformed the whole scheme of animal classification by including fossils in it.

On the basis of his vast knowledge of animal forms, Cuvier perceived that it was impossible to arrange animals in a linear series, as Lamarck had sought to do. As he rightly said, it is impossible to regard the last mammal as being less perfect than the first bird. He therefore proposed instead to divide the animal kingdom into four main groups: Vertebrates, Molluscs,

The systematic study of fossils *was Cuvier's major contribution to biology. Here is his drawing of the Megatherium, an extinct giant sloth of the Pleistocene period from South America.*

Articulates, and Radiates. This was the greatest advance in classification since Linnaeus, and it has formed the basis of all subsequent animal classification.

In thus disposing of the linear theory Cuvier was actually preparing the ground for an effective theory of evolution, had he known it. This is ironical, since he was in fact bitterly opposed to any such idea. He scathingly said that, once Lamarck's principles were accepted, 'only time and circumstances are needed for the monad or polyp to finish by transforming itself, gradually and indifferently, into a frog, a swan, or an elephant ... A system resting upon such bases', he added, presumably thinking of Erasmus Darwin, 'may entertain the imagination of a poet, but it cannot for a moment support the examination of anyone who had dissected a hand, a vital organ, or a mere feather.'

Cuvier had nevertheless to explain the undoubted presence of the fossil remains of species no longer existent, and the absence from fossil deposits of the remains of many existing species. He declared that sudden and violent catastrophes had wiped out all the species in given areas. To make this theory water-tight, he had to deny that any fossilized human bones had ever been found, and to assert that the bones of lions which had been found must be of different species from those living today. He declared that species were fixed, and that no remains of any intermediate forms had been found.

In his attempts to make sense of the fossil record on these lines, Alcide d'Orbigny, one of his followers, was driven to supposing that no fewer than twenty-seven such catastrophes must have taken place.

When Lamarck commented that a universal catastrophe which mixed up and dispersed everything was very convenient for naturalists who did not want 'to take the trouble to observe and investigate the course followed by nature', Cuvier was touched on the raw. From then on he treated Lamarck's ideas as if they were the ravings of an imbecile, and used his vast authority to bury him in oblivion.

Lamarck, blind from his microscopical studies, had to give up his lectureship in 1825 and was reduced to penury. He was forced to sell his collection of shells to the state to obtain something to live on. He had married four times: now his fourth wife died, and only his daughter Cornélie faithfully cared for him. When he died, he was buried in a grave bought on a five-year lease; its whereabouts is now unknown. It fell to Cuvier to compose the traditional eulogy given on the death of an Academician. He delivered such a savage attack that the Academy refused to print it.

Meanwhile, yet another conception of the way in which animal forms originated was being canvassed. This too Cuvier succeeded in annihilating.

Goethe in Italy: *painting by Tischbein. On his famous Italian jouney Goethe gave free reign to his scientific romanticism, disdaining patient verification of fact. But his ideas were often valid and his influence was fruitful.*

WHEN GOETHE was walking in the old Jewish cemetery in Venice, his man picked up a ram's skull and jokingly offered it as the cranium of some vanished Shylock. He let the skull drop, and it broke open along the sutures – the joins between the several bones of which the skull is composed. The idea suddenly struck Goethe that the skull might be composed of modified vertebrae. Thus was born the 'vertebral theory of the skull'. Huxley disproved it a quarter of a century later.

The idea which dominated Goethe, and which he lifted from Herder, was that all living creatures were departures, more or less, from an ideal type, or Platonic idea. There was an ideal plant, an ideal man, and ideal animals. So strongly did Goethe believe in this notion, that he rushed into the public gardens at Palermo, fully expecting to find the ideal plant. As to the ideal man, clearly he had been a Greek: one of the Classical Greeks had been the Urmensch.

Developing this idea, he argued that all existing forms had been modified by environmental circumstances from the ideal. Thus all the parts of the flower could be shown (he believed) to be modified leaves; similarly the skull might prove to be a modified backbone.

These propositions, wholly false in themselves, yet proved of inestimable value to biology, and there is no more fascinating demonstration of the importance of free speculation than the way in which these wholly intuitive Romantic conceptions, despite their falsity, yet conduced to the discovery of the truth.

As we now conceive the process of evolution, existing forms of life are derived from common ancestors, and therefore display similarities of form. Goethe's dissections, designed to show a continuous range of variation, did in fact succeed in showing that species are not distinct in the way which had been supposed. Moreover, Goethe turned to the study of embryo forms, to prove his point, seeking to find in them the origins of structures found in the adult. Thus he created the study of how forms change – morphology. (He invented the word; and gave an impulse to embryology which lasted the rest of the 19th century.)

Goethe's influence was thus considerable, though his contribution to the store of scientific facts was negligible. As Abercrombie has pointed out, it was not that he was an airy theorist, nor that he thought in abstract terms. He had a highly concrete, visual mind, and a practical bent. Among other things, he started the network of meteorological stations on which weather forecasting now depends. His trouble was that he rejected the patient erection of theory on a basis of experiment, and preferred to postulate complete systems of ideas, intuitively arrived at: experiment served merely to confirm these intuitive truths. It was substantially the method of 'reasoning' which the medieval doctors had employed. The truths were known; the task of learning was simply to validate them. His conclusions from the sheep's skull were typical.

All great scientists have moments of insight: but Goethe put forward these wild speculations incessantly. Essentially, they were based on analogy. Thus because the ivy clings to the tree, it is female.

It was these Goethean ideas which dominated Geoffroy St Hilaire, the impulsive, gifted, passionate young man intended for the priesthood, who became a chemist and anatomist, and was given a chair after the revolution at the same moment as Lamarck.

The biggest problem for those who felt all animals were modifications of a single type was to account for the differences between vertebrates and invertebrates. St Hilaire proposed that the inkfish was a vertebrate which had been folded upon itself, so that its anus lay near its mouth. Indeed, he claimed to find not only in crustaceans but in insects the remnants of vertebrae in which ribs and apophyses could be distinguished, and claimed to have discovered a breast-bone in fishes.

In 1830 Geoffroy presented to the Academy a paper by two junior scientists in which the homology between inkfish and vertebrates was asserted and which attacked Cuvier directly at the same time. Cuvier, while paying tribute to St Hilaire's services to comparative anatomy, wholly demolished this theory, and destroyed his entire plan of research, revealing that the idea of an uniform plan for the entire animal kingdom was meaningless.

St Hilaire had the sense to drop the subject of inkfish, and changed his theory of 'unité de plan' to a 'théorie des analogues', in support of which he cited the presence in varying species of certain small bones. Cuvier, dipping into his store of anatomical knowledge, exposed St Hilaire's ignorance.

Of the inkfish, Cuvier said: 'They have not resulted from the develop-ment of other animals, nor has their own development produced any animal higher than themselves.' Today, while we should agree with the latter pro-position, we should unhesitatingly reject the former. Ironically, while Geoffroy and Lamarck thought both untrue, it was the latter which really annoyed them – for the inkfish had, in their view, to lead to some higher step in the ladder of nature, and it was this link between the stages which they were chiefly looking for.

In short, Cuvier's type theory and Geoffroy's attempt to compare organs by embryological studies both contributed to the emergence of a theory of evolution. Moreover, Cuvier's achievements lit up a zeal for comparative anatomy and paleontology which lasted the entire nineteenth century.

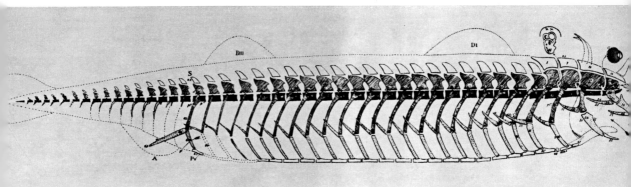

Goethe's idea *that all things had an 'archetype' or primeval form misled even such a competent anatomist as Richard Owen into proposing this 'archetype' of the vertebrate skeleton. It showed the skeleton as a series of vertebrae with rib-like attachments: from the first two, jaws developed; from others, the limbs.*

Three wings –
pterodactyl, bat, bird –
are analogous, not homologous.
The diagram shows radical differences of structure.

THE 'CUVIER OF ENGLAND', Richard Owen, the director of the Natural History section of the British Museum (and the man who got it moved from Bloomsbury to South Kensington) was the leading expert on prehistoric fossil remains in England.

Owen pointed out that in two different types of animal, the same organ may play different roles; or, conversely, different organs may play analogous roles. Thus gill and lung play analogous roles but are derived from different organs, the fish's swim bladder corresponding to the lung in mammals. Hence gill and lung are *analogous,* lung and swim bladder are *homologous*.

Owen, true son of Cuvier, was to prove one of Darwinism's most bitter opponents.

The change which was taking place in men's minds, and which was germinating in the minds of Erasmus Darwin and Lamarck, was a change from conceiving the world as held in a fixed order by the divine will, to a world which was continually in flux as a result of the competing efforts of its inhabitants. It is this which makes the work of Malthus, and his theory of the limitation of the numbers of populations by their pressure upon resources, of crucial historical importance.

And it is significant of course that this is what was happening in the world at large. In France, particularly, the established order was vanishing.

And it was the fear of such a change which lent bitterness to the rejection of evolutionary ideas, and which made the work of Lyell and the geologists alarming to the propertied classes. Equally, it was this which made them so attractive to the poorer classes.

The obscurity into which both Erasmus Darwin and Lamarck fell is to be explained by the reaction after the French Revolution and the wars of Napoleon. Lamarck could be written off by thinking of him as merely a French atheist. Darwin could be dismissed as an immoralist.

IN 1813, THREE MEN, all doctors, all Fellows of the Royal Society, announced in almost identical terms a theory of natural selection, and repudiated the Lamarckian idea of the inheritance of acquired characteristics. Their names were Wells, Prichard, and Lawrence.

The statements were quite explicit, but Prichard's and Wells's work was ignored, and Wells died four years later, lonely and embittered.

Very different was the fate which met Lawrence's *Lectures on the Physiology, Zoology and the Natural History of Man.* He put forward a theory of the selection and exclusion of hereditary factors (an idea which Charles Darwin later dismissed) and asserted that all human races had arisen from the sort of mutations which we find in a litter of rabbits. Breeding could improve a stock or ruin it – and European royalty, he said, seemed to have followed the latter course.

On the public the effect was (as Waddington has said) rather that of Marie Stopes's books after the first world war: it challenged both sexual and political taboos. The authorities were quick to see that such ideas might damage both Church and the ruling class. The Lord Chancellor examined the book, pronounced it contrary to Scripture, and refused copyright. Anonymous pamphlets began to appear attacking the 'wicked Surgeon Lawrence' and comparing him with the godless Tom Paine. Lawrence, who was thirty-six, realized that his career was at stake. He agreed to suppress the book. In due course he twice became president of the Royal College of Surgeons and was appointed Sergeant-Surgeon to the Queen.

It is not always appreciated that puritan fervour and religious fundamentalism were at their height in England not during the reign of Queen Victoria, who ascended the throne in 1837, but in the thirty years preceding her accession. In these years, the dramatic scientific issue was that posed by geology: was the earth created 6,000 years ago, or had it evolved over unimagined periods of time? But geology led to fossils, and thus to the issues of evolution. Moreover, to accept a natural account of the formation of the planet as against a supernatural one was a step which led inevitably to accepting a natural account of the origin of species as against a supernatural one. The whole structure of literal interpretation of the Bible was at stake.

It is difficult today to recapture the sense of awe which this sally into the forbidden territory of geology evoked. The rocks, as Hutton had shown, had been melted and twisted, elevated and ground down by forces so terrific that only the supernatural seemed adequate to account for them. In the strata of the earth one seemed to see the raw handiwork of God.

The Geological Society was founded in 1807. In 1813 a Chair of Geology was founded at Oxford. By the 1830's, according to Harriet Martineau, the middle classes were buying five books on geology to one novel.

Canon Buckland's geology lectures packed the Ashmolean Museum, but when he prepared his *Reliquiae Diluviae* in 1823, seeking to prove that the remains of animals found in caves are those of creatures existing before the Flood, he found the case extremely hard to make, and provoked from Bishop Shuttleworth the epigram (in imitation of Pope's lines on Newton):

> Some doubts were once expressed about the Flood:
> Buckland arose, and all was clear as mud.

Buckland's lectures attracted a young Scots law student, named Lyell. When called to the bar in 1825, he had already become a fellow of the Geological Society. In 1830 he produced the first volume of a work which constitutes a landmark: *The Principles of Geology*. Under this neutral title he cautiously but firmly set forth in detail the evidence for a prolonged and natural origin of the earth. Furthermore, he rejected the idea of an Universal Deluge, but asserted that there had been an Age of Ice. The truth

was unpalatable, but it could not be ignored. He was attacked mercilessly, but his book ran through twelve editions, while Cuvier's ceased to be sold. When Buckland, as Professor of Geology and Canon of Christ Church, finally felt obliged to deny the universality of the Flood, the day was won.

To Darwin, Lyell gave the gift of time – time in which the slow processes of natural selection could be worked out. Lyell himself discussed the struggle for existence, and recognized that some species must have been eliminated. 'I feel as if my books came half out of Sir Charles Lyell's brain,' Darwin once confessed.

It is therefore ironical that Lyell himself long resisted the theory of evolution. (Even his thesis of the evolution of the earth's crust cost him a severe moral struggle.) In his book he argued strongly that if new forms evolved, they would not be able to maintain themselves. For a time he claimed that it was only the imperfections of the fossil record which suggested that higher forms of life were absent from the earlier strata.

Buckland's lectures *on geology in the Ashmolean were attended by a young Scottish student named Lyell. Ten years later Lyell's epoch-making 'Principles of Geology' was of seminal importance to Darwin, who felt as if his work had come 'half out of Sir Charles Lyell's brain'. For the long, slow process of evolution needed unimagined aeons of time, and it was Lyell who first proved that the earth's age could be measured in hundreds of millions of years.*

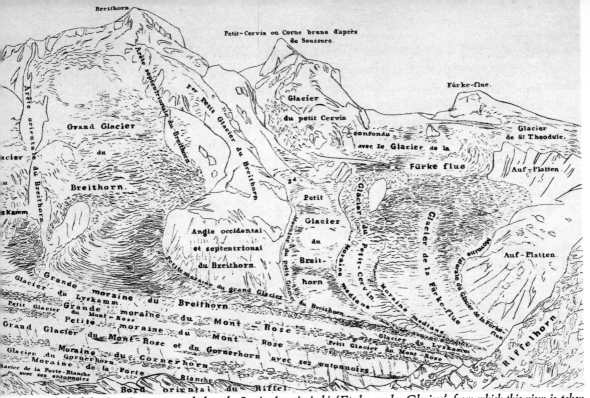

Proof of the Ice Age *was worked out by Louis Agassiz in his 'Etudes sur les Glaciers', from which this view is taken. This support for Lyell's theories helped to end belief in the Flood.*

A FANTASTIC SUGGESTION was made in 1800 by the geologist Charpentier: he published a paper asserting that the entire mountain massif of Switzerland had been carved out by vast ice glaciers, long vanished.

Louis Agassiz, a young professor of natural history at Neuchâtel, saw his chance. After eight summers' work in the Alps, with expert assistants, he published in 1846 a detailed confirmation of Charpentier's theory. He proposed that the whole of Northern Europe had once been covered by a sheet of ice, which had receded. The remains of woolly rhinoceros and cave-bear were now explicable.

Many said this was absurd: even von Humboldt reproved his rashness. But this was what Lyell had asserted. It spelled the end of the Diluvian theory. Buckland, who had attempted to controvert Lyell on this, went out of his mind and died.

Agassiz had trained under Cuvier, who had given him a stipend and a corner of his laboratory in which to write up his fish collections. Agassiz worked fifteen hours a day at the task. 'I felt within me the strength of a whole generation to work and become the first naturalist of my time,' he said afterwards.

His object was to ascertain 'what fishes lived in each of the geological epochs of creation, and to trace their characters and their relations with those fishes now living.' Living from hand to mouth, and supporting an artist – to draw his specimens for him – on his meagre income, Agassiz did a tremendous job. Like Cuvier, he learned to infer the appearance of the entire animal from a single bone. It is said that at a meeting with British scientists, he was given a single bone and asked to sketch what he thought the entire fish must have looked like. When he had finished, a curtain was removed and the entire skeleton was revealed, exactly matching his drawing.

Agassiz modified Cuvier's doctrine of catastrophes, teaching that God had recreated living things on a series of occasions, but each time he had started where he left off before 'in order to improve His creatures progres-sively until they reached the final goal, man made in God's image.'

This doctrine was acceptable to the Church, and to the conservatively-minded, accounting as it did for the facts of evolution, while retaining God as the author. Thus, where Darwin argued that the fact that amphibians, reptiles, unspecialized mammals, apes and man, all had twenty fingers and toes, implied the occurrence of a natural sequence, Agassiz claimed that it showed merely that God knew where he was going. It was precisely because Darwin proposed a mechanical explanation of evolution, thus dislodging the Deity from his last foothold, that his work was so shocking.

On Naval Timber *by Patrick Matthew:*
hidden away in an appendix this book
(published in 1831) contains a clear
anticipation of Darwin's views on natural
selection.

APPENDIX. 385

turely destroyed. This principle is in constant action, it regulates the colour, the figure, the capacities, and instincts; those individuals of each species, whose colour and covering are best suited to concealment or protection from enemies, or defence from vicissitude and inclemencies of climate, whose figure is best accommodated to health, strength, defence, and support; whose capacities

A SCOTTISH BOTANIST, so obscure that not even the date of his birth or death is known, published a paper of epoch-making importance. This was Patrick Matthew, and his paper appeared in 1831, the year in which Charles Darwin was to set off on his voyage round the world. When Darwin found out about it, after the publication of his own book on evo-lution, he was greatly chagrined, and admitted that it 'most expressly and clearly anticipated my views', and he wrote to Wallace, 'He gives *most clearly* but very briefly . . . our view of Natural Selection. It is a most complete case of anticipation.' Wallace agreed.

VESTIGES

OF

THE NATURAL HISTORY

OF

CREATION.

LONDON:
JOHN CHURCHILL, PRINCES STREET, SOHO.
MDCCCXLIV.

A best-seller of 1844: Chambers' 'Vestiges'. There were other forerunners. The idea of natural selection was in the air.

PUBLISHED anonymously, condemned by the critics as godless and immoral, *Vestiges of the Natural History of Creation* took the public by storm in 1844. Four editions appeared in seven months, and by 1860 some 24,000 copies had been sold. Speculation as to the author's identity was rife: it was even whispered that it might be the Prince Consort! Darwin and Wallace pored over it. Tennyson translated its theme into ringing verses. It made evolution 'almost a national creed'.

The author was a scientific amateur (but so were Darwin and Lyell amateurs) named Chambers, a member of the publishing house, who chose anonymity lest he harm his business. Thomas Huxley, the doughty defender of Darwin, attacked the book savagely. 'Foolish fancies', 'pretentious nonsense', 'charlatanerie' were some of the terms he coined for it.

Scientifically it contributed nothing new, while reviving some old errors. Chambers believed in a branching evolution, but attributed it partly to Lamarckian forces and partly to a divine plan, an inner directive force. Perhaps its most interesting feature was the stress placed by the author on the existence of spontaneous variations. He had good reason: both he and his brother had six fingers on each hand, and six toes on each foot.

With 'the Correct Likeness of the Fejee Mermaid', P. T. Barnum, the famous showman of the middle 19th century, also exhibited the Ornithorhynchus, 'as a connecting link between seal and duck'; two distinct species of flying fish, 'which undoubtedly connect the bird and the fish'; the Siren or Mud Iguana, 'an intermediate animal between the Reptile and the Fish... with other animals forming connecting links in the great chain of Animated Nature.'

The public flocked to see these 'missing links' – seventeen years before the publication of *The Origin of Species* – for the notion of their existence was already thoroughly familiar.

The Fejee Mermaid advertised by Barnum in the 'New York Herald' as a missing link.

The most famous ship *in the history of science: HMS 'Beagle' in the Straits of Magellan.*

IT WAS IN THIS small vessel, *H. M. S. Beagle,* that a frail young man newly down from Oxford sailed from Portsmouth, in December 1831, on a voyage of exploration which was to last five years. His name was Darwin.

He had been studying for the church, but his uncle arranged his attachment to the *Beagle* as naturalist, saying that 'though not professional, natural history is very suitable for a clergyman'. His head was full of Buckland's lectures on geology, and he took with him the first volume of Lyell's *Principles*. 'The great merit of the *Principles*', he said later, 'was that it altered the whole tone of one's mind, and therefore, that when seeing a thing never seen by Lyell, one yet saw it partially through his eyes.'

The *Beagle* was a ship of only 240 tons, and there were 76 people on board; in addition to the normal crew, and the surveyors, there was Darwin, an artist, and three Fuegians: a man named York Minster, a girl named Fuegia Basket and a boy, Jemmy Button. They had been collected – and named – on a previous voyage, and were now being returned to their home. Darwin shared a cabin with two officers, in conditions so crowded that a drawer had to be removed before he could sling his hammock.

The captain, Robert FitzRoy, who was twentysix when Darwin joined the ship, was a remarkable man, not only an expert navigator, but a good writer. His Journal gives a vivid picture of the voyage. It was he who had the idea of inviting a naturalist to join the expedition. At the same time he was a man of narrow fundamentalist views, and a martinet.

The *Beagle's* task was to complete the survey of the coasts of South America. When she reached Brazil, Darwin saw his first tropical forest; he counted it afterwards as the most remarkable experience of his life. 'The delight one experiences in such times bewilders the mind; if the eye attempts to follow the flight of a gaudy butterfly, it is arrested by some strange tree or fruit; if watching an insect, one forgets it in the stranger flower it is crawling

York Minster

Fuegia Basket

Jemmy Button

Young Darwin was lathered *and dipped in traditional style as the 'Beagle' crossed the Equator.*

over; if turning to admire the splendour of the scenery, the individual character of the foreground fixes the attention. The mind is a chaos of delight out of which a world of future and more quiet pleasure will arise.'

Darwin, now twenty-six, was not attracted by the Galapagos Islands, when the *Beagle* dropped anchor off Chatham Island in 1835.

'The fragments of Lava, where most porous, are reddish like cinders; the stunted trees show little signs of life. The black rocks heated by the rays of the vertical sun, like a stove, give to the air a close and sultry feeling. The plants also smell unpleasantly. The country was compared to what we might imagine the cultivated parts of the Infernal regions to be.'

When he went ashore, the razor-edged lava at once cut his shoes to ribbons. Nevertheless this was the place which was to start in his mind the train of thought which would make his name the best known in 19th-century biology.

He proceeded to make his usual careful collections of the plants and animals and was particularly interested in the finches. There were fourteen species, all resembling mainland species, yet all distinct, both in appearance and in habits. Some were insect-eating, others vegetarian. It was the Vice-Governor, Mr Lawson, who pointed out to him the crucial fact. Each variety of animal came from a different island. The natives could even tell from which island a tortoise had come by looking at it. For some time Darwin paid little attention to his remarks. 'It never occurred to me', exclaimed Darwin, 'that the production of islands only a few miles apart, and places under the same physical conditions, would be dissimilar. I therefore did not attempt to make a series of specimens from the separate islands.'

Soon after this discovery, the *Beagle* sailed, but as Darwin said, the subject 'haunted me'.

'I never dreamed that islands, about fifty or sixty miles apart and most of them in sight of each other, formed of precisely the same rocks placed under a similar climate, rising to a nearly equal height, would have been so differently tenanted . . .' And then he added the significant words, 'one might really fancy that from an original paucity of birds in this archipelago, one species had been taken and modified for different ends . . .'

It was to be twenty-three years before he would publicly declare that belief, and attempt to explain how the modification had been brought about.

The fourteen species of finch which Darwin found on the islands all appear to have evolved from a single species, which had presumably colonized the island from the American mainland at some remote time. One had evolved a long beak with which it attacked the bark of trees, in search of insects, like a woodpecker. But it had failed to evolve the woodpecker's long tongue and had learned to use a small twig to dislodge the insects. The fact that mainland finches did not evolve into this form, we now explain by saying that this particular mode of life was already more efficiently exploited by another bird, the woodpecker.

On his return to England, Darwin wrote a narrative of the voyage, together with scientific accounts of his material. At twenty-seven he found himself the world authority on the geology of South America, sought after not only by Lyell, Brown, and other scientists, but also such eminent men as Macaulay and Carlyle.

But more significant than what he published was the notebook – a cheap yellow-covered one, for he was frugal in all his habits – in which he began to assemble data related to the idea of natural selection. He studied bees and opened ants' nests. He observed that ducks leave ponds carrying small water plants on their backs and the eggs of small organisms on their feet, and he showed that these remain fertile for up to twenty hours in air, from which it follows that they could thus be disseminated from one lake or river to another. He took a cupful of pond mud and counted how many plants finally

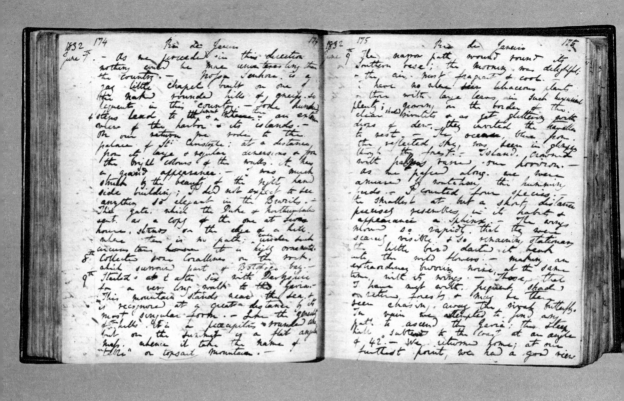

A cheap yellow-covered notebook *(which can still be seen at Darwin's house) contains his observations assembled on the voyage of the 'Beagle'. From these he began to build up his theory of natural selection. On the pages shown here he describes a walk near Buenos Aires, where he counted four species of humming birds, their wings 'scarcely visible'.*

sprouted from the seeds embedded in it: 537. He spent hours, he tells us, in gin palaces talking to pigeon fanciers and combing the files of gardeners' magazines, determined to study how artificial selection occurs; and even started breeding experiments himself, chiefly with pigeons. He did not reveal the object of these enquiries, and when as late as 1849, a friend – Hooker, the botanist – asked him, curiously, what Ornamental Poultry had to do with the barnacles on which he had published a definitive study, he replied, 'You wonder what "Ornamental Poultry" had to do with Barnacles; but do not flatter yourself that I shall not yet live to finish the Barnacles, and then make a fool of myself on the subject of species, under which head Ornamental Poultry are very interesting . . .'

Darwin's closest friend *and supporter was Joseph Dalton Hooker, here seen on the 16,000-ft Choonjerma Pass in Nepal, in a part of the country never open to travellers before or since his time. Here he studied the geographical distribution of plants – a subject of fundamental importance to Darwin's theories.*

Hooker – 'the only man from whom I have constantly received sympathy' – was becoming Darwin's closest friend, and was, in the storms which followed publication of the *Origin of Species,* to be one of his staunchest supporters. He was by general consent the leading botanist of the age: the supreme authority on the geographical distribution of plants, the study which was Darwin's main tool in exploring natural selection. To this end he explored particularly the unknown eastern part of the Indian mountain chain.

Eight years younger than Darwin, Hooker's desire to travel was sparked by reading Darwin's *Journal* of his voyage: he used to sleep with the proof-sheets beneath his pillow and read them on waking, and rising, as all day was spent studying for his medical final exams.

153

At twenty-two, he sailed as Assistant Surgeon under Ross in *Erebus,* on the three-year magnetic survey of the Antarctic which set sail in 1839. Ross, like FitzRoy, was favourably disposed towards botany, so Hooker seized the opportunity to study plankton. On returning home, his results established his reputation, and he determined to go to India to see whether plants at different altitudes varied in the same way as they do between different climatic zones. Is the sequence as one passes from the steamy valleys to the icy peaks the same as when one passes from the equatorial zone to the Arctic?

Hooker's father was Director of Kew Gardens, and his son succeeded him. When the father took over it comprised about 18 acres: today there are about 650 acres. More important, the two men turned it into the most im-portant centre of plant-distribution studies in the world, and Hooker's col-lections (those from India comprised seven wagon-loads when they were shifted from the India Office in 1858) enabled him to produce Floras for the British Colonies which remain standard works. His Flora of British India appeared in seven volumes and ran to 6,000 pages; it recorded 16,000 species. As originally planned it would have run to twelve volumes. Hooker's *Flora of the British Isles* (1870) is still a standard work for students.

There were two other important centres of plant study in the world. In Geneva, Augustin de Candolle was attempting the gigantic task of listing all known species. The work was carried on after his death in 1841. In Cambridge, Massachusetts, Asa Gray was working towards the founding of his Herbarium, and making his important studies of North American plant distribution.

Kew Gardens in 1854. Hooker, as Director, made this an important centre of plant study.

Gray had been intrigued by Hooker's monograph on the plants Darwin brought back from the Galapagos, and had turned to collections recently made in Hawaii – to find the same thing. Species from different islands in the group, though obviously similar, were not identical. Gray was at this time quite orthodox. He assumed that every current member of a species had descended from a single original exemplar (or from a pair, where sexual reproduction was involved) and that the descendants had gradually radiated from the point at which the first pair had lived. Plant distribution was discussed in terms of what we now call 'adaptive radiation'. Hooker thought in like terms, hence his astonishment at Darwin's material.

Gray addressed himself to a problem: why are many of the plants of eastern America so similar to those of China, while nothing similar is found in the area between? If the Creator had created two magnolias and set one down in China and one in Virginia, there was no problem – but it seemed rather arbitrary of Him, and it made the radiation theory unstable. Gray was able to show that in the tertiary period (about 60 million years ago) there had been a single flora over the whole area. The ice-sheets, creeping down from the Pole as the Ice Age drew on, had split it in two. The idea of radiation was therefore re-established – but some of the Asian species were no longer identical with the American ones! Gray cautiously concluded that they must be descendants from a pristine stock, and that 'variation in species is wider than is generally supposed.'

But this was in 1858. Let us go back to Darwin where we left him in the early 1840's.

Hooker: *a photograph of 1876.*

Asa Gray *in his study: about 1876.*

In the garden of Downe House, Darwin sometimes felt so happy that he 'did not care one penny how any of the beasts or birds had been formed. But at other times he felt ill – was it the five years of repeated sea-sickness or an obscure tropical disease? The notebook grew until in 1842 and 1844 he wrote two essays outlining his theories. These were never published in his lifetime, but he sent copies to one or two intimates. To Hooker he wrote: 'At last gleams of light have come, and I am almost convinced that species are not (it is like confessing murder) immutable: I think I have found (here's presumption) the simple way by which species become exquisitely adapted to various ends.'

In essence, Darwin's theory was this: small chance variations in its hereditary constitution will sometimes handicap a plant or an animal, but occasionally they will assist it to compete better with rivals for food, or in the production and protection of its young. Thus animals or plants with favourable variations will suvive more numerously, until the variation has become standard throughout the species. Over very long periods of time these variations may proceed so far that the species becomes changed to a new species. This is the theory of natural selection.

As Darwin accumulated information supporting this thesis, he occasionally tested the reactions of other scientists, but continually postponed publishing his material for fear of being met with a storm of ridicule and abuse, such as had greeted Chambers.

Then, in 1858, a letter arrived at Downe from the other side of the world, which shook Darwin to the core. It was signed 'Alfred Russel Wallace'.

This painting of Alfred Russel Wallace shows him in the jungle of Borneo with the young orang utan and the young macaque which he brought up by hand. He noted how the young orang played and cried like a human baby, and quite differently from the macaque. It learned to walk, it showed a need for affection, it cut its teeth – much more like a human than a monkey.

Wallace was a professional collector of specimens, who had spent many years in the jungles of Brazil. He was also a self-taught naturalist who in 1855 had published a paper on 'The Law which has regulated the introduction of New Species'. Each species, he said, had appeared coincident with some similar pre-existing species.

In 1857 he was in the obscure island of Ternate off the western coast of the Moluccas. He had been making comparisons between the distribution of living forms in the Indies and in South America. (The book which he published in 1876 on the geographical distribution of animals is still one of the most important works on the subject.) There, while suffering from fever, he was seized with the idea of variation of species. 'There is no limit of variability to a species, as formerly supposed,' he wrote. 'Useful variations will tend to increase; useless or hurtful variations to diminish . . .'

When Darwin received his letter, he wrote at once to Lyell:

'Wallace . . . has today sent me the enclosed . . . Your words have come true with a vengeance – that I should be forestalled . . . I never saw a more striking coincidence; if Wallace had my MS sketch written in 1842, he could not have made a better short abstract!'

Darwin at first felt he should send Wallace's paper for publication, and give him the priority of discovery. But friends suggested a more equitable solution. Lyell and Hooker would present a paper by Darwin and that by Wallace jointly. These papers were read to the Linnaean Society in London on 1st July 1858.

The effect of the papers on the scientists was dramatic: but the issue had still to be presented to the public at large. Darwin withdrew to the Isle of Wight and began to write. Wallace went on to become one of the founders of zoological geography, and his name is perpetuated in 'Wallace's line' which divides the fauna of the Malay archipelago from those of Australasia and the Pacific islands.

'Scribbling in a vile hand whole pages as quickly as I possibly can, contracting half the words,' Darwin frantically wrote the *Origin of Species* in 1858 and 1859.

On 1st October he finished correcting the last of the proof sheets, and, completely exhausted, retired to a spa to recover, stopping only to send an advance copy to Lyell. He was, he said, in a state of 'the wibber-gibbers'. Publication took place on 24th November, and every copy of the edition of 1250 was sold on the same day. Darwin realized that he had not only an intellectual success but a money-maker on his hands. Hooker reported: 'Darwin's book is out and created a tremendous furore on all hands.' The *Quarterly Review* and the *Edinburgh Review* snarled. Sedgwick, the thick-witted geologist who failed to grasp the significance of the signs of glaciation which he observed, wrote to Darwin that he was 'very pained', and when he met him told him that he had had to hold his sides with laughing. It seems a curious combination of reactions.

In January 1859, six months after the reading of the joint papers to the Linnaean Society, Darwin had written to Wallace: 'You ask about Lyell's frame of mind. I think he is somewhat staggered, but does not give in . . . Dr Hooker has become almost as heterodox as you or I, and I look at Hooker as by far the most capable judge in Europe.'

In England, the most serious opposition came from Owen. There is some evidence that Owen had himself toyed with the idea of a theory of natural selection, but finding himself forestalled, was driven to deny it. He went to the extraordinary length of writing articles against the theory under assumed names, in which he appealed repeatedly to the opinions of the famous Professor Owen. It was he who wrote the severe review of the *Origin* which appeared in the *Edinburgh Review*. 'But do the facts of organic nature square with the Darwininian hypothesis? Undoubtedly not,' declares the reviewer (Owen). The only value of the book was half a dozen ob/ servations of animal behaviour, which were 'few indeed and far apart, and leaving the determination of the origin of species very nearly where the author found it.' Darwin's observations not only failed to convince, they did not even lend colour to the hypothesis. Darwin's mind was not intel/ lectually equal to tackling such an important task, Owen said. In the same review, after approvingly citing Professor Owen two or three times, he re/ spectfully accepts Pouchet's claim to have shown spontanous generation.

'I will buckle on my armour and fight my best,' cried Darwin, goaded, but with Hooker and Huxley, not to mention Lyell, on his side, he could afford to ignore Owen's attacks. In America, however, his position was less secure. Agassiz led the opposition, maintaining 'a species is a thought of the Creator.' Among 1,500 species of fossil fish which he had examined, he said, he could see no support for such a theory. 'There is no evidence of a direct descent of earlier from later species.' Asa Gray fought to secure Darwin a fair hearing, and arranged publication of the *Origin* in the United States. Agassiz mocked: 'Mr Darwin affirms the monkey is his brother, and the horse his cousin, and the oyster his remote ancestor.'

'I am sharpening up my claws and beak in readiness,' Huxley had written to Darwin, shortly before the publication of the *Origin*. But though he intended to secure a fair hearing for Darwin, if he could, and to demolish

'In a vile hand', scribbling as fast as he could, Darwin wrote the whole of 'The Origin of Species' in 1858–59. This page of the MS, which comes from Chapter VII, is one of only ten that survive, for Darwin used up old MS sheets for making fresh notes.

breed from ~~back~~ pointers. On the other hand,
habit alone in some cases has been sufficient:
no animal — more difficult to tame than the young of the
wild rabbit, scarcely any animal is tamer than the young
of the tame rabbit; yet I do not suppose that
domestic rabbit has ever been selected for tameness; & I presume
that we must attribute to chiefly of this inherited
~~inherited~~ fer other within to other tameness
a change in instinct to habit & continued close

confinement.

Natural instinct are lost ~~feelings~~ under Domestication;
& a remarkable instance of this is seen in
those breeds of fowls, which most rarely or never
sit on their eggs.
become "broody" or will to ~~sit incubate~~.

Familiarity alone presents us seeing how
universally & largely the minds of our domestic animals
~~remarkably~~ ~~temporary~~ modified by domestication. It is scarcely possible to
have been modified. It is scarcely possible to
doubt that to look & even has become instinctive
in the dog. ~~and how changed in the largest~~
~~no dog believed~~] all ~~the character of the dog~~ water, fires, jackals & all-spring,
the Cats family, when kept quite tame, are much
eager to attack partly a sheep & pigs; & this
tendency has been found innate with, dogs themselves,
which has been brought from savages who do not keep, domestic
animals } ~~as those~~ of Tierra del Fuego & Australia)

inaccurate criticism in print, he was not out for trouble at the famous British Association meeting at Oxford in 1860. Even when Sir Richard Owen falsely asserted a basic difference between the anatomy of men and apes, Huxley contented himself with a contradiction.

But the rumour spread that the Bishop of Oxford – Bishop Wilberforce, sometimes known as Soapy Sam – would settle the heretics' hash on the last day of the month. Huxley was pressed to stay, but replied at first that he had no desire to be 'episcopally pounded'. By the strangest irony, it was Chambers – whose book Huxley had reviewed so savagely when it was published anonymously – who persuaded him to stay.

Attracted by the prospect of a set-to, some seven hundred people arrived at the Museum, and the meeting was shifted to a larger hall. The clergy massed in the middle of the room; in one corner stood a group of pro-Darwin undergraduates. The Chairman was Professor Henslow, Darwin's former teacher. One after another the clergy rose to assert their views dogmatically, until the chairman was forced to stop them on the grounds that only valid scientific arguments could be accepted.

Finally it was the turn of Soapy Sam, skilled in the arts of persuasion and pulpit oratory, insolent in his assurance, cunning in his awareness of how to appeal to prejudice. Blandly, he spoke for half an hour – until he made

'Soapy Sam' – *Samuel Wilberforce, Bishop of Oxford – led the opposition to 'The Origin of Species' at the British Association meeting at Oxford in 1860.*

his fatal mistake. Turning to Huxley he asked, was it on his grandfather's or on his grandmother's side that he claimed descent from an ape?

Huxley muttered to a neighbour: 'The Lord hath delivered him into mine hands.' There are several accounts of what followed, but here is Huxley's own: 'So when I got up I spoke pretty much to the effect – that I had listened with great attention to the Lord Bishop's speech but had been unable to discover either a new fact or a new argument in it – except indeed the question raised as to my personal predilections in the matter of ancestry – That it would not have occurred to me to bring forward such a topic as that for discussion myself, but that I was quite ready to meet the Right Rev. prelate even on that ground – If then, said I, the question is put to me would I rather have a miserable ape for a grandfather or a man highly endowed by nature and possessed of great means of influence and yet who employs those faculties and that influence for the mere purpose of introducing ridicule into a grave scientific discussion – I unhesitatingly affirm my preference for the ape. Whereupon there was inextinguishable laughter among the people.'

Darwin received the news of this victory with nervous chortles: 'How durst you attack a live bishop in that fashion? I am quite ashamed of you! Have you no respect for fine lawn sleeves? By Jove, you seem to have done it well.'

The bishop's sneer about Darwin's descent *from an ape was one that also occurred to lesser minds. This cartoon from the 'Hornet', a humorous journal of the time, puts it in fairly obvious terms.*

'I WILL LEAVE my mark somewhere, and it shall be clear and distinct – T.H.H., his mark – and free from the abominable blur of cant, humbug and selfseeking which surrounds this present world . . .' 'Few men have drunk more deeply of all kinds of sin than I.' 'If I were not a man I think I should like to be a tug.' These were three comments by T.H. Huxley on himself.

An observer's judgement: 'Huxley had more talents than two lifetimes could have developed. He could think, draw, speak, write, inspire, read, negotiate, and wage multifarious war against earth and heaven with the cool professional ease of an acrobat supporting nine people on his shoulders at once.' Darwin and Hooker said that they felt intellectually infantile compared with him. He was a born lecturer. As a writer his power of projecting his personality on to the page, by means of crystalline, much corrected prose, made his arguments appear like a personal communication with the reader.

'There is a strain of madness in him,' Beatrice Webb noted, and one of his brothers was 'as near mad as a sane man can be.' In him there was a Calvinistic streak: he was dubbed the John Knox of agnosticism, and he crusaded against intellectual dishonesty as others against the devil.

This extraordinary man was the son of a poor schoolmaster and a woman of tremendous energy and great rapidity of thought. He recalled that as a child he often wept for fear his

Thomas Henry Huxley, *whose defence of Darwin lifted him into national fame.*

mother would die. His school life was a 'pandemonium'; from the age of ten he educated himself. At first he wanted to be an engineer. At one point he almost went to Australia to become a brewer. But he became a surgeon in the navy, joining the H M S *Rattlesnake* expedition to N. Australian waters. Unfortunately the captain was not welldisposed to research, and threw his dissections overboard, while the Admiralty refused to publish the important research reports he sent home. Nevertheless, he contrived to make his name with a book on the jellyfish which swarm in these waters.

MAN·IS·BVT·A·WORM

From the worm *that crawls out of primeval chaos, Punch's fanciful evolutionary spiral leads round, through ape, anthropoid, cave-man and 'masher', to a not unsym-pathetic portrait of the brooding sage of Downe House.*

Darwin's *Origin* tore through the theological world like a plough through an anthill. It was 'an attempt to dethrone God', and 'a jungle of fanciful assumptions', even 'a huge imposture'. Books, pamphlets and sermons were hurled at the head of the author. One authority, rather unwisely, declared, 'If the Darwinian theory is true, Genesis is a lie, the whole frame-work of the book of life falls to pieces, and the revelation of God to man, as we Christians know it, is a delusion and a snare.'

In Australia, the Bishop of Melbourne asserted that it was actually the object of Chambers, Darwin and Huxley 'to produce in their readers a disbelief of the Bible'. In America, the same line was taken. 'If this hypo-thesis be true, then is the Bible an unbearable fiction . . . then have Christians for nearly two thousand years been duped by a monstrous lie . . .'

The Catholic Church did not stop at denunciation, but set up sacro-scientific organizations to combat such ideas. The Protestants followed suit, and the Society for the Promotion of Christian Knowledge published a book which declared that evolution was 'flatly opposed to the fundamental doctrine of creation.'

When in 1871 Darwin published his *Descent of Man* the brouhaha burst out again. Even the *Times* reviewer condemned it as 'an utterly unsupported hypothesis', full of 'unsubstantiated premises, cursory investigations, and disintegrating speculations', and Darwin himself as 'reckless and unscientific'.

Gradually however, the Church began to take up the position that perhaps, after all, Darwinism was not inconsistent with Christianity, that evolution might even reveal God's plan. When in 1882 Darwin was buried in Westminster Abbey, the Rev. Dr Laing was in a minority when he said this proved 'that England is no longer a Christian country'.

Approved Catholic textbooks reconciling evolution with creation, such as that of the Abbé Choyer in 1875, continued to appear, and still do.

The greatest scientific figure in England, Lord Kelvin, undermined Darwin's confidence in his theory by arguing that geological time was much more limited than Darwin supposed. For the rest of his days Darwin was unable to exorcise the 'odious spectre' of Kelvin's argument.

'I TAKE THE SUN much to heart,' groaned Darwin in 1868. For, within six years of publication of the *Origin,* the greatest scientific figure in England, Lord Kelvin, had launched an attack on the concept of unlimited geological time, on which the theory of natural selection depended, with such vigour that even Darwin's confidence in his theory was shaken.

Kelvin, a strongly religious man, wrote a number of papers – the first was in 1862 – arguing that the sun's rate of dissipation of energy was such that it must have had a short life in the past, and could not exist for many million years more 'unless new sources [of energy] now unknown to us' exist. If the sun's life was short, so must the earth's be, and by 1893 Kelvin was prepared to put it at a mere 24 million years, where Darwin had guessed at 300 million for the period since the Tertiary deposits alone. (Today, we estimate the earth's age at 24,000 million years.)

In 1865 Kelvin challenged the geologists directly in a paper titled: *The Doctrine of Uniformity Briefly Refuted.* (By uniformity he meant the view that the strata had been formed by gradual and natural processes, not by catastrophes, a view known as uniformitarianism.) He declared that his facts 'seem sufficient to disprove the doctrine that transmutation has taken place through descent with modification by natural selection'.

Darwin was flummoxed. 'I have not as yet been able to digest the fundamental notion of the shortened age of the sun and earth,' he wrote to Wallace in 1871. Two years later Kelvin was openly speaking of the 'utter futility of Darwin's philosophy'. Darwin reacted by trying to show that evolution could have been achieved in this shorter period, and was led into contradictions. At one point he modified the *Origin* by suggesting that perhaps higher organisms evolved more quickly than lower; at another, using a different argument, he suggested just the reverse possibility. Wallace thought that perhaps the earth's orbit had formerly been less eccentric, and that this might have made a difference.

The irony was, of course, that the trained physicist was wrong – he did not allow for atomic sources of energy within the sun – and the geologists, whom he thought so amateur, were right.

Darwin called Kelvin's argument an 'odious spectre': it was not exorcised until both men were dead. But soon afterwards what seemed an even more serious objection was raised. An erudite and hard-headed Scots engineer, Fleeming Jenkin, wrote an article arguing that if a new trait emerged it would at once be bred out by back-crossing. Only if it emerged simultaneously in a majority of the creatures concerned would it establish itself. But such a widespread simultaneous variation is quite different from the natural selection of chance variations, which Darwin had suggested, and suggests some interior modifying force.

Darwin wrote to Wallace, much troubled: 'Jenkin has argued in the *North British Review* against single variations ever being perpetuated, and has convinced me . . .' and he entered a footnote in the sixth edition of the *Origin* to this effect. Another writer pressed the point a few years later in *Nature,* and Herbert Spencer also took it up.

In this dilemma, Darwin lost his nerve, and began to insert little Lamarckian loopholes into the new editions of his works. In the final edition of the *Origin* he even went so far as to say, 'There must be some efficient cause for each slight individual difference . . . and if the unknown cause were to act persistently, it is almost certain that all the individuals of the species would be similarly modified.' So in the end Darwin has – while leaving in his references to spontaneous variation – come to think in terms of an unknown cause, in place of natural selection.

He did not know that the answer to Jenkin's objection had been standing on the shelves of an Austrian library, unread, from 1865, two years before Jenkin wrote. Both Darwin and Jenkin were dead before anyone dusted it off and read it. The writer was a Moravian monk, the Abbé Mendel.

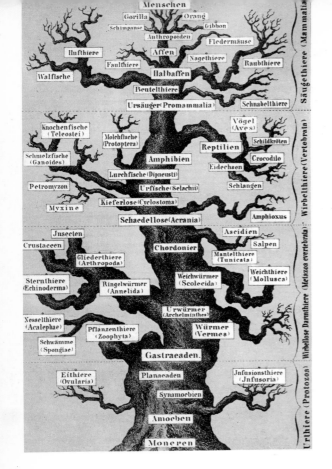

The first of the popularizers, *Ernst Haeckel, drew this 'evolutionary tree' to show the descent of man from the Protozoa. Impressed by the brilliance of Darwin's conception, Haeckel went even further and suggested that the Monera, the most primitive form of life, was itself formed from inorganic materials.*

THIS 'EVOLUTIONARY TREE', showing the descent of man from the apes, was drawn by Ernst Haeckel, an extraordinary man, half scientist, half high priest, with a dash of liberal politician thrown in. Perhaps today he would be called a publicist. Few scientists have exerted so wide an influence.

He purveyed science to the public in easily digestible form, often perverting the facts to make them more attractive and embedding them all in a quasi-religious philosophical structure, enlivened by fiery diatribe and poetic imagination. His *Riddles of the Universe* sold 400,000 copies and was translated into many languages. His conviction that the facts would be found to fit his theories resembled nothing so much as the attitude of the medieval theologians to Christian dogma. This conviction justified him, he felt, in depicting in scientific drawings structures which he could not see but felt sure existed.

He was, however, a skilled draughtsman, and his beautifully illustrated work on the Radiolaria of the Mediterranean won him a chair of zoology at Jena, which he held all his working life. Radiolaria are minute symmetrically spherical objects which live in water: they are extremely hard to draw since the entire sphere cannot be brought into focus under the microscope at the same moment. Haeckel tells us that he drew these microscopic creatures with the aid of a camera lucida; and he describes the difficulty of drawing organisms which can only be kept alive for a short time, and whose soft protoplasmic bodies protrude in all directions threads and arms which branch and rejoin in shifting tangles of infinite complexity.

Haeckel, on reading the first German translation of the *Origin*, was thunderstruck by its brilliance – it was, he thought, a superb triumph of intellect over prejudice. Inspired by it, he developed the notion of evolution still further, claiming (a) that the Monera, the most primitive form of life, was formed from inorganic materials; (b) that just as an egg-cell becomes a collection of cells, so, in the evolutionary story, unicellular creatures had clumped together to form multicellular creatures; and (c) that the gradual emergence of organs in embryonic life followed the same sequence as the evolution of these organs in historical time.

In this last claim, at least, there was a measure of truth: the 'recapitulation' of evolutionary stages in the embryo is well established. Thus the human embryo goes through a phase where it has rudimentary gills. Though not original, Haeckel's assertion helped to transform comparative anatomy into comparative embryology in the nineteenth century.

But Haeckel thought that the *Origin* had one grave defect: it did not face the question of the origin of mankind.

Examining the skeletons of various apes and monkeys and comparing them with those of a human child, Haeckel came to the erroneous conclusion that the gibbon was the nearest relative of man. It was this which inspired the Dutch anatomist Eugen Dubois to visit Java, home of the gibbon, in the hope of finding a primitive ancestor of man. Since Java had escaped the ice age, he felt it the more likely that something of the sort might have survived. When Haeckel announced his views at a congress in 1863 he was called an atheist, though some supported him, including the famous Alfred Krupp. When he told the Duke of Weimar that he proposed to write a book on the subject, the latter observed: 'One may think that sort of thing, my dear Professor, but one doesn't have it printed.'

Radiolaria, *minute spherical grains of marine ooze, drawn under the microscope by Haeckel. As they are spherical, the focus of the lens must be shifted gradually through them, and the resultant patterns interpreted three-dimensionally.*

Haeckel's *General Morphology – founded on the Descent Theory* proved to be a gigantic work, which foreshadowed even the atomic theory.

In 1877, after several foreign tours and many honours, Haeckel urged on a scientific congress at Munich that evolution be taught in German schools. Among who opposed the idea was Virchow, the Pope of German medicine, and Haeckel's former teacher, who said that such a course would lead to revolution. When an attempt was made to assassinate the Kaiser soon after, Haeckel was accused of being morally guilty of the crime.

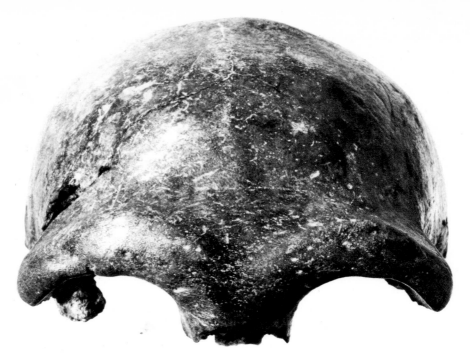

Was this the missing link? *Found at Neanderthal near Dusseldorf in 1856, this skull, with the ape-like ridges over the eye-sockets, set off furious arguments among scientists.*

A CRANIUM of strange appearance with bony ridges above the eye-sockets was unearthed in a quarry in Rhenish Prussia in the year 1856. Though not the first skull of this type to be discovered, it was the first to undergo scientific scrutiny, and thus the first skull of a genuinely extinct variety of man ever to be seriously examined. Its owner was dubbed Neanderthal man, from the valley near Dusseldorf where these remains were found.

Was it the skull of a genuine missing link between man and the apes? This was the burning question which Darwin's book made all the more pregnant. Estimates ranged from a cautious 'yes' to scornful assertions that it was the putrefied remains of a Cossack killed in the Napoleonic wars. No one could agree whether the owner had been young or old, normal or abnormal. The great Virchow pronounced the bones pathological: those of a man who had suffered from both rickets and arthritis.

Not enough was known about the sequence of geological strata to date it with certainty. (Even today the Neanderthal remains present many problems.) The jawbone had vanished and only a few odd bits of the skeleton remained. Lyell, however, declared it to be genuine.

It was not until 1886 when two complete skeletons were discovered in a cave near Namur, surrounded by very primitive hand-tools and ornaments, in layers which could be confidently dated, that conviction came.

Improbable, gigantic animals from the remote past brought crowds to museums. Here is a nineteenth-century exhibition at the American Museum of Natural History, New York.

HUNTING in the soft chalk of a dried-up river bed in Kansas, Othniel Marsh, then thirty-eight, stumbled over a small, hollow, fossil bone about six inches long and an inch in diameter. It looked like the tibia of a bird – a gigantic bird – but no living bird possessed such a joint as this bone did, for it permitted a freedom of movement in one direction 'that no well-constructed bird could use on land or water'.

The only joint like it that Marsh could identify was possessed by the pterodactyl, the flying reptile of Jurassic deposits in Europe. On the basis of this one bone, Marsh made a reconstruction of the entire animal: it emerged as a toothed pterodactyl of fish-eating habits, with a wing span of twenty feet, which he named pteranodon. He had discovered the first American 'flying dragon'.

Three years later a complete skeleton was dug up in Europe. Marsh, outbidding Agassiz, bought it for $1,000. Other discoveries followed.

Huxley commented: 'The discovery of the toothed birds by Mr Marsh removed Mr Darwin's proposition that many animal forms have been utterly lost from the region of hypothesis to demonstrable fact.' Darwin wrote, 'Your old birds have offered the best support to the theory of evolution.'

In the previous year, Marsh, excavating an old well in a lake bed in Nebraska, had found bones which could only be explained as belonging

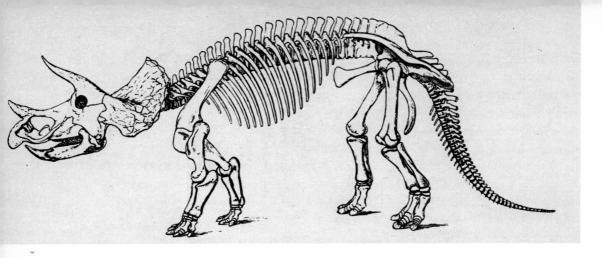

As the railways were built *across the country, Marsh followed them, penetrating into geologically unexplored territory and reporting on his finds to the U.S. Government. This drawing of a Triceratops, about forty feet in length, is from one of his reports.*

to an ancestor of the horse, standing three feet high. In the next six years at least a further thirty specimens from various stages in the sequence from Protohippos to the modern horse, came to light. The horse, it appeared, was not European but American.

But this was only the beginning: the fact is, the middle west of the United States was, all unsuspected, a palaeontological paradise. The bed of a dried-up sea, it was littered with the bones of weird, gigantic animals, still unknown to man: stegosaurus, brontosaurus, diplodocus, triceratops. As the railways were built across the continent this geologically unexplored territory was opened up. Following his election to the presidency of the American Academy of Arts and Sciences, Marsh travelled out to Benton, Wyoming, in 1868, the whole length of the Union Pacific; the last mile was finished with rails which his train brought up. A quick reconnaissance convinced him that here was material for a life's work. He returned to Yale, enlisted the help of young, adventurous Yale men, induced the United States army to provide escorts, engaged Buffalo Bill and Pawnee Indians as guides, and proceeded to make a killing.

March pursued his campaign to make Yale the greatest paleontological centre in the world with the ruthless acquisitiveness of an industrial tycoon. But he had a rival in the field: E. D. Cope, the greatest comparative anatomist in the United States. Both were men of initiative, ambition and wealth.

Battle was joined in 1877 when an English school-teacher, Arthur Lakes, found some gigantic vertebrae in Colorado sandstones. He sent one to Marsh, but when he failed to reply, sent the remainder to Cope. Marsh, on discovering this, at once telegraphed Lakes to keep the whereabouts of the find a secret, and wired his agents to buy up all the fossils, including those despatched to Cope. Just as Cope was about to publish a paper, he was ordered to return the bones, while Marsh, on the strength of an 8-foot femur, hastily wrote a paper on *A New and Gigantic Dinosaur*.

A long dinosaurian struggle ensued. Often each man would find bones within a few days of the other, and name them within a matter of hours. Cope took to telegraphing his papers to the American Philosophical Society, in order to ensure priority. In 1872 he attempted to telegraph a description of a new species, Loxolophodon, 'a document probably unique in paleon-tological history'. Cope spent more than $80,000 and was obliged to sell his home to secure his fossils. He accused Marsh publicly of breaking up fossils which he could not use himself in order to prevent others using them, and of hiring men to obstruct his rivals' work.

Marsh's triumph came when the newly-formed United States Geological Survey ordered Cope to turn over his collections to the National Museum in Washington, of which Marsh was honorary curator! But Marsh too had to mortgage his house and take salaried work. When he died at sixty-eight he left no personal bequests and only $200 in cash.

Marsh was blue-eyed and sandy-haired, his beard almost red. His stiff, rather pompous manner contrasted with the warmth of the more likeable Cope. Up to 1869 only a few dinosaur bones had been found. The 1871 edition of Lyell's *Elements of Geology* did not mention the word 'dinosaur'. Marsh, who described 34 genera, made it a household word.

The descent of the horse *from Eohippus, a remote ancestor three feet high, was worked out by Marsh from fossil remains. In this comparative table the evolution of the hoof can be clearly seen. Huxley's waggish comment (while on a visit to Marsh in 1876): Eohippus ought to have an Eohomo on its back! And so he drew it.*

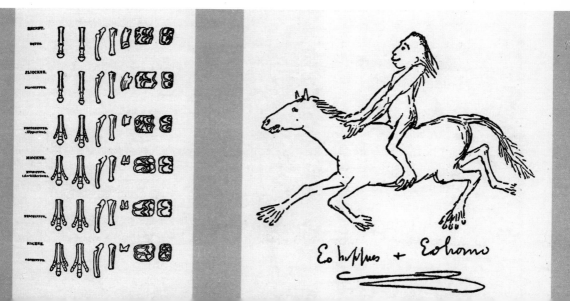

Eohippus + Eohomo

Two-thirds of the earth's surface remained a mystery, despite the 19th century's frenzy of exploration. To remedy this, Her Majesty's Ship 'Challenger' sailed nearly seventy thousand miles on the first great voyage of oceanography. Opposite, the 'Challenger's' main deck, showing the winch, and a deep-sea dredge slung outboard.

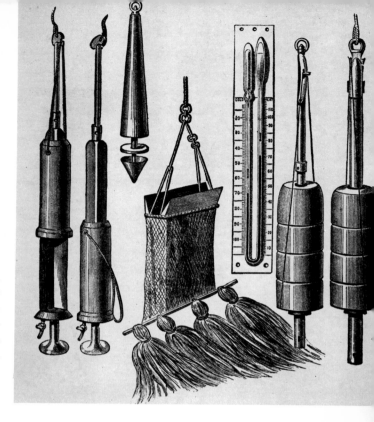

New instruments were devised or old ones adapted, to enable the 'Challenger' to dredge from hitherto unsampled depths. On the left is a water-bottle: lowered in the first position, as soon as it touches bottom the sleeve falls, trapping a small quantity of water.

WHEN HMS 'CHALLENGER' docked at Spithead in 1876, after a voyage of 69,890 miles over the oceans of the world, she had laid the foundations of a new branch of science; oceanography. This voyage, like those of Cook and Columbus, had added a new region to knowledge – the depths of the oceans, until then a total mystery.

Edward Forbes, the first man to put a naturalist's dredge down to any depth, had brought up starfish and other animals from 1,300 feet in the Aegean, but in such small numbers that he concluded that at about 1,500 feet down life ceased. But when, in 1860, a telegraph cable was hauled to the surface for repair, between Sardinia and Africa, animals were found to have established themselves on parts known to have been lying at a depth of over 6,000 feet. These and other clues inspired Charles Wyville Thomson (Forbes's successor as Professor of Natural Philosophy at Edinburgh) to explore this so-called 'azoic zone'. In short summer cruises, in which he made several trawls at depths of over 12,000 feet, he recovered living things.

Encouraged by this, he enlisted the help of the Royal Society and the Admiralty to organize the most comprehensive and important oceanographic expedition there has ever been – nothing less than a survey of the ocean depths and its floor over the entire planet. Despite the frenzy of exploration which had been going on, two-thirds of the earth's surface remained a mystery. Even today we know less of the geography of the ocean bed than we do of the surface of the moon.

Thomson and his team of scientists designed apparatus never seen before to sound and dredge the deeps. Ripping out seventy-four of the ship's seventy-six guns, they built in a chemical laboratory, a natural history laboratory, and even a dark-room for photographic development. They took with them 144 miles of sounding rope, and 12½ miles of sounding wire; and quantities of 'spirits of wine' for preserving specimens. There was also a parrot, rather dilapidated, which perched on the wardroom hatpegs and observed from time to time: 'What! Two thousand fathoms and no bottom! Ah, Dr Carpenter, FRS!'

In the three and a half years' voyage they had many adventures. Once the ship rammed an iceberg in a storm. They rescued two brothers who had

Seventy-four guns *were removed from the 'Challenger's' tween-decks to make room for labs and workshops. Above: the natural history laboratory.*

Examining a haul *from the ocean depths on the deck of HMS 'Challenger'. Astonishing forms of life were brought to the surface, from depths as great as 26,850 feet (5 miles).*

marooned themselves on Inaccessible Island for two years. In the course of the trip, seven men died from one cause or another.

Their deepest sounding was at 26,850 feet – not far from the deepest sounding ever made. (The figure stands currently at 34,440 feet – about 6 miles – and was recorded by a United States vessel in 1950.)

With the new trawls, astonishing forms of life were brought to the surface, many of them related to extinct forms. They brought home a colossal collection of specimens, such as naturalists had never seen. The findings, when eventually published, comprised fifty quarto volumes. The *Challenger* team had discovered 715 new genera, and 4,417 new species of living things – for each of which a place had now to be found in the evolutionary tree. The hope, however, that many primitive animals, corresponding to groups only known in fossil form, would be found was disappointed, though there were a few such.

On the geographic side, the *Challenger* mapped many features of the main ocean basins, incidentally disproving the existence of a drowned continent of Atlantis.

The existence of the living slime, *Bathybius haeckeli,* which had so fascinated Haeckel, was also disproved. Huxley believed he had observed this almost structureless protoplasm, and Haeckel claimed that it covered the floor of

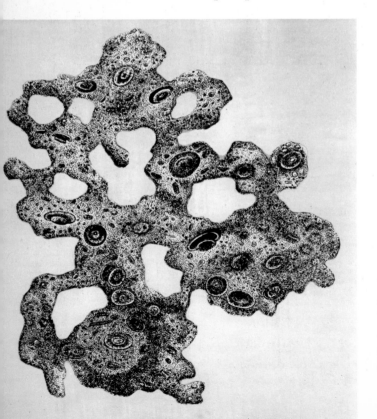

The 'living slime', *Bathybius haeckeli,* claimed by Haeckel to be an ocean-wide 'reservoir of life', turned out to be merely fine sand particles embedded in a precipitate of sulphate of lime, formed from the sea-water and preserving alcohol.

A modern 'Challenger', *the Danish oceanographic ship 'Galathea', reaped a rich harvest of specimens in the South Atlantic in 1952. Like their predecessors, the Danes relied much on the deep-sea trawl: the one being hoisted inboard here, from nearly 12,000 ft (3,500 m.) in the Gulf of Panama, came up so heavily laden that it had to be lashed into three parts to lessen the strain on the net.*

The first American mastodon *to be exhumed, reconstructed and shown to the public was found in a swamp in Ulster County, New York, in 1799. Charles Willson Peale, the artist, paid $300 for the remains – which he wrongly insisted were those of a mammoth – and painted this lively picture of the excavation. He included himself in the scene: he is the black-coated figure standing at the edge of the pit, holding one of the full-scale drawings from which the bones were identified.*

the oceans, a reservoir of life. Searching for it in vain, the *Challenger* chemist discovered the answer. When specimens are preserved in alcohol and sea water, an amorphous sulphate of lime is precipitated and clumps around fine sand particles: this was the supposed *Bathybius*.

From the material collected, Sir John Murray developed three major lines of research: the study of the formation of coral reefs, the study of the distribution of the minute floating plants and animals known as plankton, and the study of oozes from the ocean bed. It was Murray who was chiefly responsible for seeing the findings into print, for Thomson, his health undermined by the voyage, could do little, and died in 1882.

Geological specimens from the almost uninhabited Christmas Island proved to contain valuable phosphates, when Murray came to compare them with *Challenger* material, hoping to throw light on his theory of coral-atoll formation. He induced the British government to annex this island, and to grant a concession to work the deposits to a company which he formed. The government soon received in revenue far more than it had put into the entire expedition!

By 1880 everyone was having second thoughts about natural selection, including Darwin. Both Darwin and Haeckel began to introduce Lamarckian elements into their schemes. A 'Neo-Lamarckian' school emerged: in particular Samuel Butler (the author of *Erewhon*), in a book published in 1878, criticized Darwin personally, in strong terms, and proposed an alternative, Lamarckian, explanation of evolution.

At this point natural selection found a new champion in August Weismann, a professor of zoology at Freiburg and former private physician to the Archduke Stephan. Weismann cut off the tails of a family of mice for twenty-two generations, mutilating in all 1,592 mice. They showed no signs of producing tailless offspring, which he took as a disproof of the inheritance of acquired characteristics.

This rather ill-conceived experiment, obviously inspired by Lamarck's remark about one-eyed babies, gives a less than just impression of Weismann's contribution, however. He introduced a valuable concept, known as continuity of the germ-plasm. He pointed out that it is those cells which produce new eggs or sperm which are important, from the view-point of heredity. There is no reason why damage or disuse of cells in other parts of the body should affect this 'germ-plasm'. Equally it is only variations in this germ-plasm which can affect future generations. These germ-plasm cells are immortal, while bodily cells are destined to die.

Actually, 'immortal' is too strong. A better metaphor would have been a family, in which some children in each generation are childless, while others carry on the line.

Weismann also predicted the central features of the mechanism of inheritance. He realized that there must be particles of some kind – he called them 'ids' – which were transmitted through the germ-plasm, conveying the hereditary determinants. Today we know that it is not discrete particles, but long chainlike molecules of the complex substance known as DNA which carry the hereditary message, and that the precise structure of these molecules varies throughout their length. Thus Weismann was on the right track.

In concluding, let us be clear what it was that Darwin achieved. Three things he did *not* do: (1) He did not propose the theory of evolution. That had been widely held for many years by all except the Church and the pious middle class, who were inhibited by a literal belief in the Bible from accepting such a view. (2) He did not *invent* the idea of natural selection as possibly the agent which effects evolutionary change. That stemmed from Lawrence and others. (3) He did not prove decisively that natural selection was in fact the agent. What he did do was to synthesize a great mass of information and show (a) that it was consistent with a belief in evolution, and (b) that most of it was consistent with natural selection being the agent.

Darwin did not find any case where natural selection could be shown conclusively to have operated – that was not to come for nearly another century. Nor did he prove that natural selection was adequate to account for the conversion of one species into another. And this was really the crucial question – socially as well as scientifically – because if species do change, then the Genesis account is inadmissible.

To the Victorian middle classes, always impressed by evidence of Herculean labour and minute care, Darwin's mass of fact brought conviction of the fact of evolution, while his modest way of life made it difficult to dismiss him as an atheist. To science, Darwin's work brought a new way of looking at things which made possible a great spate of enquiry and readjustment of ideas. The world could no longer be seen as static.

The least admirable feature of Darwin's behaviour was his ungenerous attitude to his predecessors: his grandfather he described only as having 'anticipated the erroneous ideas of Lamarck', and he kept the contemptuous references to Erasmus and to Lamarck in the preface of his *Origin* even after he had begun to adopt Lamarckian ideas himself.

Lamarckian assumptions run all through his *Expression of the Emotions* (1872), and he believed that children would inherit the moral qualities acquired by their parents. When Brown-Séquard announced that guinea pigs, in which epilepsy had been induced by an operation, transmitted it to their children, Darwin noted it in the next edition of the *Origin,* commenting: 'On the whole we can hardly avoid admitting that injuries and mutilation . . . are occasionally inherited.'

Survival of the fittest. *Darwin never found a visible example of evolution actually proceeding. Today, much work has been done on this, particularly with 'industrial melanism' in moths. The Pale Brindled Beauty moth,* Phigalia pedaria, *has a colouring to match the lichened tree trunks on which it rests* (above). *During the last century, with increasing industrial pollution, it stands out conspicuously on a tree stained with factory smoke* (below), *and a mutant black form of the same species blends better with its environment. Predatory birds attack the conspicuous form; the mutant's camouflage helps it to survive and, by natural selection, to spread. A classroom example of evolution, studied by Dr H. B. D. Kettlewell.*

Nor was he straightforward on the question of natural selection in his work, but sought to confuse the issue, making Lamarckian assertions at one point and 'Darwinian' ones at another, as if anxious to be right whatever the outcome might be. The first edition of the *Origin* contains forty-five references to 'my' theory, but never explains what the theory is: evolution itself, natural selection as an agent, or a mixture of natural selection and direction. In successive editions he gradually dropped the 'my' for 'the'.

As Professor Waddington has said, Darwin 'was able to put his ideas across not so much because of his scientific integrity, but because of his opportunism, his equivocation and his lack of historical sense. Though his admirers will not like to believe it, he accomplished his revolution by personal weakness and strategic talent, more than by scientific virtue.'

Charles Robert Darwin: *a portrait taken towards the end of his life by the Victorian photographer Julia Margaret Cameron.*

7

THE COMMON FACTOR

THE FIRST DRAWING EVER MADE OF CELLS, the building blocks from which all organisms, both plant and animal, are composed, was made by Hooke and published in his *Micrographia* in 1665: a year previously he had commented on the 'microscopical pores' of several kinds of wood.

More than 170 years were to pass before biologists realized that both plants and animals are composed of cells, and that cells have an independent life. The discovery of this common factor in all living things was the greatest single generalization in biology, and more fertile in its effects even than the concept of evolution. It threw light not only on the working of the body, and on the nervous system, but was the essential preliminary for an understanding of heredity. Among many other consequences, the whole conception of disease mechanisms was transformed.

The idea is so simple and so sweeping that it is hard to realize how difficult it was to attain. Each step was taken almost with reluctance.

For a long time, cells were thought of only in connection with plants – for animal cells are hard to see, being smaller and highly transparent. Except for some specialized forms, such as eggs, sperm and blood corpuscles, animal cells were not seen in any convincing way until the improved achromatic microscopes, devised by Lister in 1827, and developed by Amici, came into use. But even in plants, cells were not at first conceived as blocks or building units. A contemporary of Hooke, Grew, referred to plant cells as 'bladders', and declared, in 1682, that the sides of the bladders were not membranes 'but so many Ranks or Piles of exceedingly small *Fibrous Threds* . . . which is to say, that the *Pith* is nothing else but a *Rete mirabile*' or wonderful network. Thus the idea that cells were no more than the interstices of a network of fibres was given currency.

Early in the 19th century, a new conception began to emerge. One worker managed to separate the cells of a buttercup bud from one another; another observed that the cells sometimes varied in colour from one cell to the next; so they were units, not just the gaps in a lace-work. But cells were still

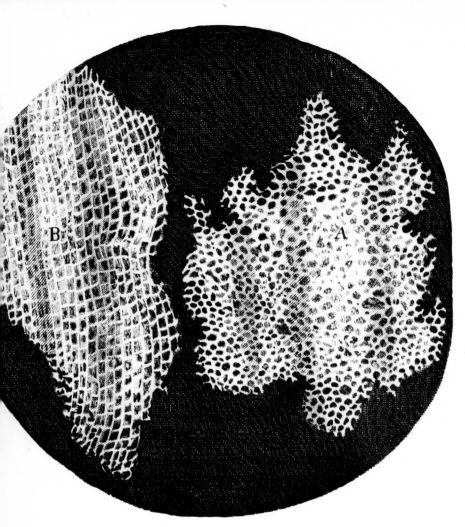

The first drawing ever made *of cells, the basic material from which all organisms are built up, was published by Robert Hooke in his 'Micrographia' in 1665, These 'microscopical pores', as he called them, are what he saw when he examined a piece of cork under the microscope.*

thought of as walls enclosing a fluid, rather than as building blocks. It was recognition of the presence within them of a characteristic substance, what we now call protoplasm, which was the essential step to the latter view. This did not come until the middle of the century.

A dark object of unknown purpose was seen embedded in plant cells in 1831 by Robert Brown, using a single lens of only $^1/_{32}$ inch focal length. This was the nucleus. What was its significance? As we now know, it controls the running of the cell – if it is removed, the cell dies, if it is reimplanted reasonably soon the cell revives again. It also carries the hereditary information which controls development. But this did not emerge until the end of the century.

Brown's main contribution was to show that nuclei are a regular feature of *all* plant cells, not just an occasional phenomenon.

Now discoveries began to come thick and fast. In 1836, Valentine saw the analogy between plant cells and the skin cells of animals, and in 1837 Henle observed that the growth of each proceeded on similar lines. Prior to this, Purkinje and Mueller had observed the cells in embryonic cartilage, in which a definite cell wall can be seen. The moment for a sweeping generalization was at hand, but they failed to take the crucial step. It was left to a brilliant young pupil of Mueller's, Theodor Schwann, to draw the logical inference of their identity.

'One of the strangest scientific personalities of the age', Matthias Schleiden, ex-barrister and failed suicide, changed the course of biology by propounding a theory of the cell which, within fifteen years, was proved totally incorrect.

After an unsuccessful attempt to shoot himself, he took up biology and became a doctor both of medicine and of philosophy. He was thirty-four when he published the short paper which brought him fame. Attracted by Brown's discovery of the cell nucleus in plants he decided it was a 'nucleus of crystallization'. Cells, he declared, crystallize out of a fluid round these nuclei, which then disappear. To prove his point, he studied – as fate would have it – almost the only biological plant material which would give colour to his belief: the embryo sac in flowering plants. In this embryonic, rapidly-growing material, no cell walls appear (see p. 184).

His paper reeks of nature philosophy, with its references to 'noble juices', 'potentiated cells' and the like, but – and this was the point – it quite consciously presents the *plant* as a community of cells. He even calls it a Polypstock, or mass of polyps. He was halfway to the modern cell theory.

Stimulated by this success, he set out to convert botany into an exact comparative science, and four years later published a textbook of botany. Soon after came his *The Plant and its Life*. With its clear figures and stimulating style, full of striking reflections and outspoken criticism of contemporary botanists, it put botany on the map. (In the American edition, several passages were suppressed as irreverent.) In particular, Schleiden's work stimulated Hofmeister and Nägeli to enter the cytological field, and it was largely Schleiden who induced the young Zeiss to devote himself to optics.

In complete contrast with Schleiden, who roundly abused the most famous botanists of his day (excepting only Brown and Mohl) was the meek, devout and friendly Theodor Schwann, who refused the professorships constantly offered him by German universities, because, as he said, he did not like the way German histologists quarrelled.

In Berlin he had studied under J. P. Mueller, and had been stimulated by him to do several bits of important work; notably he discovered and named pepsin, the digestive ferment of gastric juice.

Fontana saw these 'globules' (cells) in the slime of an eel in 1751. His sketch even shows the nucleus, though he naturally did not realize what it was.

The idea *that not only plants but animals also are built from cells which are fundamentally similar occurred to Theodor Schwann, a brilliant young pupil of Mueller's, in 1838. He drew these pictures comparing plant and animal cells to prove his claim, and launched the greatest generalization in the history of biology.*

Schleiden, *ex-barrister, failed suicide, was 34 when he declared that plant cells were formed from 'nuclei of crystallization'. He studied embryonic material in flowering plants and published this sketch of the process, as he saw it, in 1839.*

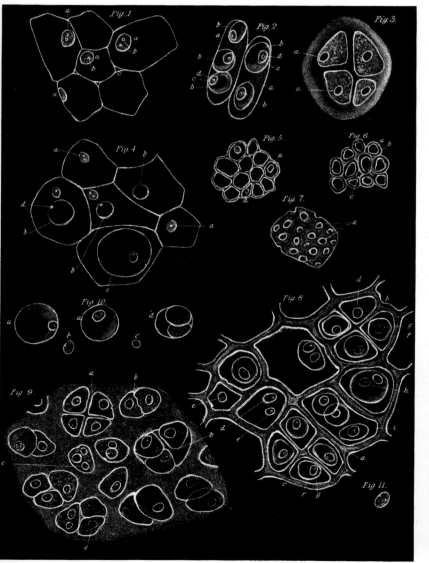

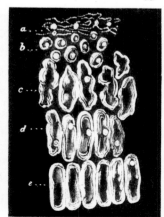

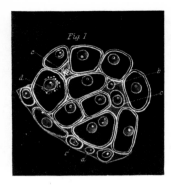

Taking over *en bloc Schleiden's erroneous theory of cell formation,
Schwann published this picture to show how, as he believed, he had
seen new cells emerging between the old, in animal material. He
announced his theory in 1839.*

The acid test *of the cell theory was: how does the egg, which has
no cellular structure, develop into a cellular organism? Koelliker
was one of many biologists who worked on this problem: he drew
these brilliantly clear pictures in 1844 to show the young eggs
of cuttlefish dividing.*

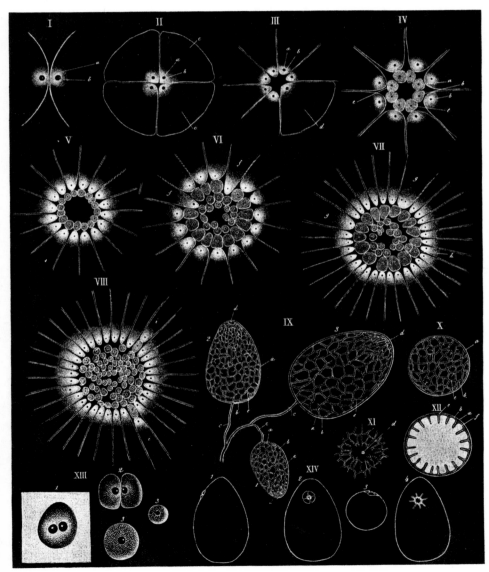

In October 1838, according to his biographer, a famous dinner-table conversation occured. Schleiden, over the coffee cups, told Schwann of his newly-published theory. Schwann immediately recognized the similarity between Schleiden's plant-cell nuclei and structures he had seen in animal nerve tissue. They went at once to his laboratory in the Anatomical Institute, where Schwann teased some of the cells out of the notochord (primitive backbone) of a tadpole, and showed Schleiden the similarity. Plants and animals were composed of units basically identical! It was the greatest generalization in the history of biology.

In 1839 Schwann published his theory, in a paper called *On the Correspondence in the Structure and Growth of Plants and Animals,* and the cell theory was launched.

Schwann took over *en bloc* Schleiden's erroneous theory of cell-formation and drew a picture (see p. 185) to show how the new cells emerged between the old. He, too, thought the nucleus was a transitory thing and that the cell was hollow.

Despite these errors, he proceeded to make valuable discoveries. By studying the cell-formation in embryonic tissue, and tracing the tissue into adult life, he was able to show that tissues which are not obviously cellular in the adult are in fact of cellular origin. Thus he helped to show the cell was an almost universal building block.

Schwann next applied these studies to distinguish five main types of tissue (as against the 21 types distinguished by Bichat). (1) the blood, in which cells are independent; (2) skin (in which they are flattened); (3) bone and cartilage (in which they are calcified); (4) tendons and ligaments (in which they form fibres); and (5) muscles and nerves. He coined the term *metabolism,* for the chemical process within the cell. It was Schwann, too, who suggested that eggs are essentially cells, despite the great differences in appearance due to the variation in the amount of yolk present.

The notion of the universality of cells was immediately accepted, and histology – the study of tissues – became a science. (Leydig, who applied the new approach to insects with great industry, has sometimes been called the founder of histology.) The idea of early physiologists, that tissue could be subdivided indefinitely, vanished.

Thus, if any one man can claim the credit for demonstrating the universality of the cell as a unit of life, it is Schwann, not Schleiden. Schleiden, however, gained the greater part of the credit by his bragging and his polemic style, and thanks to the modesty of Schwann.

A closed-circuit breathing machine was one of Schwann's inventions. Ironically enough, for Schwann the discovery of the universality of the cell meant scientific collapse. Pondering it, he felt the whole organic world had become nothing more than a machine. Later, he explained his feelings thus. Imagine, he said, bees endowed with intelligence. They would say to themselves, the cylinder would be a better form of honey-cell than the hexagon, for it contains more for a given area of wall. If they then followed their reason, rather than their instinct, the whole species would become extinct. Appalled, Schwann threw himself into the arms of the Catholic church, embracing a God 'more sensitive to the heart than to reason'. He never again made a discovery of importance, but became a teacher much loved by his pupils. In his machine for continually re-breathing the same air, can one see a symbol of his life?

Schleiden, on the other hand, drifted from appointment to appointment – at one stage he held a chair of anthropology at Dorpat, with the rank of Russian councillor. He died in Germany one year before his junior.

What made Schwann's book so immediately striking was the fact that, as he himself said: 'The great barrier between the animal and vegetable kingdoms, viz. the diversity of ultimate structure, thus vanishes.' Used as we are to the idea of there being both plants and animals, it is difficult for us to see how strange it is that a world should be peopled by two distinct orders of complex organisms, employing two completely different mechanisms of maintaining their growth and development – the one relying on the sun's energy to convert simple chemicals into complex ones; the other, parasitic on the first, consuming those complex molecules and deriving energy by breaking them down again.

Invented by Schwann – a closed-circuit breathing apparatus.

This dichotomy had bothered the earliest physiologists, who attempted to explain it with their theory of the vegetable and animal souls. It formed a difficulty in arranging living things in a coherent scheme of classification. To recognize the common origin of both forms was a precondition of accepting a theory of evolution.

To resolve this great dichotomy would have been progress enough. But the cell theory was to prove of even wider application.

However, first let us glance back at a curious predecessor of Schwann's.

A brilliant shot in the dark was made at the cell theory, more than thirty years before Schwann and Schleiden's papers, by the semi-mystical Oken, one of the more extraordinary figures in the history of biology. Ockenfuss, as he was originally called, was a South German peasant, who after severe privation managed to maintain himself at a series of universities, and finally became an esteemed professor. He was probably the first man to organize annual scientific conferences – the first was in 1821: the biologists had to meet in secret because Oken, an ardent patriot, agitated for the unity of Germany, and was suspect to the authorities in the reaction after the War of Independence. The meetings were imagined to be political in character.

Lorenz Oken –
'a shot in the dark'.

M. J. Schleiden –
outspoken but wrong.

Theodor Schwann –
'the universal cell'.

The teacher ⟨

Though Oken did some good routine biological work, and published an excellent guide to nature study, he made no important contribution to natural science. He himself valued his fantastic theory of Natural Philosophy. The first sentence of this gnomic work runs: 'The highest mathematical idea, or the basic principle of all mathematics, is that Zero = o.' Then we are told that God and the world = o + —, while God alone or the primal idea = o, and space is o = + o —. Number mysticism recurs in his works, and, rather like Swedenborg, he compares the entire animal kingdom to a great animal, the various parts of which correspond to different animal forms. The parts of a plant correspond to the four elements: the root is the earth-organ; the stem the water-organ; the leaf the air-organ; and the flower the fire-organ. Lacking the poetic imagination of Goethe, or the logical consis-tency of a great philosopher, his speculations are as grotesque as they are irrational.

Yet this mystical mode of thinking led him, as early as 1805, to the follow-ing amazingly prescient statement:

'All organic beings originate from and consist of vesicles or cells. These, when detached, and regarded in their original process of production, are *the infusorial mass or primeval slime* whence all larger organisms fashion themselves or are evolved.'

This pregnant sentence not only postulates the cell theory, but also implies the theory of evolution, not to mention foreshadowing the idea of proto-plasm, a term not then invented. Indeed, Oken goes on to speak of these 'mucous vesicles' gradually forming themselves into particular species by union or combination. And although in his day the term Infusoria com-prised a wider range of creatures than it does now, including some we now know not to be unicellular, yet we can see here the recognition of the fact that protozoans are simply creatures consisting of a single cell.

188

...liant circle of German biologists was J. P. Mueller (left). Among his pupils: (l. to r.): Koelliker, Henle, Virchow, Remak.

Equipped with the new achromatic microscopes, a new generation of German biologists proceeded to develop the cell theory far beyond the conceptions of Schwann and Schleiden. In complete contrast with the nature-philosophers, these men were immensely industrious, immensely cautious and worked with the detailed thoroughness which the world has come to regarded as 'typically Germanic'. This group of men was so remarkable, and achieved so much, that we should make their acquaintance.

The father-figure was Johannes Peter Mueller, the son of a poor shoe-maker, of whom it is said that he 'introduced experimental physiology into Germany'. He gathered round him a school of brilliant pupils: Schwann, Koelliker, Henle, Virchow, Remak, Reichert, du Bois Reymond. One of them said of him: 'He never taught dogmas, only a method.'

His personality was 'a curious combination of nervous unrest, proud egoism and deep melancholy'. He had a tendency to hallucinations, which he studied scientifically; in fact he observed the manifestations of his own senses to the point of 'shattering his nervous system', and had to abandon this. He died in circumstances never explained – the body, at his own request, was never autopsied – and is believed to have committed suicide.

Mueller is best remembered for his monumental *Handbook of Human Physiology,* a mine of novel facts and ideas, and for his law of specific nerve energies, to which we shall come in the next chapter. His doctoral thesis was numerological, like the work of Oken. In old age he bought up all the copies he could find of this immature effort and burnt them.

He became one of the greatest marine zoologists the world has seen, and vigorously supported the idea of special research stations for this work. Zoologist, paleontologist, embryologist, neurologist, biochemist, comparative anatomist, pathologist and psychologist, he was one of the last great poly-histors, with a fund of almost universal knowledge.

189

A very different personality was his pupil Koelliker, of whom it was said that he made 'a new discovery in histology every year'. Jovial, approachable, a keen horseman and huntsman until the age of eighty, he was a dogmatic teacher. On his appointment to the Chair of Anatomy at Zurich in 1845 (when he was twenty-eight) he stirred up the sleepy department, chivvying the university into putting up the money for one of the new microscopes, and bringing in another of Mueller's able pupils, Henle, as prosector.

Koelliker did more to establish the cell theory than anyone else. He was one of the first to recognize the ovum as a cell, and the first to point out that spermatozoa were cells, which he did in his doctoral thesis in 1840. His *Handbuch der Gewebelehre* (1852) was the first systematic book on histology; his *Entwicklungsgeschichte* the first book on comparative embryology. In fact, it was Koelliker who first applied the cell theory to embryology.

Moving to Würzburg, where the gymnasium had been languishing in Jesuit hands, he galvanized the department of anatomy, getting in another of Mueller's pupils, Virchow, to lecture, and also taking with him, Henle. Here he created a group of able pupils, of whom the most important was Gegenbaur.

A forceful personality, unable to brook contradiction, Gegenbaur showed in 1861 that *all* vertebrate eggs are simple cells. Until then it had been thought that some eggs, notably those of birds, were multicellular. He spent most of his life proving the views of Darwin by making comparative studies of different animal forms. 'The ultimate aim is phylogeny,' he declared, and imposed this view on a whole generation.

'The Pope of German medicine,' Virchow made it his aim to acquire 'an all-round knowledge of nature from the deity down to the stone.' At school he was a stormy petrel, though his academic record was brilliant: his schoolmates nicknamed him 'the king'.

In 1848, when an epidemic of 'hunger typhoid' broke out in Upper Silesia, Virchow was sent on a commission of investigation. In a brilliant sociological analysis, he showed the causes lay in the poverty of the people, to the annoyance of the state. He made it his life's work to reform the German public health services, and became a prominent liberal, clashing with Bismarck.

When he arrived in Mueller's laboratory, the animal cell had just been identified. Subsequently Remak, a fellow-pupil and friend of Virchow's, showed that blood cells are formed by the division of cells specialized for this purpose. Virchow soon generalized this discovery into the great doctrine: *omnis cellula e cellula* – every cell comes from a cell. From this he went on to the generalization that all disease is ultimately disease of cells – in contra-diction to Bichat who, sixty years before, had declared that all disease was disease of tissues. As if this were not enough, he spent the latter part of his life in anthropological studies. On his death, Germany lost her leading pathologist, anthropologist, sanitarian and liberal.

Yet another of Mueller's pupils, Reichert, linked cell theory with embryology, by showing that the segments into which eggs divide, divide again and again, until only cells can be seen. He made many other contributions to histology.

Shooting off at a tangent, at the suggestion of Mueller, du Bois Reymond explored the subject of animal electricity – generated by cells of a special type – and proved that the nervous impulse is electric in nature, as I shall tell more fully elsewhere.

At the end of all this work, where did the cell theory stand? Three great extensions of the original thesis had been solidly proved. First, the origin of cells was clear: all cells come from cells. Second, the universality of cells was clear: every kind of plant and animal tissue is composed of cells, or is derived from them, as in the case of collagen. Third, it had been shown that eggs and sperm, whether plant or animal, are cells, and divide to form tissues. Histology, the study of tissues, had been born.

Yet one more extension remained: the group of small water-creatures we now call Protozoa, or first living things, may be regarded as organisms consisting of a single cell. It was another German biologist, Siebold, who gave formal expression to this view.

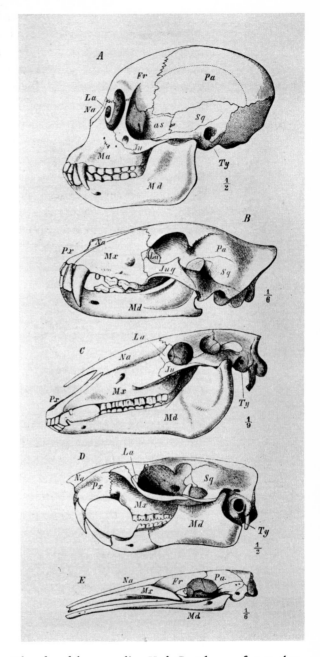

That forceful personality *Karl Gegenbaur – first to show that all vertebrate eggs are simply cells – made important studies in comparative anatomy to confirm the views of Darwin. Above are his drawings of the skulls of the ape, tiger, horse, capybara and anteater, which he published in 1898.*

The whole biological picture had been simplified.

These advances were not always accepted with enthusiasm. The *British Medical Journal,* for instance, reviewed the English edition of Virchow's *Cellular Pathology* with a hostility which recalled the treatment of *The Origin of Species* by the *Edinburgh Review* a year previously. All the evidence, the reviewer declared, went to support Schleiden's crystallization theory.

Meanwhile, attention was gradually turning to the contents of the cell, the protoplasm and the nucleus, and the study of cytology was emerging.

Protoplasm was a mysterious substance, even when viewed by the crude methods available in the 19th century. It was irritable: under the influence of an electric current it would round up. Within it, streaming movements took place. Much later, it was discovered that it could ingest droplets of liquid from its surroundings and pass them rapidly towards the nucleus. Today we know it to be a most complex system of membranes and specialized energy-producing bodies, known as mitochondria, as can be seen in the electron micrograph on p. 195.

But in the 19th century biologists were disposed to regard it as a simple liquid, or (after colloids had been discovered) as a colloid. The improved microscopes of the 'seventies gave pause to this idea, since they vaguely revealed the presence of bodies within it, and it began to be visualized as a system of fibrils or granules.

Dujardin, who called it sarcode, was the first to study it: he observed that it was elastic and contractile (which inorganic substances are not) and by 1841 reported that it was common to embryos and lower organisms. The idea of an universal substrate to life was spreading, and Purkinje, who knew from his theological training the word Protoplast, a term applied to Adam, suggested that sarcode be renamed protoplasm. By 1884 Gilbert could make Pooh Bah in *The Mikado* trace his ancestry back to 'a primordial protoplasmic globule', and be sure of getting a laugh.

It was von Mohl, who analysed the contents of the cell in a series of brief but weighty papers, who established it as a determinate substance and not just a 'living slime'. He described the starch grains and granules of chlorophyll within it, and studied the contractile vacuole.

In 1892, Otto Bütschli, the son of a Swiss pastrycook, put forward the theory that protoplasm was composed of a fine foam. To prove his point, he mixed oil of cloves with a finely-powdered soluble salt, and then placed a drop of the resulting paste in a liquid in which the salt was soluble. Placing this under a microscope, he watched as the liquid diffused into the paste and distended each fragment of salt into a minute bubble, enclosed in a film of oil. The foam thus formed looked, under a low-power microscope, very much like protoplasm.

The dodo became extinct *about 1681, but from surviving skeletons and old descriptions, reconstruction was possible. This painting shows one specimen being reconstructed at the Museum of Natural History, Paris. Zoological collection, classification and study helped to form the atmosphere in which Darwin launched his theory of natural selection, and extinction of a species showed the process of evolution at work.*

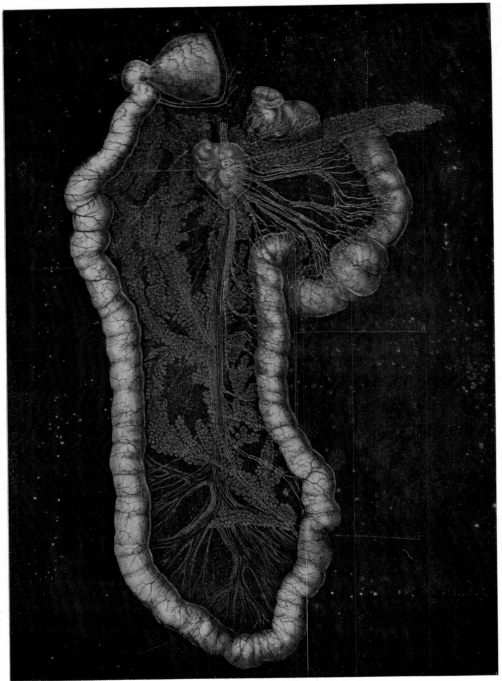

With an intricate tracery *of ducts and blood vessels, Claude Bernard shows the pancreas of a rabbit shortly after an all-meat meal. Emulsified fats show white through the gut wall, from a point where the pancreatic duct enters it (upper right). Bernard's work on the pancreas in the early 19th century advanced our knowledge of how digestion works.*

Streaming movements took place within the foam. From the surface emerged protrusions like the pseudopodia of amoebae. The droplet even moved through the liquid in which it was immersed. True, it could not maintain itself for long, and certainly could not duplicate itself. Yet it seemed to show some of the phenomena of life, suggesting they might be based on physico-chemical interactions.

Most of his fellow-cytologists made fun of his demonstration, some suggesting that he got the idea from watching the making of whipped cream in his father's confectionery shop. Yet his point was valid: vital phenomena can be analysed in physico-chemical terms. It was his fellow-workers who were still thinking in obsolete, vitalistic terms.

The modern conception of the cell was established by Max Schultze, who in 1861 defined it as 'nucleated protoplasm' – thus recognizing the irrelevance of the cell-wall, the original hall-mark of cells – and labelled it 'the physical basis of life'. Working without a microtome, Schultze brought cytology to the farthest point possible with existing methods.

The development of methods of fixing and staining, and of methods of slicing tissues with the microtome, opened up the second great chapter in the history of the cell – the exploration of the nucleus, a step which made possible the development of modern genetics.

Von Mohl thought the nucleus was a conglomeration of the granular substances in the cell: thus he moved away from Schleiden's view that it was a 'nucleus of crystallization' without arriving at a correct interpretation. With the microscopes then available the nucleus seemed to appear at the time of cell division and then to disappear again, which led biologists away from regarding it as a permanently-organized structure.

With superb skill, von Nägeli made these observations of the nucleus with its chromosomes in 1842, half a century before they were positively recognized and named. He did not, of course, know what they were, and called them *bâtonnets*.

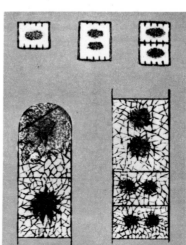

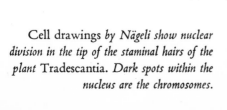

Cell drawings *by Nägeli show nuclear division in the tip of the staminal hairs of the plant* Tradescantia. *Dark spots within the nucleus are the chromosomes.*

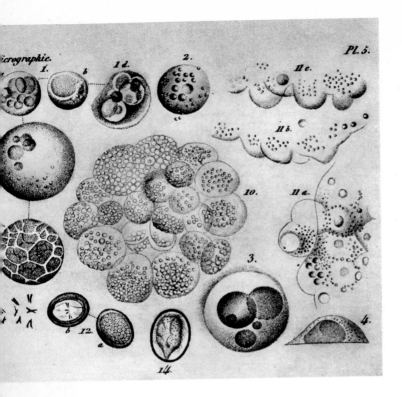

The interior of the cell as revealed by the modern electron microscope is seen to be far more complex than the 19th-century biologists could possibly have guessed from the resources at their disposal. In this picture (magnified x 23,000) the elongated oval shapes surrounding the nucleus are the mitochondria, the specialized energy-producing bodies.

The contents of the cell were studied by *Félix Dujardin* in the 1840's. What we now call protoplasm he named sarcode, and described it as the universal basis of life, both plant and animal.

No one added more to cell theory than the delicate von Nägeli, a Swiss, who studied under de Candolle and did his first experimental work under Schleiden. He set himself to throw light on the origin of cells by examining the growing point of plants and the development of seeds under the microscope. He soon saw that the nucleus does not bud off new cells – as had just been suggested – and proved that cell formation follows the same pattern in lower and higher plants, and corresponds to cell-formation in animals, as Koelliker had held. Organs, he declared, are built from cells 'in accordance with mathematical rules'.

Above all, he showed that the various parts of plants, from bark to the internal vessels, are all composed of cellular material.

Taking up von Mohl's work on protoplasm, he showed that it contained nitrogen, and thus differed from the starch grains within it and from the cell-walls. He also did good work later in bacteriology, but his main field of interest was heredity.

Nägeli recognized that there must be some part of the cell which is responsible for its specific qualities: it must be rigid, and he named it idioplasma. In the ten years before his death it became clear that the chromosomes

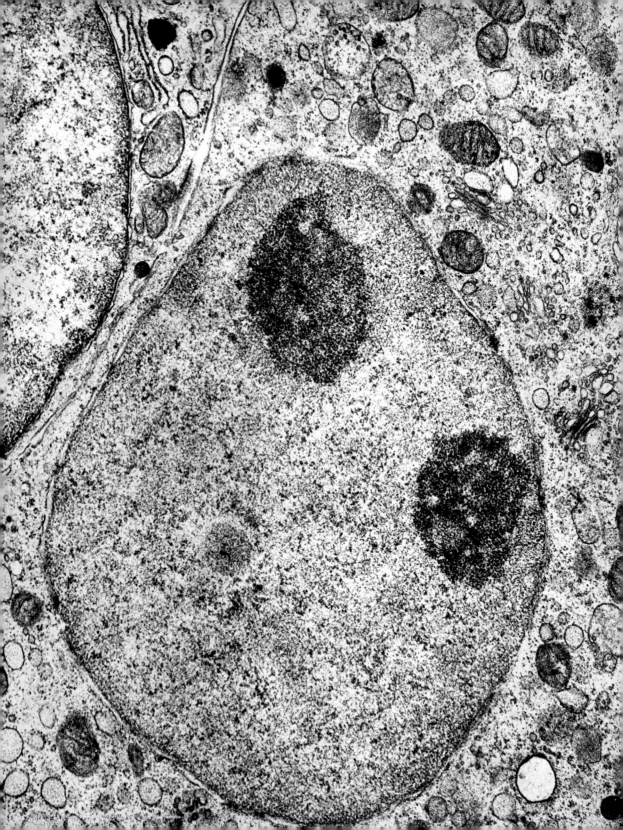

actually were the mysterious, rigid idioplasm, the existence of which he had inferred.

By a double irony, Nägeli was also (unlike Darwin) aware of Mendel's work (as I shall relate in a later chapter) and thus had the second clue to genetics in his hands. This he also failed to understand.

Having discovered that tissues could be analysed into cells, many workers began to ask whether perhaps the cell was not composed of still smaller units – speculations which were stimulated by the molecular view of matter. Herbert Spencer spoke of 'physiological units', Darwin of 'gemmules', Haeckel of 'plasticules', Weismann of 'biophores', Hertwig of 'idioblasts', de Vries of 'pangens'.

The cell does indeed contain smaller units, but the elucidation of these was to remain a task for the mid-20th century. None has proved to be a unit of life, as the term was understood in the 19th century. It was, in fact, in the nucleus, not in the cytoplasm, that the next step forward was to be made.

Improved methods of slicing *tissues made examination of the cell nucleus possible. This early microtome by the Swiss anatomist Wilhelm His can still be seen at Basle University.*

8

THE PERSONAL EQUATION

Bell, Magendie, Ramon y Cajal

'THE ORGANS OF AMATIVENESS, Philoprogenitiveness, Adhesiveness, Combativeness and Destructiveness were largely represented and influenced his character in a striking degree.' Such was the verdict of a phrenologist after inspecting the skull of Dr Francis Gall, which can still be seen in the Anthropological Institute in Paris.

A British paper gave this description of him: 'He is rather thin and pallid (and has) a capacious head and chest. The brilliancy of his penetrating eye left an indelible impression . . . much urbanity, with some self esteem and inflexibility of design.'

Widely, but inaccurately, supposed to be the inventor of phrenology, or the art of assessing character by feeling the contours of the head, he has been condemned by history as a charlatan or a fool. In point of fact, he was a brilliant anatomist, who radically changed our knowledge of the brain. Why he should be condemned for an incorrect theory, when so many other scientists who did good experimental work but held incorrect theories are not, is one of the mysteries.

He found a new technique for dissecting the brain: previously it had simply been sliced in various planes, as if by a bacon slicer. Gall dissected out the numerous structures within it, distinguishing the commissures, the pathways in the central nervous system, and the groups of fibres which connect the outer shell, or cortex, with the inner part. In particular, he traced the nerve tracts which lead from the eyes to the visual cortex at the back of the brain.

He distinguished the grey matter and the white matter. Hitherto the former had been thought 'a kind of slime'. He showed it was a network of nerves. The white, hitherto thought to be a sort of gruel, he showed was a mass of fibres. These, we now know, are the inter-connections of the cells. He explained why the brain surface is folded: to increase the area – for it is the cells of the surface layer which perform the complex associations on which mental activity depends. He described how the nerves gradually grow a sheath of myelin: as we know, they cannot conduct a nerve impulse until they do.

He established that cerebral nerves do not originate in the cerebrum, and disposed of the 18th-century idea that the spinal cord was a kind of tail of the brain. He realized that the brain was the seat of all faculties and of feeling (contrast Lord Jeffrey's declaration: 'There is not the smallest reason for supposing that the mind ever operates through the agency of any material organ . . .'), and declared that mental disease was brain disease, at a time when French doctors were blaming the nerve centres in the stomach.

The theory which Gall pursued was that the brain consisted of a number of organs, or distinct functional parts, linked together in a confederation by nerve tracts. This was a highly novel idea: following Aristotle, medieval thinkers had regarded it as a *sensorium commune* – an organ capable in some inexplicable way of mediating all the functions of the 'mind' or 'soul' to the body, and had thought this *sensorium* located in the ventricles (or spaces), or in the cerebrospinal fluid. The study of brain function since Gall's time has been one long ding-dong battle between these two conceptions, which is still not fully resolved. Today we know that while functions such as memory appear to pervade the whole brain, and while it can compensate for the removal of considerable sections, yet in other respects localization does occur. We know, for example, that visual impressions are dealt with at the back of the head, that the central portion is concerned with maintaining bodily functions, that general alertness is controlled from the brain stem, and so on.

Gall, however, developed his hunch in the wrong direction. He sought to associate parts of the cortex with temperamental differences. He plumped for 37 distinct organs, each responsible for a 'sentiment' or propensity. He was led to this theory by noticing the temperamental differences of fellow students at Vienna: in particular he considered those who had prominent eyes were those who learned readily by heart. Seeing a man of great determination with a bulging forehead, he got the idea that personality traits (moral qualities, as they were then termed) could be diagnosed from appearance, an idea already popularized by Lavater.

The sexy type is contrasted phrenologically with the childloving woman. Spurzheim, from whose book these two are taken, was the first to use the word 'phrenology'.

A brilliant anatomist of the brain, Franz Gall, has been wrongly condemned as a charlatan for his supposed invention of phrenology.

Gall's first lectures in Vienna caused a sensation, but in 1802 he was ordered by the Court, at the Church's instigation, to desist; the Church held that to explain personality in such a mechanical way was blasphemous. Three years later he left Vienna on a tour which proved a triumph. Reil, after attending his demonstrations at Halle, said: 'I have seen in the anatomical demonstrations made by Gall more than I thought a man could discover in his whole lifetime.' He often announced new discoveries in his lectures, many of which were appropriated by listeners and announced as their own.

One of those who eagerly picked up Gall's conception was a man called Spurzheim, who became his pupil from 1800 to 1804. He moralized Gall's studies, claiming to be able to distinguish the rich from the poor by appearance alone, the honest, sober faces of the former contrasting with the dissolute and bestial faces of the latter. It was Spurzheim's efforts which brought Gall's work into eventual disrepute. It was he who, in 1815, introduced the word 'phrenology', a term Gall declined to use. Indeed, Gall refused to read Spurzheim's books.

Gall, it is time to recognize, established the modern conception of the anatomy of the brain: no advance of significance was to occur for more than a century.

Cartoonists made laboured fun *of the phrenology craze, as in this print by 'L. Bump' after 'J. Lump'. Among the lecturer's examples are busts of Gall and Spurzheim, and a jar of gall on the shelf adds to the merriment.*

Ladies and Gentlemen
Having thus concluded the hundred and thirty ninth article, under the Head *or* Section of **Propen**
Talkativeness with Gulling, *standing* First *and further beg to testify, beyond all do*
Under Evident Contradictions, *Stands beautifully develop'd to a* **Surprising** *and* **Promi**

BUMPS

LIFE'S (A) DUMPER

TONY LUMPKIN

Consequence

ABSTRACTION

SUSPICION

PRYING

Dr Ville

Gall

CONCLUDING ADDRESS

J.Bump delt. L.Bump s.

shall take my leave until the next lecture, by clearly elucidating in my own person an instance of Due Proportion of Faculties:
ndow of contradiction, that on the Craniums of this highly gifted and scientific Audience the Organ of Implicit faith
e Dear Ladies, Worthy Gentlemen, adieu.

When the privilege of decapitation, *previously confined to the nobility, was extended to all classes by the proposal of Dr Guillotin in 1789, scientific curiosity was aroused by the idea that life could continue briefly after the head was cut off.*

CHARLOTTE CORDAY blushed when the executioner held up her severed head for the crowd to see. Such was the story: it reveals the interest which people then felt in the question of whether life continued after decapitation by the new democratic method. For decapitated animals appear to go on living for some moments. Impressed by this, Legallois made serial sections of the mid-brain and upper spinal cord. He discovered that cutting the medulla, at the point at which the vagus nerve departs, stopped breathing. Thus 'almost by accident' as he said, he became the first to locate a physio-logical centre in the brain. This was termed the 'vital knot'.

The search for such centres continued, with results rather different from those which had been expected. The brain, it turned out, did have certain kinds of specialization. Thus Magendie's pupil Flourens, by systematic re-moval of parts of the brain, showed that the cerebellum served to co-ordinate movement, that intellect and volition were confined to the cerebrum; and that excitability and sensation were connected with the spinal cord. (Rolando, who was the first to apply electrical stimuli to the brain, had thought the cerebellum a kind of power-station, secreting electric fluid into the nervous system.) Flourens' work was considered to have destroyed completely any possibility of localization of function in the sense of a specific brain area controlling a specific act or function. But observations were already being made which would renew the doubt.

In 1831, a patient was admitted to a hospital for the insane near Paris, who was mentally normal but could not talk. Thirty years later he died. The surgeon Broca, who had examined him carefully in life and had discovered that he had no defect of the speech organs, nor was he imbecile, immediately performed an autopsy and found damage to a particular point in the left temporal lobe of the brain. Taking other such cases into consideration, Broca concluded that the man's trouble was an inability to recall words, and that a centre which performs this task is located at the point in question. On the strength of this, he postulated centres for all the main intellectual functions, thus reversing the position of Flourens and reverting to Gall's after a mere thirty years.

A few years later, the concept of localization received another powerful impetus. Two thirty-two year old German students attempted to stimulate the cerebral cortex electrically. This had been tried many times without success by others and it was firmly held that it was totally insensitive. But these earlier workers had stimulated the rear of the brain, which is easier to approach in most animals, and had caused bleeding and damage. Fritsch and Hitzig, using very weak currents, found that when they stimulated a particular area towards the front of the brain, they got quite specific muscular movements. Stimulation of this point would cause the lip to curl, of that make the eye move. The English neurologist David Ferrier extended this work to a variety of animals, and produced such clear-cut results that denial was impossible.

To many this specificity seemed quite incredible and committees were set up to check the findings. They confirmed them.

A search for similar sensory areas followed, and Cushing, the brain surgeon, produced this chart in 1909 on the basis of stimulations done during brain operations.

Strange to say, however, parallel with this work went discoveries which tended to the opposite conclusion. Goltz removed similar parts of the brain in different animals, such as dogs, frogs and monkeys, in an attempt to assess

The centres of sensation in the brain, *first located by inference from brain damage, were mapped in 1909 by Harvey Cushing, the American brain surgeon. This 'map' shows his findings.*

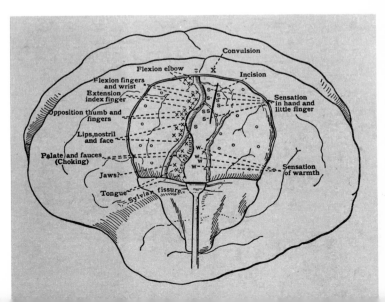

the amount of sensation lost. To his surprise, he found that the loss seemed to be proportional to the amount of cortex removed, regardless of which particular bits were excised. Early in the present century, Lashley, an American psychologist, made scores of transverse cuts in the cortex of rats which had been taught to run mazes, and found that their ability was little impaired. On the strength of this he propounded the doctrine of 'the equipotentiality of the cortex'. This states that all parts of the cortex are equally effective in carrying any type of memory, save only visual memories which are stored at the back of the brain, in the area served by the optic nerves.

While memory remains a mystery, today we know that Lashley would have got different results if he had made his cuts parallel to the surface of the brain and not at right angles – for it is the paths down into the centre of the brain, and up from it, which are of the greatest importance. Meanwhile the motor cortex has been explored in detail, chiefly by Wilder Penfield the Montreal brain surgeon, who has stimulated hundreds of unanaesthetized patients in the course of brain operations. On the basis of this work, he drew these two homunculi, which serve to show the relative amounts of brain tissue available for different sensory and motor functions. It can be seen, for instance, that the amount of brain serving the thumb is as great as that serving the entire lower limbs. Note also the relatively vast area devoted to sensation from the lips, a fact related to the charm of kissing.

Meanwhile, other workers were exploring the nervous system in the body as a whole. Only one crude technique was open to them at first: cutting nerve-roots in living animals to see what function was then lost.

The next step in brain mapping *was to determine the relative areas of the brain concerned with sensation and movement of the various parts of the body. Information gained from hundreds of brain operations is summarized by Wilder Penfield in these graphic figures. Note the disproportionate space occupied by sensation from the lips, and movement of the hand.*

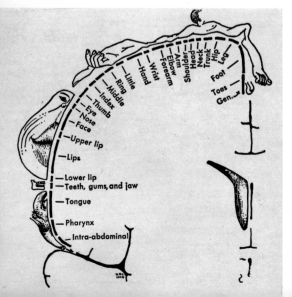 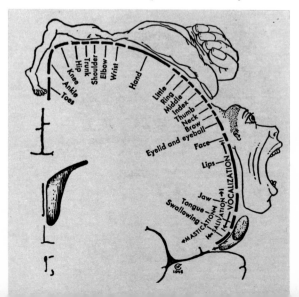

A wounded soldier *with tetany, drawn by Sir Charles Bell on the field of Waterloo.*

THE 'RARE TALENT for drawing' of Sir Charles Bell is seen in this Fuseli-like picture of a soldier suffering from tetanus on the field of Waterloo. Bell had hurried there with his friend and colleague John Shaw – their only passports being their surgical instruments. After three days operating on British soldiers, sleeping only one and a half hours in twenty-four, till his arms were 'powerless with the exertion of using the knife' he turned to the French, many of whom had been lying in the woods, untreated, for a fortnight. Even in the stress of these events, his clothes stiff with blood, he made sketches and notes, and brought back specimens of skulls and amputated limbs. He later wrote a treatise on gunshot wounds. He was then forty-one.

Four years previously he had written to his brother: 'My new anatomy of the brain is a thing that occupied my head almost entirely. I hinted to you formerly that I was burning, or on the eve of a grand discovery. I consider the organs of the outward senses as forming a distinct class of nerves from the other. I trace them to corresponding parts of the brain, totally distinct from the origins of the others.' This, the distinction between afferent nerves (leading *to* the brain from sense organs) and efferent nerves (leading *from* the brain to muscles), has been called the most important discovery in physiology since Harvey's demonstration of the circulation of the blood.

Bell was a complex character. One of the four talented sons of a poor Scots minister, he 'received no education but from his mother'. He did badly at school, and was deprived of his first job by an opponent. In 1804, he arrived in London with suicidal thoughts; he earned no fee for the first fifteen months after he set up in practice, and the floor of his house collapsed. Only when he set himself up as a lecturer did he meet with some success.

Though ambitious he could not bring himself to publish. After elaborating on the passage just quoted, he added: 'My object is not to publish this, but to lecture it – to lecture to my friends – to lecture to Sir Jos. Banks' coterie of old women, to make the town ring with it, as it is the only new thing that has happened in anatomy since the days of Hunter . . . But I must still have time.'

In March of the next year: 'I write to tell you that I really think I am going to establish my Anatomy of the Brain on facts the most important that have been discovered in the history of science.' He then proceeded to describe his experiments, and in August 1811 published, for private circulation, a pamphlet called *Idea of a New Anatomy of the Brain,* which has been described as the Magna Carta of neurology.

None of the scientists to whom he sent it for comment troubled to reply, and Bell seems to have put the subject aside for ten years. Though pressed by his friends and relations to publish his results he steadfastly declined.

Just what Bell discovered has become the focus of one of the bitterest personal controversies in the history of biology. The other side of this controversy is represented by the French doctor and neurologist, François Magendie. In contrast with Magendie, Bell was reluctant to perform painful experiments on animals. 'I should be writing a third paper on the nerves,' Bell wrote in 1822, 'but I cannot proceed without making some experiments which are so unpleasant to make that I defer them. You may think me silly but I cannot perfectly convince myself that I am authorised in nature or religion to do these cruelties – for what? – for anything else than a little egotism or self-aggrandisement . . .' Magendie felt no such inhibitions. An American doctor who attended his demonstrations commented: 'Mr M. has not only lost all feeling for the victims he tortures but he really likes his business. . . . In many cases the experiments are unnecessarily cruel and too frequently reiterated.'

Magendie was 'the prototype of vivisectors' in English eyes. Certainly this extraordinary, arrogant man performed a long series of ruthless dissections on living animals with total disregard for their sufferings, as well as treating his human patients with almost equal ruthlessness. He seemed to have a taste for the bizarre: his early papers concern swallowing and vomiting; he was particularly interested in a boy who had learned the trick of swallowing his own tongue. After an experiment in which he fed a dog on a protein-free diet until it died, he analysed the intestinal gases of four executed criminals, stressing that their youth made them especially suitable for the investigation. One of his star demonstrations, often repeated, was the progressive removal of parts of the brain of a rabbit, designed to show the loss of areas of sensations and types of movement. The wild movements of the tortured animal made

François Magendie, *French neurologist and surgeon.*
Behind the dreamy romanticism of this portrait is a
ruthless operator who scorned anaesthesia and seemed to
relish inflicting pain.

the dissection particularly difficult to perform, and its aichevement was regarded as a *tour de force*.

The suspicion that there was something a little abnormal in his attitude is reinforced by his opposition to the introduction of anaesthetics. In a speech to the Academy of Science, he attacked doctors who 'intoxicate their patients to the point of reducing them, so to speak, to the state of a corpse which one can cut and slice at will without causing suffering.' 'Pain?' he exclaimed, 'Pain is one of the prime movers of life. As for myself, I should never allow my body to be handed over to a surgeon in a defenceless state.'

Still more oddly, he produced as a further reason that some criminal might take advantage of a defenceless female in this state of intoxication. In a subsequent meeting of the Academy, ether was again the topic of discussion. Flourens and Serres read papers on its action. Magendie rose in reply. What he had in mind, he said, was almost too delicate in nature to mention even in the bosom of the Academy of Science, but what he was really disturbed about was the erotic hallucinations evoked by ether. 'Females thus inebriated had been seen to hurl themselves upon the operator, with gestures and propositions so expressive, that in this singular and novel situation, the danger was not for the patient but for the surgeon. (Prolonged hilarity, interruptions.)'

As Magendie grew older, his experimentation grew steadily rasher. At one point, when removing a cataract from a female patient, he deliberately and repeatedly touched the retina of her eye with his scalpel, causing her to

207

see flashes of light but to feel no pain. Thus he confirmed that nerve endings are specialized, and that only the appropriate nerves can register pain.

On one occasion, summoned to a patient with hydrophobia from a dog-bite, he injected two pints of water into his veins, while six students held him down. This calmed the patient, and stopped his seizures, but he died nine days later. Magendie declared that he had cured the hydrophobia, and that death was due to a local disease unconnected with it, which may have been true, since he doubtless introduced countless micro-organisms with the injection.

Magendie's reputation soared, until after many repetitions of the outcome, the public lost faith in such a lethal cure.

On another occasion he found that cutting a certain bunch of nerve fibres in the brain of a rabbit caused it to roll over sideways, repeatedly. Assuming the animal would soon stop rotating, he left it in the laboratory overnight, and was surprised on his return to find it had been rolling over and over all night and was enveloped in the straw on which it had been placed 'like a bottle of precious wine'. In this way he discovered 'circus movements', as they have been called.

Magendie's attention was drawn to Bell's theories and experiments by Bell's paper to the Royal Society in 1821, and by a demonstration (thoroughly botched) that John Shaw performed for him in Paris in the same year. Thus it was that in 1822 Magendie came to publish his classic paper on 'the functions of the roots of the spinal nerves', and the controversy was in being.

The man who performed the critical experiment of severing first the forward set of nerves, and then the rearward, and noting that in one case movement was lost, in the other sensation, was unquestionably Magendie. It is true enough to say that he would probably not have proceeded to such an experiment without the stimulus provided by Bell, though he declared that he had been thinking of trying it for some time.

It is clear from what Bell wrote that he, for his part, was primarily concerned to prove something about the brain, not the nerves: he wished to localize sensory functions in one part, motor control in another; he appreciated that this implied two groups of nerves, and indeed he realized that there must be a special set of nerves (which he called vital, but which we call the autonomic) regulating the bodily organs and functions. He performed an experiment on the two sets of nerves, primarily in order to demonstrate his theory about the localization of functions in the brain. What he did was to *press* on the forward nerves, whereupon the muscles of the animal's back were convulsed. When he pressed on the rearward nerves, nothing happened. He concluded from this merely that the forward nerves were insensitive,

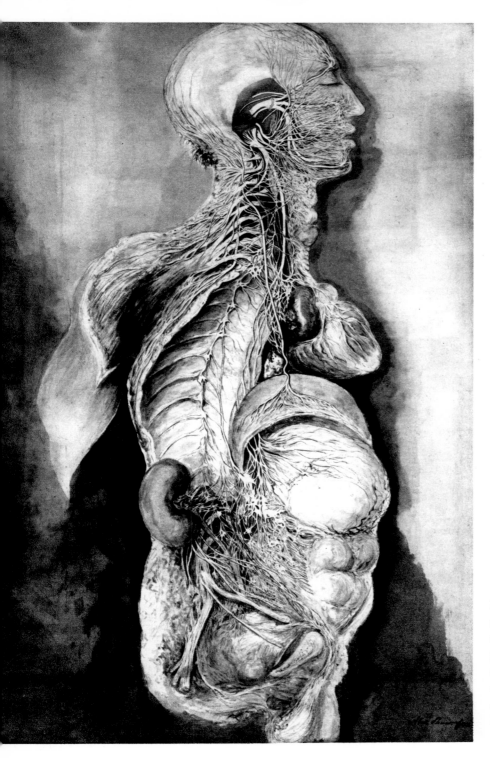

Bell was an artist
*as well as an
anatomist: this
painting of the nerves
of the head and
thorax hangs in the
Medical School of the
hospital where he
taught.*

a thing he thought very odd. His comment on the experiment was: 'Such were my reasons for concluding that the cerebrum and cerebellum were parts distinct in function . . .'

While Magendie remained eminently fair, publishing Bell's papers in full as soon as they were brought to his attention, and claiming no part in his general theories of nervous anatomy, Bell became incensed, and publicly accused Magendie of stealing his ideas. He even republished his original papers, quietly making changes from the original version, designed to strengthen his case. This controversy has never been closed, and was bitterly fought out over again by proponents of both schools of thought in 1911. But the facts are clear.

The Bell-Magendie law, as it is now known, launched a great wave of exploration of the nerve tracts in the spine, the exploration of which lasted the whole of the rest of the 19th century. It is difficult today to appreciate what a flood of light was let into the dark confusion of the nervous system by these experiments. Within a century of the discovery of this law, the motor and sensory patterns in the nervous system were largely mapped out.

Technically, these experiments were awkward to perform, as the two sets of nerves lie close together; but they were no more awkward than those done by Galen. The discovery might have been made at any previous time.

THE MAPPING of the nervous system depended, however, upon a number of technical advances, and above all on the newly-born study of electricity. It was in 1771 that Galvani, an Italian physiologist, discovered that if he hung up a frog's leg by the nerve from a brass hook, with the toe touching a silver plate, it would kick convulsively. The two dissimilar metals were producing an electric current which stimulated the leg-muscle to contract, thus breaking the circuit, which was renewed when the leg fell again.

Galvani's experiments *with frog legs, schematically represented in a contemporary engraving.*

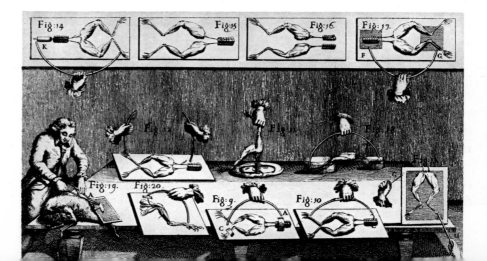

The magnetic tub, *one of Franz Anton Mesmer's methods of cure by 'animal magnetism'*.

Galvani did not know, and never learned, that he was making two discoveries at once; he was demonstrating an electric current, and also showing the electric nature of the nervous impulse. Nor did he know that the current would be named after him, 'galvanic current'. He concluded that animal tissues generate electricity (1791). (They do, but this was not an instance.) But if electricity, why not magnetism? Mesmer had cured patients with iron magnets in 1766. When he found he could effect the cures equally well without the magnets, he concluded his 'personal magnetism' was the cause: hence the belief in animal magnetism.

When Volta (1800) had invented a method of producing electricity which did not involve animal tissues, and the galvanometer had been designed to detect its passage (1811), the next steps became possible, for now nerves could be stimulated electrically, a method much subtler than merely cutting them.

J. P. Mueller formulated the 'law of specific nerve energies'. This says, in effect, that the sensation produced by a stimulus depends on the end-organ, not on the nature of the stimulus. Thus a stimulus to the eye will only produce a flash of light – as Magendie also noted. Damage to the nerves of the ear produces a noise, and so on. This is true whether this stimulus is mechanical, electrical or chemical.

In 1841 another Italian, Mateucci, showed that a current flows from the surface of a muscle to a wound in it. The burning question now arose: is the nervous impulse itself electrical?

WITH THIS device, known as a myograph, or muscle-measurer, du Bois-Reymond showed that, when an impulse travels along a nerve, there is a change of electrical state. By 1871 he had discovered that the interior of the nerve is negative, and that the impulse consists in the spreading of the negative charge inside to the outside.

Thus the electric nature of the nervous impulse was firmly established. It was a decisive moment, for it brought the whole conception of nervous

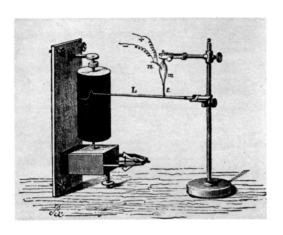

A telltale mark on the revolving *drum shows the twitch of the muscle caused by passing an electric current through the nerve. This apparatus was devised by Emil du Bois-Reymond.*

activity out of the realm of 'animal spirits' – conceived as a mysterious property beyond the scope of scientific investigation – into that of natural science. Du Bois-Reymond himself drew the conclusion that there was no real difference between organic and inorganic nature.

Other workers contributed the fact that, after a nerve has discharged, it remains inexcitable for a brief but definite time, known as the 'refractory period'. The batteries, as it were, are recharging themselves.

Du Bois-Reymond, with others, also showed that chemical changes occur in a muscle whenever it contracts, these changes being triggered by the nerve impulse. In short the basic facts of nerve-impulse conduction had now been established. The detailed physico-chemical explanation of what occurred would have to wait for the more delicate techniques and more detailed knowledge of the 20th century.

HOW FAST does a nerve impulse travel? Von Haller (after considering the rate of movement of the tongue in pronouncing the letter R) had said 9,000 feet a minute – not far from the truth. Other estimates ranged as high as 57,600 million feet per second – about sixty times the speed of light! Mueller thought it must be comparable with the speed of light, and that it would probably never be measured, since one cannot compare its propagation through immense distances.

Yet within a few years his former pupil, von Helmholtz, had shown it to be only about 90 feet a second, much slower even than sound. With the apparatus shown below, and using his own arm, he measured the delay between stimulus and muscle-twitch for different lengths of nerve. To check if sensory transmission were similar (for, since Bell and Magendie's work, one could not assume this) he stimulated a man upon toe and thigh, and noted the difference in reaction time.

The fact that human beings take time to respond to a stimulus had first been noticed by astronomers, oddly enough. When observing the moment at which the sun's disk occulted a fixed star, different observers, with different reaction times, turned in slightly different results. At first the slower observers were thought to have been incompetent. When it was realized that everyone has an individual pattern of response to a stimulus, astronomers sought to calculate a 'personal equation' to compensate for these differences.

The discovery that the nerve impulse is not transmitted instantly was of great psychological importance. Previously the will and the action seemed one: now the decision of the mind and the response of the body were seen to be separate. It seemed a victory for materialism.

Helmholtz in 1863 compared the nervous system to an electric telegraph – a simile only recently seen to be misleading. At the time, this came as a thunderbolt. It dramatized the idea that human behaviour could probably be explained in physical terms. It tore a rent in the curtain which veiled one of the great mysteries of life.

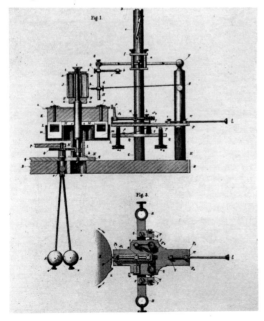

The speed of the impulse *along the nerve was measured by von Helmholtz with this apparatus, which registered both the electric shock and the muscle twitch. About 90 feet a second was the answer – much slower than had been thought.*

Why do we automatically withdraw a hand or foot that approaches fire? Descartes propounded a theory, and drew this diagram to illustrate it.

THE BURNT BOY withdraws his foot. Thus Descartes pictured what we now call reflex action: that is, movements carried out without conscious decision. Sneezing and the regulation of the iris diaphragm of the eye are other well-known examples.

Robert Whytt, a Scot, demonstrated before 1751 that such reflexes do not involve the brain: the sensory impulse fires off a motor impulse as soon as it reaches the spinal cord. Whytt used the frog, but in 1833 the physiologist Marshall Hall extended our knowledge by sectioning the spinal column of a snake at successive points, showing that it is not simply a nerve trunk: it is a chain of reflex arcs. He fought hard to establish the point. The idea that action can take place without any awareness seemed strange to people. Hall's purpose was to clarify the distinction between conscious and unconscious; the effect was to reveal the body, more and more, as functioning like a machine.

Thus the concept of reflex action had already prepared the way for the mechanical interpretation of human behaviour when the electrical nature of the nerve impulse was discovered. Fired by this, investigators now resumed the study of the reflex with new enthusiasm.

In 1877 Strumpell described the case of a boy, aged sixteen, who had no sense of taste or smell, and whose skin was insensitive to touch, as to heat or pain. Even his muscles gave him no sense of tiredness after use. In addition, he was blind in the left eye and deaf in the right ear. If the other eye and ear were closed, he fell within two or three minutes into a deep sleep. He could only be awoken by shining a light on his good eye, or by a sound in his good ear. Shaking had no effect.

This, and similar cases, aroused intense interest in Russia, where, fourteen years before, in 1863, a young doctor had published a startling book which these cases seemed to confirm. It maintained that thought was not a mysterious psychic process, but merely the product of reflexes which were not carried through to their conclusion in action. 'A thought is the first two-thirds of a psychical reflex,' he said. So materialist did this view seem, that the authorities not only banned the book but took court action against the author for undermining public morals.

The writer was I. M. Sechenov, the son of a landowner. Turgenev took him as a model for Gazarov, in *Fathers and Sons* – the type of the rising intelligentsia, a young doctor who spends his time dissecting frogs, to the disgust of his genteel family. He was the first Russian to use experimental methods in physiology, but his work has remained little known in the West until recently.

Sechenov was moved to write his book because of an experiment he had conducted just previously. He found that certain reflex movements of decerebrate frogs are inhibited by stimulating a certain point in the brain with an electric current, or – and this was the method he actually used – by applying a crystal of salt. This discovery profoundly impressed du Bois-Reymond and other experts in the field, because it was thought until then that inhibition only occurred in organs, such as the heart, regulated by nerves specialized for the purpose.

Though Sechenov proclaimed that psychic processes could be studied by the objective methods of science, he did not attempt such enquiries himself. It was left to Pavlov to attempt this.

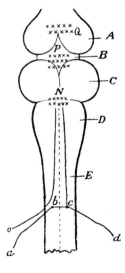

At the spots marked X in the frog's brain Sechenov placed a crystal of salt, establishing that this inhibited reflex action. This proved that muscular movement was not, after all, controlled entirely by the will.

The first Russian *to use experimental methods in physiology: Ivan Mikhailovich Sechenov in his laboratory at the St Petersburg Medico-Chirurgical Academy. Beside him dangle three of the frogs whose spinal reflexes he studied.*

Human chemistry *in bottles: Thudichum's pioneer preparations.*

IN 1941, BIOCHEMISTS at the National Institute of Medical Research analysed the contents of these bottles of strange substances, found in the brain by an almost-forgotten 19th-century chemist with the odd name of Thudichum. Using the powerful modern technique of chromatography, they found that his analyses – ridiculed at the time – were as good as the best modern analyses. Thus was vindicated the memory of a remarkable and unjustly neglected biochemist who can claim to be regarded as the father of brain chemistry.

For, while the physiologists were slicing and stimulating, the chemists were beginning to analyse: the bases were being established for the modern view of the brain as a chemical as well as an electrical device. Thudichum extracted a series of novel and complex substances from brain tissue: cephalin, sphingomyelin, phrenosin, kerasin, glycoleucine; he discovered and named the cerebrosides.

Thudichum, the son of a German minister, had been refused an academic post because of his sympathy with the revolutionary side in 1848, had abandoned Germany and had become naturalized British. He had anta-gonized his German colleagues by this, no doubt, as by the wide range of his researches, and by his rough polemic style when criticized. In 1874, when he was forty-five, he had published his first paper on brain chemistry. He was at that time a successful medical practitioner, specializing in an operation for the removal of nasal polyps (he had also invented an operation for the removal of gallstones, still used in difficult cases) and a chemist to the local government board. He had been first director of the Pathological Laboratory at St Thomas's, until three years previously, when he had re-signed to devote more time to his practice.

Three years later the attack was launched. A scathing, anonymous attack by Gamgee was followed by detailed criticism by Professor Hoppé-Seyler, the greatest physiological chemist of his day. Of the structures which Thudichum assigned to the substances he found, Gamgee said: 'One might as well supply a formula for bread and butter.'

So successfully did they establish his reputation for inaccuracy that for long afterwards German chemists, rediscovering in the brain substances which Thudichum had first found and named, felt entitled to rename them and to claim rights of first discovery, on the grounds that Thudichum's preparations had been hopelessly impure.

Thudichum lost his grant from the British government, as a further consequence, and his book on the brain was not published until 1884, nor in Germany until 1901. Thudichum, never elected to the Royal Society, was forgotten on his death. He was a man of gaiety as well as energy, who translated odes in praise of wine from the Greek, wrote poems to his daughters on their birthdays and sang in a fine tenor voice. He wrote a book on cookery, as well as a monograph on public health, and counted Ruskin, Burne-Jones and Sickert among his friends.

His gift for combining research with relaxation, in a way all too rare among scientists, is revealed by a story from his days as a medical student at St Thomas's. At a dinner in the garden of the hospital, 'There were thirty-three in number including myself. We drank, from two o'clock in the afternoon until seven in the evening forty-four bottles of wine, consisting of white and red, Hungarian, Burgundy and Sauternes. The alcoholic content of the total was an aggregate of 4,000 grammes of absolute alcohol. All the urine passed from two o'clock till six next morning was collected and distilled – only ten grammes of alcohol were collected. The rest was burned in the system.'

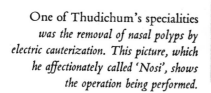

One of Thudichum's specialities *was the removal of nasal polyps by electric cauterization. This picture, which he affectionately called 'Nosi', shows the operation being performed.*

THE 'PURE BEAUTY of the cerebellar cortex' is seen in these pictures of different types of nerve cell in the brain, and their interconnections. They were made by the Spanish microscopist Ramon y Cajal to illustrate the numerous discoveries he was able to make in 1888 and 1889 with the aid of a new method of staining microscopic sections.

The fine processes which sprout from nerve cells are quite resistant to ordinary biological stains, and until this time it had been impossible to examine them in detail. An Italian, Camillo Golgi, discovered that silver chromate could be used to pick out nerve cells to the complete exclusion of all others, the minute branches appearing in brownish black against a translucent yellow background. He announced his methods in 1880 but they were generally ignored.

But in 1887 Ramon was shown the technique by a young doctor who had come across it on a trip to Paris. At that time scholastic discipline was such that no pupil of a famous scientist would use any methods except those taught by his master: to employ the methods of a rival was a kind of disloyalty to the man and (where the rival was a foreigner) to one's country. Ramon, however, decided he must take up this marvellous new technique, and, if possible, make it more reliable, for it was rather capricious. (Ironically, the young doctor who told Ramon about it abandoned it for this very reason.) Ramon had the inspired idea of applying to *embryo* material: to his joy he found that not only did it work more reliably, but the nerve processes, being less fully developed, were less tangled, and could be seen more clearly.

Immediately he made a flood of new discoveries. A bewildering variety of types of nerve cell, equipped with many different patterns of cell process, was discovered as he applied the new technique to different tissues – the spinal cord, the olfactory endings, the retina, various parts of the brain. A nerve cell has two kinds of extension, many short branching ones called dendrites, and a long one called an axon, which often ends in a fine branching system called an arborization. Waldeyer named such nerve cells 'neurones'.

As Ramon studied his preparations, the truth rose up in his mind 'like a revelation'. The branches of the axons come in contact with the dendrites of neighbouring cells, he realized, but do not fuse with them. In particular, where the axons enter the mass of fibres in the grey matter, the principle remains true; these fibres are not a continuous network, with every cell thus connected ultimately to every other cell, as Golgi and most other neurologists supposed (a view known as the reticular theory). On the contrary, each cell is connected with certain specific other cells, and with them only. 'Protoplasmic kisses' was Ramon's name for these inter-neuronal contacts; today they are known as synapses. The reticularists continued to oppose the synaptic theory bitterly, until the last of them died in 1939.

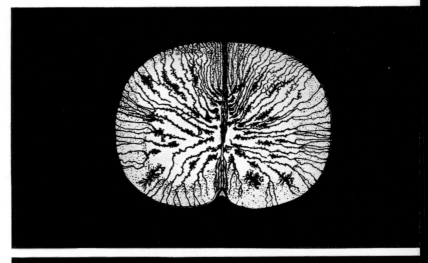

A long step forward *in the study of the nervous system: cross-section of a cerebellar convolution, stained by the Golgi method and drawn by Santiago Ramon y Cajal.*

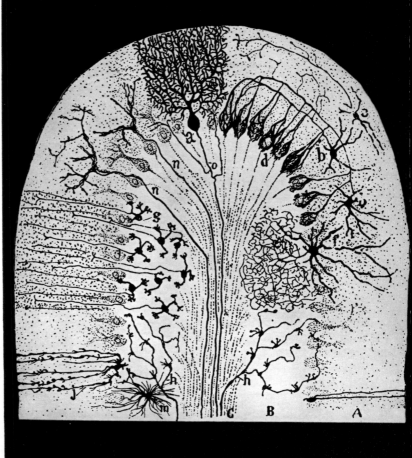

Nerves of the embryo *or the newly born are easier to study, as they are less fully developed and less tangled than adult nerves. With silver chromate staining, the cerebellum of a newborn mouse, drawn by Ramon, shows up the nerve processes in beautiful clarity.*

Working like a fury, for fifteen hours a day, Ramon proceeded to chart the growth of the neuronal processes: to do this he had to make long series of preparations from embryos at successive stages of development. He showed how these processes search about until they find the type of cell they are looking for: the end of the growing portion is amoeboid. When contact has been made, unsuccessful strands are reabsorbed. The arborizations then proceed to climb the main stem of the axon and the dendrites, like ivy on a tree. He showed that the nerves grow by extension of the axon: the whole nerve is derived from a single cell, even when several feet in length. This demolished earlier theories that several cells fused to form a nerve, or that incomplete cell-divisions occurred.

So enormous was his output at this time that he could not get his papers published without delay, and was in danger of losing his claims to priority. He therefore sank every penny into founding a scientific journal: in some issues, every article was from his pen!

In addition to endless contributions to the detailed anatomy of the neurones, Ramon was to make one other major discovery. He found how to stain the neurofibrils–fine fibres, hitherto only imperfectly seen, within the nerve-cells. His new method showed how they passed down the axons, and that they did *not* pass into the adjoining cells, as the reticularists, fired with new hope, had claimed as soon as they were discovered. Ramon did not sleep for several days, so active was his brain with plans for exploiting this new breakthrough.

Ramon was a man obsessed with the idea of accurate vision. The aspect of neurology which chiefly fascinated him was the mechanism of seeing. Photography was his hobby; his life's work was making clear what had been, quite literally, obscure. Chess was also a hobby: he was accustomed to play four games at once, and could even play without looking at the board, so vivid was his power of visualization. His gift was in the tradition of Velasquez.

At seventy, he turned again to the study of the eye – this time to the compound eye of insects. He hoped to show it was relatively simple, compared with the mammalian eye, but it proved bafflingly complex. Ramon was unable to reveal any general principle by these studies, and finally abandoned them in disappointment.

When Ramon died at eighty-two (in 1934), he had entirely transformed our picture of the nervous system by revealing the fine details of its structure, and had laid the basis for understanding what goes on in the brain. His work put the coping stone on the structure erected by the 19th-century neuroanatomists. The next developments were to come through quite different methods of attack.

9

THE SECRET AGENTS

Pasteur, Koch, Beijerinck, Stanley

IN THE 17TH-CENTURY PICTURE on page 222 we see illustrated the recurrent idea of a 'living contagion' as one of the causes of disease. Aristotle had suggested it. The extraordinary Jesuit, Athanasius Kircher, in 1658, after a severe visitation of the plague in Rome, declared that it was due to an 'innumerable brood of worms which are imperceptible to the eye', but which can be seen under a good microscope. Indeed, Fracastorius had advanced a theory of invisible living *semina,* or seeds, which spread disease, as early as 1546, before there was any microscope capable of verifying the idea.

After a great plague at Marseilles in 1720, an English botanist, R. Bradley, produced a well-reasoned argument for the existence of a 'living contagion' – but the credit for the first proof of the existence of such an agent goes, not as many people suppose to Pasteur or to Koch, but to a half-blind Italian law-student named Agostino Bassi. Though law was his subject, he had studied under such famous scientists as Volta and Spallanzani. When his eyesight went, he retired to a farm, and here he saw the devastation wrought by a silkworm disease known as muscardine, in which the worms are afflicted by white patches. Bassi found that, if material from the white patches was inoculated into healthy silkworms, they also fell prey to the disease. And under the microscope, he found in the inoculum a parasitic fungus, now known as *Botrytis bassiana.* In his little book describing his investigations, he hesitantly remarks: 'Perhaps some of my readers will respond with a smile to my doctrine of living contagions.' This was in 1835; in 1844 he asserted that smallpox, bubonic plague, spotted fever and syphilis were also due to 'living parasites'. The world remained unimpressed, and Bassi died in the very year in which Pasteur started his studies of bacterial action.

But the subject was in the air. Zoologists were studying the various small organisms they could see with their new microscopes. In 1849 a veterinary surgeon named Pollender saw anthrax bacilli in the blood of sheep which had died of this disease; but his claim that they were the causes of the disease were dismissed.

The next important step was taken by a French investigator, Davaine. He found he could transmit anthrax from sheep to rabbits by inoculating the rabbits with the blood of diseased sheep. But the experiment did not work every time, and his critics declared that the 'bacterides' – as Davaine called the bacilli which he could see in the blood. – were not the cause of the disease but merely a by-product. Furthermore, the disease tended to be confined to certain districts: was it not perhaps due to something in the soil?

Some ten years later, a young German medical officer named Robert Koch, who had settled in a tiny country town in an area where anthrax was rife, decided to attack the problem again. He had the idea of inoculating mice with 'bacterides', and then studying their blood continuously. Working at home, he discovered that the anthrax bacilli multiplied in the blood, and eventually formed spores. And these spores were tough: they could survive outside the body in conditions that would instantly kill the bacilli. Then, on

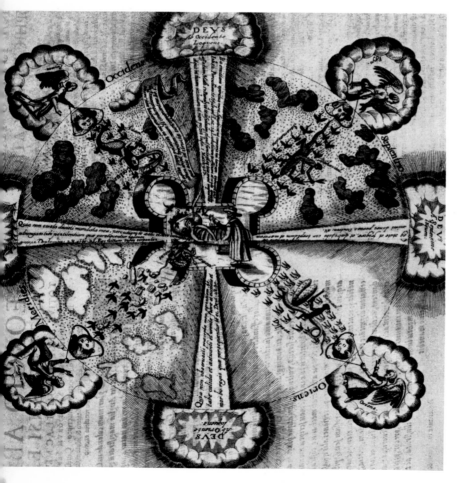

Invading hordes of disease-carrying organisms breach the walls of the citadel of health. An intuitive belief in 'living contagions' was held before bacteria could be seen in the microscope.

re-entering the body of an animal, they gave rise to more bacilli. So the mystery was explained. It was the first time in history that the mechanism of an infectious (bacterial) disorder had been demonstrated beyond a doubt.

Three years before Koch's paper, one Obermeyer had discovered a bacterium to be the cause of relapsing fever, but he had promptly died, and his discovery had not been followed up.

Koch, still working in his improvised laboratory, now showed how to culture bacteria – that is, how to grow them in the laboratory – and how to destroy them. Furthermore, it became clear that each disease has its specific bacterial cause: a bacterium cannot give rise to different diseases, nor do bacteria change their type. Obvious as this now seems, it all had to be discovered and proved.

The germs of anthrax were sketched by Koch in 1876 to illustrate how the spores developed; and in 1877, having invented ways of staining and

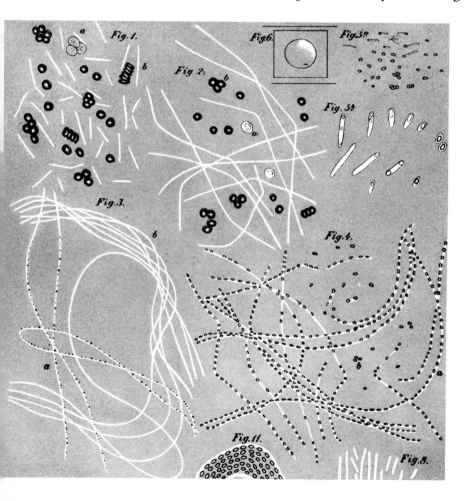

The germs of anthrax, drawn by Koch in 1876. Immature bacilli (Fig. 1), among the red corpuscles, grow longer (2), and develop spores (3). The spores increase in size and break off (4), to start the cycle afresh.

223

fixing the bacteria, he published very clear microphotographs. His work sparked off a chain of discoveries. In 1879 the gonococcus – the cause of gonorrhoea – was discovered; in 1880, the typhoid bacillus, the leprosy agent and the protozoon which causes malaria.

Among those who were stimulated by Koch's work was Pasteur, the great French chemist whom we have already met in connection with the question of the spontaneous generation of life. His work on this had convinced him of the existence of bacteria, but he saw them primarily as causes of fermentation and decay and did not pursue their possible connection with disease. For ten years or so he continued to work on the fermentation of wine and the brewing of beer, and then at the request of the French Minister of Agriculture turned to the problems of the French silkworm industry, which was menaced by a silkworm disease. It was as he was finishing this work that Koch's paper appeared, causing Pasteur to throw himself into the problem of anthrax, which was at that time decimating the French sheep population; he also studied fowl cholera.

A large crowd of doctors, vets and journalists gathered at Melun, near Paris, on the 31st May, 1881, to see Pasteur inject virulent cultures of anthrax into forty-eight sheep, half of which had previously been 'vaccinated' with his newly-developed attenuated anthrax culture. The test was the focus of national attention. Pasteur had discovered the principle of attenuation by chance, when, in the course of following up Koch's work on anthrax, he had inoculated some fowls with a culture of chicken cholera which happened to be several weeks old. The birds proved to be immune to subsequent inoculations of the unattenuated virus, and Pasteur christened such attenuated inocula 'vaccines', by analogy with Jenner's cow vaccine. But his announcement of this discovery was met with general scepticism, and a public test was arranged.

Two days after the injections at Melun, twenty-two of the unvaccinated sheep were dead and the other two were dying, while all the vaccinated sheep were alive. 'The whole of France burst out in an explosion of enthusiasm.'

From anthrax Pasteur passed to child-bed fever and to rabies. He found that the rabies virus could be propagated in the brains of dogs and rabbits and hence he was able, as all the world knows, to develop an effective vaccine.

Nevertheless, Pasteur hesitated to apply it to man. The whole medical profession was opposed to the deliberate injection of disease agents into man, and even his associate Roux turned against him, although he returned when Pasteur became the object of bitter attacks in the Academy of Medicine.

However, Pasteur's hand was forced in 1885, when the nine-year-old Joseph Meister was brought to him, bitten on the hands, legs and thighs some sixty hours before. Pasteur believed that the disease was too well established for the vaccine to prove effective, and feared that if the boy died his vaccine would be discredited. Nevertheless, he felt he could not refuse him the chance of life. He inoculated and Meister lived. Within the next fifteen months, no fewer than 2,490 persons received the vaccine, though at first Pasteur was dubbed a murderer by sceptics.

Meister later became gate-keeper of the splendid Pasteur Institute, erected by a grateful nation in Pasteur's old age. In 1940, fifty-five years after Pasteur had saved his life, he committed suicide, in order to avoid being compelled to open to the German invaders the crypt where Pasteur lies buried.

Model crystals of tartaric acid, made for Pasteur. With crystals like these, at the age of 22, he performed one of the classical experiments in the history of science.

IT WAS WITH two crystals that Pasteur's scientific career began. Tartaric acid had long been known to occur in wine fermentation vats, and in 1820 a second form, having smaller needle-like crystals, had been noticed. In 1844, a German chemist noticed that if light was passed through the commoner form, its plane of vibration was rotated to the right (as happens with various other substances) but that with the rarer form no rotation occurred.

Pasteur, then aged twenty-two, felt sure that some chemical or physical difference must exist to account for this. He prepared crystals of the rarer form, and inspected them under the microscope. At first they all seemed identical; then, as he later recalled, 'my heart stopped beating' – he realized that *two* types of crystal were present: some were the mirror-images of the others. Sedulously picking out one variety from the other, he prepared solutions of each, and showed that one solution rotated light to the right, the

The young Pasteur *received his baccalaureate in 1842, with 'mediocre' in chemistry. Seven years later, aged 27, he became professor of chemistry at Strasbourg.*

Sceptics called him a murderer, *but in fifteen months from the first anti-rabies inoculation he treated 2,490 patients with the vaccine. Above, with some of the children he inoculated. Mortality from hydrophobia is now less than one per cent.*

'These three things – *will, work and success – between them fill human existence', he wrote. The photograph on the right show him dictating notes to his wife even during his convalescence from a mild stroke.*

Fifty years after *his 'mediocre' for chemistry, Pasteur received an international ovation at his jubilee in the Sorbonne. The gowned figure in the centre with hands upraised is Lord Lister, who saw the applicability of Pasteur's work on microbes, and introduced revolutionary measures of surgical asepsis.*

226

other to the left. Mixed together, the two rotations cancelled. It was one of the classical experiments in the history of science.

Biot, the great crystallographer who had first discovered these rotations in 1815, summoned him to the Collège de France and made him repeat the experiment before him. As the predicted rotation showed up on the polarimeter, the famous old man seized Pasteur by the hand and exlaimed: 'My dear son, I have loved science so deeply that this stirs my heart.'

All his life Pasteur remained obsessed by the idea that asymmetric bodies are always the product of living processes. 'The universe is an asymmetrical whole . . .' he said, 'Life is dominated by asymmetrical actions.' He had large magnets made, to see if this would affect the development of crystals; and planned to grow plants wholly in sunlight reversed by a mirror, to see whether they would produce substances with crystals of opposite symmetry to those found in nature. This fantastic vision he carried with him to the grave.

'Moderation! This is a word which is rarely applied to me', said Pasteur. He defended his views in dramatic language, when attacked, but in his work he was the embodiment of caution and self-discipline. When cogitating a problem he would remain tensely silent for long periods, even with his own family. When it was solved, he expected everyone to share his joy. He counted that day wasted when he did not work, and spent his evenings reading and writing detailed notes. At forty-six he became partially paralysed, but he ignored this, as he later ignored old age. 'My only strength', he said, 'lies in my tenacity.'

But his most striking characteristic was his fear of dirt and infection. He avoided, as far as possible, shaking hands to avoid contamination, and at table carefully wiped his plate and glass. One of his assistants recalls: 'He minutely inspected the bread that was served to him and placed on the table-cloth everything he found in it: small fragments of wool, of roaches, of flour-worms. Often I tried to find in my own piece of bread from the same loaf the objects found by Pasteur but could not discover anything . . . This search took place at almost every meal and is perhaps the most extraordinary memory that I have kept of Pasteur.'

In 1882 came another major discovery. Koch, now equipped with proper research facilities, announced his discovery of the bacillus of tuberculosis. Hitherto TB had been generally supposed to be due to poor nutrition. Even though no cure was yet available, at least the disease could be diagnosed effectively. Within a few months, a world-wide outbreak of cholera began to create alarm. When the disease, spreading from the Orient, reached Egypt, Koch hurried there and soon identified the comma-shaped bacillus of cholera.

In 1891 a splendid Institute for Infectious Diseases was set up for Koch in Berlin and he held the directorship for the next thirteen years.

More and more investigators flocked to this rewarding field of research: erysipelas, tetanus, diphtheria, pneumonia, meningitis, bubonic plague, sleeping sickness, all yielded their specific bacterial cause. In 1905, the culmination came with the discovery of the *spirochaeta pallida,* the agent of the dread disease of syphilis.

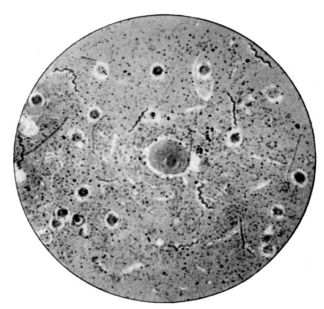

Spirochaeta pallida, *the bacillus of syphilis, magnified about* x *1000.*

Seven spirochaetes, and – in the centre – a red blood-cell can be seen in this sketch from the original paper by Schaudinn, the discoverer. The cause of this disease had been strenuously sought for twenty years or more, and many a false hope had been raised. As Dr Lassar sarcastically remarked, just before Schaudinn's success, 'One hundred and twenty-five causes of syphilis have been established during the last twenty-five years'.

In the same year Koch received the Nobel prize; soon he was elected to the Prussian Academy of Sciences, and was given the title of *Excellenz.* Then, to the intense indignation of the entire German nation, to whom he appeared almost as a god, he suddenly divorced his wife and married a young actress. He died of heart disease soon after.

The impetus which Koch's work gave to research was enormous, though many resisted the idea of bacterial infections. To the end of her life, Florence Nightingale denied the existence of germs.

The question of how the body resists disease began to loom large. Was there, perhaps, some agent in the body which did battle with bacteria? But if so, why is a person who has had measles, say, immune from further attacks of measles, but not from other diseases? In some sense the body must 'recognize' the invading agent. A similar question arises from the acceptance or rejection of a skin or tissue graft.

'A certain inhabitant of Bruxels, in a combat, had his nose mowed off, and addressed himself to Tagliacozzus, a famous Chirurgeon living at Bononia, that he might procure a new one; and when he feared the incision of his own arme, he hired a Porter to admit it, out of whose arme, having first given the reward agreed upon, at length he digged a new nose. About thirteen moneths after his returne to his owne countrey, on a suddaine, the ingrafted nose grew cold, putrified, and within a few days dropt off . . . it was discovered, that the Porter expired near about the same punctilio of time, wherein the nose grew frigid and cadaverous.'

This story, borrowed from van Helmont by an English writer in 1650, is clearly an account of the failure of a heterograft, as we should now say. A graft of tissue can only be successfully made between one part of the body and another, or between identical twins (homograft). In any other case, as soon as the blood vessels of the host have begun to grow into the donated tissue, it dies and sloughs off (heterograft).

But how does the body of the recipient discover that the tissue is not its own? Today we are still unable to answer the question exhaustively, but since about 1900 considerable progress has been made. We know that the blood contains an unique substance – gamma-globulin – which combines with foreign particles, causing them to clump together, and which renders them inactive; and that it does not do this to the body's own constituents, even when they appear to be very similar. The first clue had come at the end of the eighteenth century.

When Edward Jenner, not yet twenty, was apprentice to a doctor in Sodbury near Bristol, a young woman came to him for medical advice. When smallpox was suggested, she replied confidently that she was immune from it, as she had had cowpox. Later, when Jenner was a country doctor, he often spoke of this belief, and urged that it be tested, but no one would take the risk. However, in 1796, he decided to take the plunge: he obtained some pus from the arm of a dairy-maid afflicted with cowpox, and inserted it in a nick made in the arm of a healthy eight-year-old boy, James Phipps. Six weeks later, he inoculated the boy with smallpox lymph, and anxiously waited to see whether he would develop smallpox. He remained perfectly healthy.

After three more successful inoculations, Jenner submitted a paper to the Royal Society: it was returned with the friendly advice that he should not publish it, lest he injure his reputation. When he published it himself, there

Cosmetic surgery *of the 16th century. Why such a graft can succeed but a graft from a donor (except an identical twin) will fail to take, is still not perfectly understood.*

Inoculation with cowpox *lent itself to obvious ridicule, as in this cartoon by Rowlandson, but the benefits soon became even more obvious. Why vaccination should give immunity against smallpox remained a mystery for another hundred years.*

was controversy but the idea was soon taken up. Napoleon ordered all his soldiers vaccinated, and Thomas Jefferson in the USA had several members of his family vaccinated. The Empress of Russia urged all her subjects to be vaccinated. The British Parliament voted Jenner an award of £10,000, and five years later another £20,000. So great was his fame, that when a relation of his was taken prisoner by Napoleon, and Jenner wrote to ask for his release, Napoleon at once released him, exclaiming, 'To Jenner I can refuse nothing!'

So immunity could be conferred: but what was the explanation? Almost a century passed before any gleams of light appeared.

CHARLES RICHET was one of the more original characters in the story of biology. As early as 1890, he built himself an airplane; he wrote two plays which were performed in Paris at the Odéon; he took a leading part in the investigation of the medium Eusapia Palladino, and for many years was president of the Society for Psychical Research. He had wished to be a writer, but his father pushed him into medicine.

In 1888 Richet found that when he injected rabbits with blood from dogs suffering from staphylococcal infections he bestowed immunity to such infections on the rabbits. (The discovery was a chance one: he had been investigating tumours in dogs, and, finding one dog infected with staph, had sought to transfer the tumour to another species.) Blood-serum alone, without the corpuscles, would confer the immunity, he found. (Indeed, if he did not remove the corpuscles, the animal died.) In 1890 the first attempt was made to induce immunity in human beings in this way: it soon became clear that the immunity was specific, and the recipient became immune only to the one disease from which the donor had been suffering.

This focused attention on the serum as the site of the mechanism, and before long a pupil of Koch's, von Behring, discovered in the serum substances which he called anti-toxins, and which we now call antibodies.

Fourteen years later Richet made – again by chance – a second crucial discovery. He had been experimenting with the venom of the Portuguese man-o'-war, trying to establish what dose would kill a dog. One day, he gave 'a fine large dog called Neptune' a second dose, one-tenth the lethal amount. To his amazement, Neptune keeled over and died within a few minutes. The first injection had somehow made it abnormally sensitive. It was another instance of a recognition process.

Richet called the phenomenon 'anaphylaxis' – a lifting up or removal of protection. He had discovered the principle which underlies the allergies. For this he received the Nobel prize, though the mechanism of sensitization is still mysterious.

A new piece had been added to the puzzle in the previous year by an Austrian pathologist, Karl Landsteiner. It was already known that if the blood of one animal is mixed with that of an animal of different species, the red blood cells will clump together, or agglutinate, though no one knew why.

Landsteiner conceived the idea of mixing the red blood-corpuscles from the blood of one person with the blood serum from another. The result was somewhat unexpected. 'Sometimes the corpuscles clumped, sometimes they did not.' Landsteiner was puzzled. Was it perhaps because some of the people donating blood were ill, or in some way abnormal?

Taking blood from all the members of his laboratory staff and combining the corpuscles and serum in every possible combination, Landsteiner worked out that there were three categories of blood; in the following year, the existence of a fourth was demonstrated.

Here again the same problem was implicit as was implied by the work of Richet. In one case, how did the blood of one person 'recognize' the blood of another as being of the same or of a different group? In the other case, how

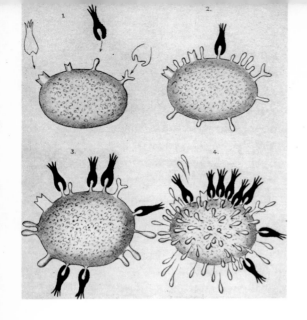

Ehrlich drew this diagram *to illustrate his 'lock-and-key' explanation of the mechanism of immunity. The cells have different locks, and the invading bodies have keys; when the key fits the lock immunity is established.*

did the blood of an immune person 'recognize' an invading bacterium as of the same type as had invaded it before?

The great German bacteriologist, Paul Ehrlich, the discoverer of salvarsan, the drug which destroys the spirochaete of syphilis, drew this diagram to explain what he thought occurred. Basically, his idea was that a lock-and-key type of mechanism must be present. The blood-corpuscles have different keys, the serum has different locks. Normally, in a given person's blood, the key does not fit the lock. But when a mixture is made which brings the keys up against locks which fit, they enter, and clumping occurs.

Ehrlich thought there must be four kinds of locks and four kinds of keys, but Landsteiner showed that the observed facts could be explained by assuming only two kinds of each. The four blood-groups could be formed by assuming that either key, or both, or neither, was present. That is, the four blood-groups were: A, B, A + B and O. Before long, it was established that these were inherited according to the normal Mendelian laws (described in chapter 13).

Landsteiner then turned his attention to immunity: he created new chemical structures unknown in nature and showed that the body could learn to recognize them, thus proving that the recognition system was not predetermined and that it depended in some way on chemical structure.

Landsteiner was always convinced that blood is as unique to each person as his finger-prints, and he proceeded to discover more and more identifiable blood-factors. Moving to the Rockefeller Institute in 1923, he showed the existence of factors M and N, and in 1937, after studying the evolution of these factors in apes, he discovered the rhesus factor. This in itself would have been enough, no doubt, to have won him a Nobel prize, but he had already been given it for his basic discovery, which had made safe blood transfusion possible.

Since then, it has become clear that these 'recognition' systems are widespread in the body. They account for the fact, already noted, that tissue from one person cannot be grafted into another, except between identical twins. No doubt they explain why sperm of one species will not normally fertilize eggs of another species. Furthermore, certain diseases, including possibly arthritis, are due to the body making the mistake of treating part of its own tissue as if it were foreign.

Simultaneously with all this, a rival theory of body-defences had been launched in 1882 by a mercurial Russian named Metchnikov. Like many others Metchnikov was impressed by Darwin's work, and spent the opening years of his scientific career exploring how sponges and other lowly creatures develop their various layers of tissue, a study which threw light on the sequence of evolution. In particular he studied the stomachs of starfish; he fed them carmine and noted how the particles of the dye were absorbed into the digestive cells. (Thus, incidentally, he was the inventor of 'vital staining', i.e. staining living tissue.)

Is the body protected *against bacteria by phagocytes? Metchnikov (here seen in his laboratory in Paris, where he worked for a time under Pasteur) was 37 when this 'new thought flashed across his brain' as he studied starfish larvae in the Straits of Messina. He received the Nobel prize in 1908.*

In a later study with frogs, he noticed that pigment particles were absorbed by cells of a different kind: the white blood-corpuscles. Then he moved one step nearer his discovery: he noted that blood corpuscles sometimes ingest bacteria. But still the penny did not drop. It was in 1882, when he was studying starfish in the Straits of Messina, that 'a new thought suddenly flashed across my brain. It struck me that similar cells might serve as the defence of the organism against intruders.'

Metchnikov felt so excited by this insight that he started striding up and down the room, and finally went down to the seashore to collect his thoughts. Here he devised an experiment to test his notion. He knew that when a splinter enters a man's flesh mobile cells, called lymphocytes, congregate at the spot. Could this be a mechanism of defence? Suppose, if so, that one inserted a splinter into the semi-transparent starfish larvae which he had been studying, would one see the mobile cells congregate at the spot? Fetching some rose-thorns from his small garden, he introduced them under the skin of some of his larvae.

That night he was too excited to sleep; he arose very early and went to see what had happened. It was as he had surmised. 'That experiment', he recalled, 'formed the basis of the phagocytic theory, to the development of which I devoted the next twenty-five years of my life.' The word phagocyte, which Metchnikov coined, means 'cell-eater'.

This new 'cellular theory of immunity' aroused strong opposition. Metchnikov asserted that inflammation is an important defence-reaction, and a sign of the struggle between the defending phagocytes and the invading bacteria. His opponents said: on the contrary, the white cells provide a means of transport for the bacteria, and so actually spread the infection.

When von Behring discovered his anti-toxins, Metchnikov's views seemed to be wrong. But in 1903 Sir Almroth Wright discovered that the blood of immunized animals contains substances which greatly assist the phagocytes in destroying bacteria. He named them 'opsonins', from the Greek word 'to prepare food', since they seemed to prepare the bacteria for consumption. Bernard Shaw made a lot of fun of the 'opsonin index' in *The Doctor's Dilemma* and thought it just a new fad. Today we call these substances anti-bodies, and realize that the two mechanisms work hand-in-hand.

Thanks primarily to Richet, Metchnikov and Landsteiner, the science of immunology had been created. Despite extensive work, the precise mechanism by which 'recognition' is achieved, and its role in allergy and anaphylaxis, remain obscure. However, at least we no longer feel the need to fall back on magical and vitalistic explanations of disease resistance.

Meanwhile, another agent of disease had begun to appear upon the scientific scene: the virus.

The first man to demonstrate *the existence of a virus – Professor Beijerinck of Delft University. He did not consider it a particle at all; he thought it was an infectious fluid, and named it virus – 'poison'.*

'A MAN OF SCIENCE does not marry,' declared the tyrannical Professor Beijerinck of Delft, dismissing an assistant for getting engaged. A bachelor himself, he lived with two sisters, and often remained silent for hours at a time. He started his lectures with the words 'Gentlemen and ladies!'

Such was the man who performed the crucial experiment which demonstrated the existence of the infective particles, far smaller than bacteria, which we now call viruses.

Probably the first person to see a virus was Buist, the superintendent of an Edinburgh infirmary, who in 1887 stained and examined a smear from a patient with pox. He thought they were bacterial spores, although his efforts to cultivate them failed. Early in the 20th century other workers saw the viruses of fowlpox and rediscovered the cowpox viruses, without establishing what they were.

It was Beijerinck who extracted the juice from diseased tobacco plants, filtered it and showed that the clear filtrate could transmit the disease to healthy plants. The filtered juice from these would transmit it to a third group and so on indefinitely. It followed that the infective agent was multiplying, in much the same way as a bacterium does, for otherwise it would have eventually become diluted to ineffectiveness. The idea of something too small to see under the microscope, capable even of passing through the sub-microscopic pores of filters of porous clay, which yet could multiply like a living thing, seemed too fantastic to contemplate. Beijerinck, for one, did not take this view: he considered that he had an infectious liquid, and called it virus, which in its original sense simply means 'poison'.

237

Six years before Beijerinck's experiments, a Russian named Dmitri Iwanowski had come within an ace of making this historic discovery. He had had the idea of filtering the juice from diseased tobacco plants, and inoculating it into fresh ones, in 1892, and obtained infection just as Beijerinck did. But the conclusion he drew from this was that either his filters must be defective, or that he was dealing with a bacterium which produced some toxin which passed through them and damaged the inoculated plant. Unlike the persistent Beijerinck, he failed to inoculate from the second plant into a third, and then into a fourth and thus failed to discover that the invisible agent was replicating itself, and therefore could not be a simple toxin.

The method having been shown, it was a logical step to apply it to other unexplained infectious diseases. Almost immediately, in 1898, two German scientists discovered that a virus was the cause of foot-and-mouth disease. Three years later, the first disease of human beings to have a viral cause was established: yellow fever. Many others followed, from measles to smallpox.

But in each case the presence of a virus was inferred simply from the ability to produce infection with filtrates. No one knew how the infective agent worked, or even what it looked like. Indeed, as late as 1913, Beijerinck was still claiming that life was 'compatible with the fluid state'.

In 1928 the mystery deepened. Elford, at the National Institute of Medical Research, succeeded in devising filters with pores of known sizes, and some of them too small to pass a virus. Thus by seeing which filter it would pass and which stopped it, size could be estimated. The answer seemed unbelievable: from 10 to 3,000 millimicrons, depending on the type. A millimicron is a millionth of a millimetre, or a twenty-five millionth of an inch. Such a figure is more appropriate for a large molecule than a living organism, and it was hard to conceive how the virus could pack the machinery of life into so small a compass.

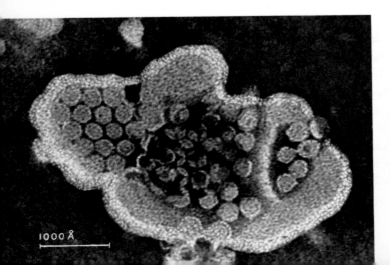

Viruses are of many shapes and sizes. *This modern electron micrograph shows the polio virus being formed within a cell. The scale, 1000 Ångström units, is 100 millimicrons, or one ten-thousandth of a millimetre.*

1000 Å

In August 1915, Félix d'Hérelle, a French bacteriologist, was asked to investigate a severe outbreak of dysentery in a French cavalry squadron. Previously to this, he had been fighting a plague of locusts in North Africa by infecting them with a bacterium, and he had noticed that on his culture plates of bacteria, clear spots appeared, where the bacteria had been destroyed. Perhaps a virus which attacked bacteria was responsible?

He decided to see whether the dysentery bacterium might have a similar viral enemy. He therefore filtered the faeces of a dysentery-stricken cavalryman, and let the filtrate act on dysentery bacteria. For the first three days, he had no success. He tried again. 'The next morning, on opening the incubator, I experienced one of those rare moments of intense emotion, which reward the research worker for all his pains: at the first glance I saw that the broth culture, which the night before had been very turbid, was perfectly clear: all the bacteria had vanished, they had dissolved away like sugar in water: what caused my clear spots was in fact an invisible microbe, a filterable virus, but a virus parasitic on bacteria.' Thus was discovered the existence of viruses which attack bacteria: d'Hérelle named them bacteriophage, or bacteria-eater.

The thought immediately occurred to him that the bacteria in the intestine of the sick man might have dissolved likewise. He dashed to the hospital, and in fact the patient was greatly improved. D'Hérelle felt sure that he had found a wonderful new agent against disease, and spent the rest of his life in experiments to prove it. But the results were confusing and disappointing: in epidemic conditions improvement was sometimes obtained; in other cases, the disease seemed to grow more resistant than before. The world remained sceptical and thought him a visionary or a humbug. Bacteriophage itself remained invisible, and some denied that it existed, claiming that the effects were due to a ferment released by the bacterium itself. D'Hérelle himself thought the virus was a non-living protein molecule.

Curiously enough, the same discovery was made almost simultaneously in England by F. W. Twort, who, like d'Hérelle, believed it would prove a new weapon against disease. His laboratory equipped with new instruments, and supported by the Medical Research Council, he set out on the task (impossible, as we know now) of culturing it. By 1944, when his lab. was destroyed by a bomb, the true nature of bacteriophage had begun to become clear, and the University took the opportunity to terminate his work. But to his death Twort continued to believe that he had been foiled in the last stages of success. Unlike d'Hérelle, he believed that it was a living agent.

Phage, as it is usually known, did not prove of clinical value. But, as we shall see in the last chapter, it was to prove a tool of inestimable value in unravelling the secrets of life.

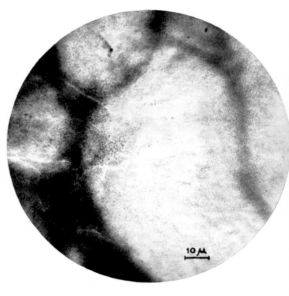

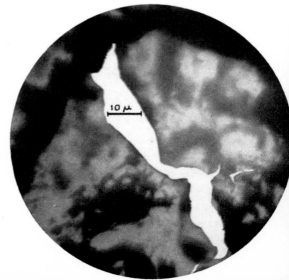

The first 'super-microscope' *(opposite, top left)* was demonstrated by Professor E. Ruska in 1933. He pointed out that, whereas an optical microscope could never resolve points less than half a wavelength of light apart, or, say, 250 millimicrons, an electron microscope using high-velocity electrons should be able to achieve much better results than this. In the event, Ruska's instrument magnified 12,000 times, and resolved points only 40 millimicrons apart.

An improved version *of this apparatus (opposite, below) was devised by L. Marton of Belgium; he was able to protect biological materials from the eroding effects of the electron beam by impregnating them with the salts of a heavy atom, osmium, and conducting away the heat by an aluminium foil half a micron thick.*

The first electron micrographs *ever taken of biological material are shown opposite, representing the cells in two kinds of seaweed.*

Progress *in electron microscopy has been extraordinarily rapid. Magnifications approaching one million diameters can now be achieved, and points no more than ten Ångström units (one millionth of a millimetre) apart can be resolved. On the right is a modern descendant (Siemens & Halske, 1954) of the primitive instruments opposite. The clarity that can be achieved with modern instruments is shown in the picture of tabacco mosaic virus overleaf.*

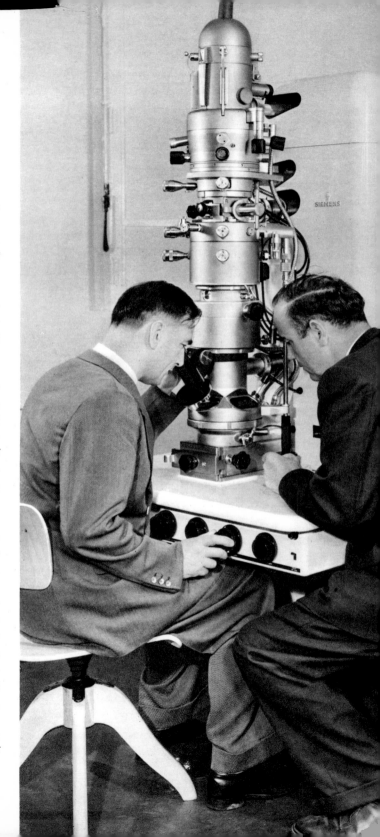

In 1932, THE DIRECTOR of the Rockefeller Institute in New York offered a new job to a twenty-eight-year-old assistant, Wendell Stanley. Would he like to go to the new plant pathology department of the Institute to work on the chemistry of plant viruses? Stanley replied that he might be interested, but what were viruses?

'That is what you are going down there for,' said the director, 'to find out what viruses are.'

Stanley studied the literature, and concluded that d'Hérelle had been on the right track: viruses were non-living protein molecules and not living organisms. He knew that several proteins had recently been prepared in crystalline form. (A crystal is a structure in which the molecules are arranged in regular rows, like bricks in a wall, a thing which is only possible when dealing with units which are identical in shape and size.) He decided to try to make a crystalline preparation of a virus. He chose for the purpose the virus which produces a mosaic pattern on the leaves of tobacco plants, known as TMV, or tobacco-mosaic virus.

For two years he grew infected Turkish tobacco plants, and processed the leaves. Pail after pail of the juice which he extracted was treated with chemical reagents and poured through filters. Then he had to test both the liquid which passed through and the cake of precipitate to see which contained the virus, by inoculating more tobacco plants with each. To remove the other substances present he tried every trick in the chemist's repertoire, even juggling with the electrical charge on the molecule to eliminate some of the other proteins. Finally, he was left with a liquid which shimmered and turned into needle-like crystals. He had a pure solution, and the crystals proved up to a thousand times as infective as the juice with which he had started.

He was by then thirty-one and almost bald. He had reduced about a ton of tobacco plants to about a tablespoonful of infective crystals. As someone said afterwards, it was like capturing the flea in an elephant's ear by boiling down the elephant to a saucepanful of caramel.

But the scientific world was not enthusiastic: it seemed inconceivable that a crystal could multiply itself within the body of another organism, like a living thing. The older bacteriologists said that plant viruses must be different from animal viruses; attempts to repeat the trick with animal viruses did not seem to work. Stanley's preparations, said others, must be contaminated with the disease agent; the crystals were not the disease itself.

Tobacco mosaic virus, *magnified 120,000 times in an electron microscope. This rod-shaped virus is the one most commonly used in fundamental virus studies. It is easy to grow, and is not infectious to humans.*

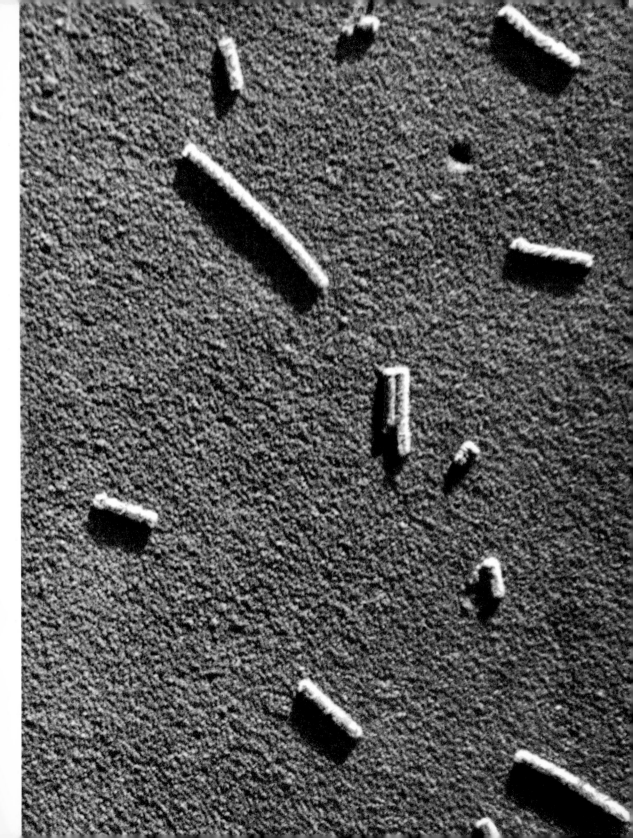

To prove his case, Stanley wrote and published frenziedly for the next five years, and lectured on every available platform in the U.S.A. and Great Britain. British biochemists – Bawden and Pirie – repeated Stanley's crystallization but found traces of phosphorus in the crystals. Phosphorus is not a constituent of ordinary protein. They showed that it came from a type of acid known as nucleic acid, which is peculiar to living things. Stanley checked and was obliged to concede that they were right. The virus seemed to partake so closely of the character of both living and non-living that people asked: 'Is it an organule or is it a molechism?'

The answer was so remarkable and so complex that it must wait for another chapter.

The man who first crystallized *the tabacco mosaic virus in pure form, Dr Wendell Stanley (right), examines infected tabacco plants with Dr Heinz Fraenkel-Conrat at the University of California. In the foreground are uninfected plants.*

10

THE ADVANCE GUARDS

Purkinje, Bernard, Spemann

PURKINJE, THE CZECH PHYSIOLOGIST, waited seven years before the university of Breslau agreed to supply him with the microscope, a fine Ploessel, in the picture overleaf. As he was a Czech – or rather an Austrian, for the Czechs had not yet become a nation – the German professors objected to him. Though himself a professor, he was given a small, dark room to share with others. Attempts were made to create a rival lectureship in physiology, so that his lectures should be neglected. And when he introduced practical work for the students, the old guard wrote to the Ministry of Education to have such an unheard-of thing stopped. Purkinje's applications to the Ministry to create a physiological institute at Breslau were intercepted and destroyed. It was, his enemies declared, unneeded.

Purkinje had to transfer all his work to his own house: as his young wife and two of his children had been carried off by typhoid and cholera, there were rooms to spare, even though he still had two other children to bring up. As a new and more sympathetic University Curator reported later, when supporting his scheme for establishing an institute of physiology, 'Not a single room is without bottles, instruments and preparations, and the health of Purkinje's family is seriously endangered.'

But once he obtained the magic instrument – for it was one of the new achromatic microscopes – there was no holding him. In his own vivid words: 'With wolf-like hunger, I have investigated tissues, both animal and plant of every type, and have become convinced that the potentialities are inexhaustible. Almost every day yielded new discoveries, and I felt a need to share this visual privilege with others, just to enjoy the satisfaction it gave them.' He invented a projection microscope so that his students could all see the preparations as he lectured.

Purkinje looked at teeth, at nerves, at the brain, at warts, and eggs, and pretty well everything he could lay his hands on. He was a second Malpighi.

Purkinje drew these pictures for one of the first great biological congresses in history – organized by Oken – in 1837. We can see, in Fig. 10, nerves

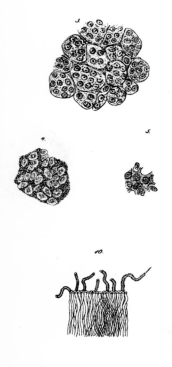

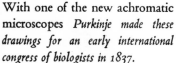

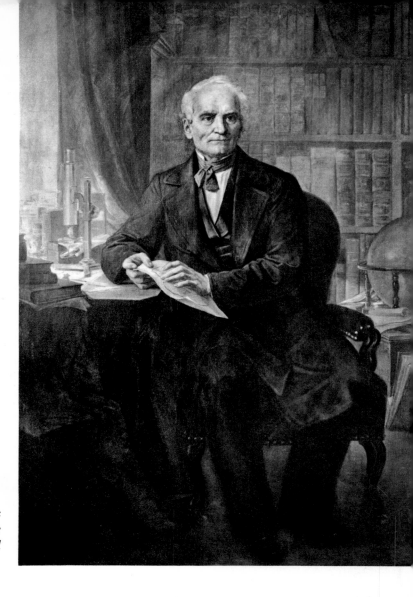

With one of the new achromatic microscopes *Purkinje made these drawings for an early international congress of biologists in 1837.*

straggling from their myelin sheath. In Figs. 3, 4 and 5 we can see cells of different types. Purkinje, indeed, foresaw the cell theory a year before Schwann, asserting that there are three fundamental structures in living organisms; fibres, fluids and cells. No one saw the significance of this generalization, and Schwann – a German – never acknowledged him.

I have already mentioned that it was Purkinje who invented the word 'protoplasm'.

Before he got his microscope, he studied the developing hen's egg, with a hand-lens, and saw, what scores of earlier investigators had overlooked, the nucleus. The fantastic implications kept him awake at nights. He had an extraordinary capacity for observation. As a successor remarked, many have seen things under the microscope which others could not see, but no one has failed to see what Purkinje has seen. Goethe, who approved him on account of a little book on colour-vision written in his student days, wrote an epigram on him:

> Let your delighted eye behold
> All things that Plato knew of old
> And if yourself you can't quite do it
> Purkinje'll come and help you to it.

More unusual, he was at the same time a highly ingenious technician. He invented many dyes and stains to bring out the details of microscopic preparations – ink, for instance, to reveal the canals in the teeth – and found that alcohol and glacial acetic acid could be used to make the tissues more transparent. He invented an early form of microtome to cut thin sections and devised the technique which we still use of sealing the preparation on the slide with Canada balsam.

Nor did he stop at microscopic technique. He devised the stroboscopic device seen below to show the movements of the heart. On looking through a slit as the disk revolves, the picture seems to move. When a penniless student, whose only food was bread sent by his mother from the village, and soup bought at an inn, he found a line of investigation even he could afford: he studied the reflection of a candle flame within his eye.

Jan Evangelista Purkinje,
scientist, teacher and inventor.

Devised by Purkinje *to demonstrate the beating of the heart, this stroboscope disk was viewed through a slit as it revolved, giving the illusion of movement.*

247

Several candle flames can be seen reflected in these figures, drawn by Purkinje, because the image has been reflected from the front and rear surfaces of the lens, and from the cornea, sometimes becoming inverted in the process. An image may also be formed within the optic jelly. With these simple tools – a candle, a mirror and his own eye – Purkinje discovered much about the structure of the eye, and laid the foundations of modern methods of ophthalmoscopy. As a student he also experimented on himself, with poisonous substances such as camphor and cocaine, having, as he said, 'a strong constitution', and gave classic descriptions of their effects.

He was the first to study the ridges on the hand and to classify the types of fingerprints. He worked on vertigo, and on dreams as an index to personality.

His many-sided activities make him a good symbol to place at the beginning of the nineteenth century. His enduring monuments are the structures we still call Purkinje's cells and Purkinje's fibres, and the Purkinje phenomenon (a peculiarity of colour-vision).

The many-sidedness of Purkinje is shown by his drawings of the reflection of a candle flame in the eye and of the ridges on the skin of the hand. The star-shaped object is a section through a wart.

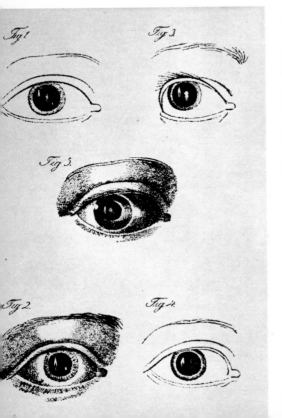
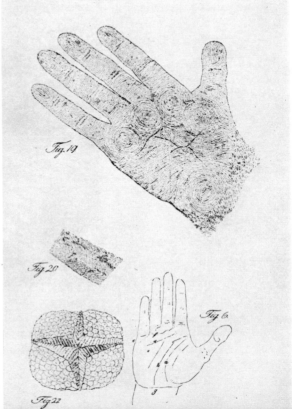

IT WAS in front of this building, the store of the American Fur Company on the small island of Mackinac in Lake Huron, that a 25-year-old French-Canadian, Alexis St Martin, was accidentally shot in the stomach from a distance of three feet, in the year 1822. The local doctor, called to the scene, gave him twenty minutes to live. Not only had clothing and wadding been driven into the wound, but the lung and stomach were protruding through the wound, and food was pumping out from a hole in the stomach.

By a freak of nature, the edges of the hole in the stomach attached themselves to the edges of the wound. This saved St Martin, for the wound could be dressed and the dirt could not enter the body cavity. But it left him with a permanent fistula, or opening into the stomach. The doctor, William Beaumont, when the county refused to support the boy, took him into his house.

To be exact, he was not a doctor: in frontier fashion, he had been licensed to practise on the strength of having acted as apprentice to a doctor, and this had been enough to get him a post as army surgeon. He was now a so-called 'Post-doctor'. His salary was $40 a month, and two to four rations daily. Three years passed before it struck him that he had in his house an unique opportunity for research. He wrote in his notebook:

'When he lies on the opposite side, I can look directly into the cavity of the stomach, and almost see the process of digestion . . . I have frequently suspended flesh, raw and wasted, and other substances into the perforation to ascertain the length of time required to digest each . . . This case affords an excellent opportunity for experimenting.'

The following January, he published papers on the time taken to digest various substances which he had lowered into the stomach on a silk thread, and experiments with gastric juice which he had extracted.

Below is the famous fistula of St Martin, as Beaumont portrayed it in his book on the gastric juice in 1833.

St Martin appears to have become somewhat exasperated by Beaumont's constant poking about in his interior, and when Beaumont took him to the city of Plattsburgh to show him off to the medical profession, he slipped away to Canada. It took Beaumont four years to locate him – St Martin was now married with two children – and a good deal of talk and money to get him back the 2,000 miles to Fort Crawford where Beaumont was now stationed. Two years later, he ran away again. Beaumont then contrived to get him enrolled in the army, and placed under his orders, so that he could pursue him as a deserter if he went over the hill another time. He lived to be 82 – fifteen years more than Beaumont attained.

Beaumont can claim to be the first American physiologist. His work, much of which remains standard, caused a sensation in Europe, where doctors did not look to the backwoods to find physiological advances.

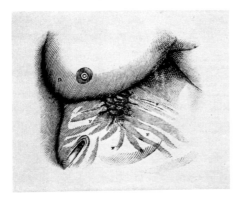

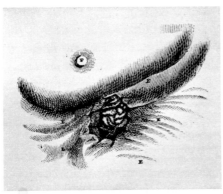

The hole in St Martin's stomach as drawn by *William Beaumont: (above) eighteen months after the wounding, and (below) seven years after. This historic fistula was a window onto the process of digestion.*

'WHY THINK, when you can experiment? Exhaust experiment and then think!' This was the oft-quoted dictum of Claude Bernard, who, more than anyone else, was the founder of modern experimental physiology. 'One must live in the laboratory,' he said. His was 'a dark, damp tannery', and most of his animals died of secondary diseases, not from his experiments. A visitor in 1859 gave this description of it: Bernard was standing before his animal table 'with his tall hat on, from beneath which escaped long locks of greying hair; round his neck was a muffler, which he scarcely ever took off, and his figure seemed a little bent, even at his age (46). His fingers were nonchalantly thrust into the open abdomen of a large dog, which was howling mournfully. He turned towards his visitor with a benevolent glance, asking him to wait a moment, and went on with his experiment.'

Bernard's wife, unfortunately, was a bigoted Catholic, a pet-lover and an ardent antivivisectionist. She was also intensely preoccupied with money. None of these qualifications fitted her for life as Bernard's wife. One can rather sympathize with her, however, when one reads how Bernard brought home to their small apartment one Sunday morning, 'a dog having an open wound in its side from which internal fluids were drawn off from time to time: a dog in a state of extreme emaciation, yet with a voracious appetite, pus running from its nostrils, coughing as it was led up and downstairs and suffering from diarrhoea, its faeces being of particular interest to the master of the house.'

Mme. Bernard stood it for another twenty years, then there was a legal separation.

'The most atrocious suffering which the imagination of man can conceive' must accompany death from curare poisoning, declared Bernard, after his experiments with this substance, a quantity of which he received as a gift in 1844.

In 1815, Watterton and Brodie had injected curare into an ass. It died. They then made an incision into its windpipe and inflated the lungs for two hours with bellows. The ass raised its head and looked round. The bellows were stopped, and it fell back as if dead. Artificial respiration was then continued for another two hours, and the ass got up none the worse. Its wounds healed and it became 'fat and balky'.

The fact is, as Bernard realized after trying the stuff on a number of animals, that curare acts at the junction of nerves and muscles, and blocks the nerve impulse. The victim is therefore unable to move a muscle, though completely conscious, and eventually dies from respiratory failure. 'Can one conceive of suffering more horrible than that of an intelligent being realizing the gradual loss of all its functions,' exclaimed Bernard with some relish, 'and finding itself, as it were, entombed alive in a dead body!'

The experiment furnished a final proof of Haller's doctrine of the irritability of muscle. However, Bernard's fame depends not on this work, but on three great contributions to physiology, which I shall now briefly summarize.

Pancreatic digestion: Dissecting rabbits which had been fed on a 100% meat diet, he noticed that the intestines were filled with a white substance – emulsified fats – from a point about 40 cm. below the exit from the stomach. He reasoned that some substance must reach the stomach from the pancreas, the ducts of which enter at this point – a substance which could emulsify fats. To test this theory he tried to depancreatize dogs, but in the absence of sterile routines, his attempts failed. Had he succeeded, he would have made them diabetic, and who knows whether he might not have discovered insulin.

The pancreatic juice also converts starch to sugar and digests proteins, but Bernard never felt he had succeeded in showing this. But he did establish that digestion is not wholly a matter of gastric action.

Glycogenic function of the liver: After feeding a dog on a meal containing neither starch nor sugar, Bernard found sugar in the blood leaving the liver. Thus he proved the glycogenic (sugar-making) power of the liver. The drama in this was that up to this time it was strongly held that the body could only break down substances, not build them up.

Bernard, as a result of this discovery, regarded the liver as an 'organ of internal secretion' and later pointed out that the thyroid and adrenals were also organs of internal secretion. The term offended those who could not see how a gland unprovided with ducts to the blood-stream could secrete.

In a larger sense, the real importance of all this work was that it was the first attempt to explore directly the fate of foods after entering the body. Prior to this, it had been like 'trying to tell what is happening inside a house, by watching what goes in at the door and what comes out of the chimney'.

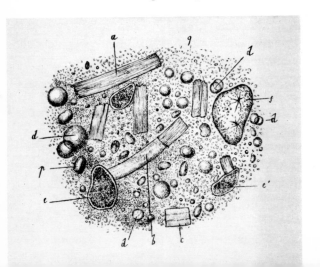

Bernard's painstaking analysis
*of the digestive process was largely carried out
on dogs. This drawing details the contents of
a dog's pylorus after a mixed meal.*

Bernard demonstrating *the function of the vasomotor nerves in his laboratory at the Sorbonne.
In this reconstruction of the scene by the painter Lhermitte, nearly fifty years later, Bernard is about
to apply electrical stimulation to the vasomotor nerves of a hare; the effect would probably be observed
in an alteration in blood flow into the basin.*

Bernard also discovered the existence of the *vasomotor nerves,* which constrict the blood vessels and reduce the blood supply to the corresponding part of the body – or which relax and increase it, as in blushing.

There is no space to tell of Bernard's countless other experiments, which included many experiments on himself. Let me add only that in 1848 he founded the first society for the study of 'phenomena pertaining to the science of life'.

Physiology had been launched, but one cannot say this without mentioning that enchanting personality Carl Ludwig, whose physiological institute at Leipzig became a Mecca for students from all over the world, after 1865. It is estimated that 200 prominent scientists were once his students. He is credited with no major discoveries, though he invented useful techniques, including one for maintaining organs alive outside the body. He was genial, kindly, unselfish, a passionate lover of music, and a skilled draughtsman. And perhaps he was more creative than history supposes, for most of the work he did, he published solely under the name of the students who aided him in it, a rare thing in science.

WHEN X-RAYS were discovered by Roentgen about 1895, they were at first little more than an amusing stunt with a possible interest for surgeons. But a 26-year-old Harvard graduate immediately realized that they could aid the research physiologist: he would use them to study the waves of contraction within the stomach. His name was Walter Cannon. To make the stomach more clearly visible he decided to mix bismuth, which blocks X-rays, with food and feed it to a cat. He drew these diagrams of the contractions of a cat's stomach while it is digesting – the first pictures of their kind ever made.

But in 1895 he noticed that when the cat was alarmed or disturbed, the waves vanished: as his cats were often alarmed at their situation, it seemed a serious check to his studies. He found that there were also other signs: gastric secretion stopped, and the rate of heart-beat increased, for instance. Then, one wakeful night, the idea flashed through his mind 'that the bodily changes in fear and rage could be interpreted as preparations for extreme effort in flight'.

This observation provided a starting point for a lifelong study of the relationships between the endocrine glands and the emotions. His claim that the secretion of adrenalin rose when the sympathetic nervous system was stimulated was challenged by two Cleveland doctors. Cannon, to justify his position, worked out a technique for removing all the nerves supplying the heart, while keeping it beating. He found that, even with all the nerves cut, the animal's heart speeded up when it was excited. Obviously, some chem-ical stimulant must be reaching it through the blood. In this way he came to discover sympathin, which he regarded as a hormone, but which is in fact secreted by the nerve endings. (Actually, there are two sympathins, one which dilates the blood vessels, and one which constricts them.)

Cannon propounded the doctrine that organisms are so constructed that they constantly seek to return to a stable state, known as the doctrine of homeostasis. Thus he carried further a dictum of Claude Bernard, who said that a free existence depends upon the stability of the 'internal environment'. This notion of an internal environment has proved very stimulating.

These are but a few highlights from the story of nineteenth-century physiology. Everywhere physiologists were isolating body-fluids, such as the cerebrospinal fluid, the lymph, pus and blood, and studying them. Work was done on the kidneys, on the mechanism of muscle contraction, on the senses of smell, hearing and vision. Of the advances in the understanding of the nervous system I have already told.

The nineteenth century also saw the first real progress in solving the most obstinate biological problem of all – that of how the egg develops into a complex organism.

Early use of X-rays: *Cannon's tracings of a cat's stomach.*

It was difficult to think of methods by which the subject might be approached, but towards the end of the nineteenth century, several ingenious experimental ideas were devised. The facts which they disclosed seemed, however, to make the matter more mysterious rather than less.

Hans Driesch, then 24, was working at the Marine Zoology Station at Naples when he decided to repeat a curious experiment performed three years earlier, in 1888, by Wilhelm Roux. Roux was influenced by Weismann's idea that in the egg lie units, which he called primordia, each of which is ready to develop into a complex organ. The egg (he held) is a mosaic of undeveloped bits. To test this, he took frog's eggs after their first division, and killed one of the two cells with a red-hot needle. He expected that if the remaining cell developed at all it would develop into half a creature. And indeed, it formed a half tadpole. It seemed that Weismann was right.

Driesch, however, used a slightly different method, employing the eggs of sea-urchins – more readily available to him at Naples – and shaking them at the two-cell stage until the two cells separated. Next day he found to his amazement that each had formed a perfect sea-urchin larva, somewhat smaller than usual. Not only Driesch was amazed: the entire biological world was excited. For here was implicit the ancient controversy between preformation and epigenesis, but with a new twist. For even the epigenesists had not supposed that the egg could adapt to a change of circumstances as radical as the loss of half its initial material. Thus, while disproving preformation, it made epigenesis more mysterious than ever.

Driesch found the result 'uncanny' – although Siamese twins are an example of the same effect – and as he continued to pursue the subject, it seemed to become uncannier. For example, if he compressed the cells be-

Siamese twins *had puzzled biologists for centuries, until Driesch threw light on twinning in 1891.*

255

tween two microscope slides, they grew out, necessarily, into a flat disc and not a sphere. But the moment the pressure was removed, the disc rounded up into a ball and carried on normally. Again, he managed to press two of the scarcely-visible eggs together until they fused. The giant egg resulting grew into a single giant larva.

It seemed to him that the normal laws of nature were transgressed by such purposive behaviour, which resembled human purposive behaviour, and concluded that 'in the embryo, and similarly in other vital phenomena, a factor is active which is fundamentally different from all physico-chemical forces, and which directs events in anticipation of the goal.' This factor he called – reviving a term of Aristotle's – *entelechy,* that is, 'carrying its goal within itself'. He seems to have thought of it as a 'life force'. This was vitalism, as against the mechanistic assumptions of Roux.

Roux's experiment was particularly irritating to Driesch because here the force of entelechy seemed to have abdicated. But eventually he showed that, in the right circumstances, even the frog's eggs would develop, like those of sea-urchins, into whole creatures, despite maltreatment.

Driesch conceded that the environment exerted some effect on development. Indeed, he showed that if eggs are immersed in a calcium-free liquid, the resulting cells fail to cohere, and therefore do not form an embryo. Again, mechanical damage to the protoplasm of the egg is not fully repaired. But he

Jacques Loeb *produced sea-urchin larvae from unfertilized eggs. The egg (top left) is put into a weak solution of saponin and sea water, and eight minutes later (middle, top) it has formed the membrane which is a sign that the egg is fertilized. If it is taken out of the solution at this stage, washed, and put into strong sea water for half an hour, it will develop into a normal larva. Otherwise the protoplasm dissolves, as remaining drawings show.*

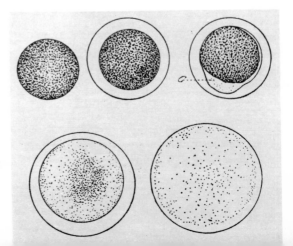

concluded that life, or at least the development of the embryo, 'is not a specialized arrangement of inorganic events; biology therefore is not applied physics and chemistry. Life is something apart . . .' He became steadily more mystical, and abandoned biology for philosophy and parapsychology.

In 1901 the mechanists again scored a victory, when Jacques Loeb developed a method of bringing the sea-urchin's egg to the larval stage without it being fertilized. Some twenty years before, Oscar Hertwig had observed that on being treated with strychnine these eggs surround themselves with a membrane, just as they do when they are fertilized. Picking up this clue, Loeb found that if the eggs were placed in an acid solution, then in sea-water of unusual salinity, and then in ordinary sea-water, development started. He brought eggs to the larval stage and later succeeded in bringing them to adulthood. Soon Bataillon, a Frenchman, found that frog's eggs would develop into tadpoles if pricked by a needle.

Once again, excitement was intense. The switch which launched development having been found, the rest of the process would soon become clear. Loeb produced a simple chemical theory, and wrote his book *A Mechanistic Conception of Life,* in which he over-generalized wildly, and ignored the inconvenient exceptions to his statements. The larve thus parthenogenetically produced are not, despite his claims, invariably typical, and the mystery was far from solved.

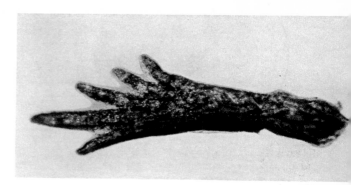

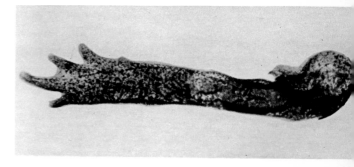

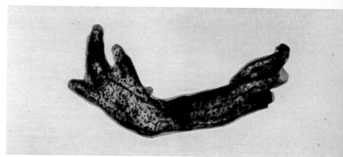

Toads parthenogenetically produced *are often physically imperfect. The hind foot, for instance, instead of the normal five toes (top), can have anything from three toes to six.*

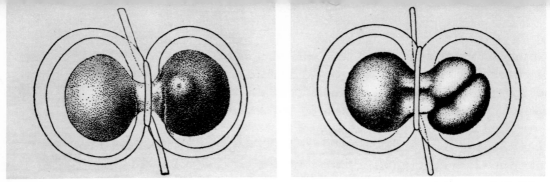

Spemann's ingenious experiment *with the newt's egg. Where the hair confines the nucleus to one half (left, in the one-cell, and right, in the two-cell stage), that half develops normally while the other becomes a confused mass of intestinal organs.*

THE SON OF A SMALL PUBLISHER in Stuttgart, Hans Spemann, devised a new mode of attack: transplantation. He began by picking up the work of Driesch.

Taking from a baby the finest of possible hairs, he looped it round a newt's egg, and constricted it into hour-glass shape. In some cases, the egg developed into two complete embryos; in others, one half developed normally, the other into a confused mass of intestinal organs. Observing closely, he found that when the constriction ran through a dark patch on the egg known as the 'grey crescent' development of both segments was normal. But when the crescent was wholly in one segment, only that segment developed normally. Presumably, the crescent contained some factor vital to complete development.

When eggs develop, they form a hollow ball of cells; then one side of the ball turns inward, as if one had pressed the surface with a thumb, and becomes a tube which finally reaches the opposite wall, where a hole forms. The tube thus formed is the primitive gut, the newly-made hole the anus, and the hole at the other end, the mouth. Spemann observed that this turning inward (known as invagination) always started from the region of the grey crescent, and he began to think of it as an 'inducer' region. To test this idea, he therefore decided to see if he could cut out this vital region and transplant it elsewhere. He invented a micro-pipette and a fine glass needle, and using his hair-loop to hold the egg, he contrived, in 1921, after many attempts, to cut out the inducer from the embryo of a light-coloured variety of salamander and to implant it in the future belly-area of a dark-coloured one. Both inducers worked: two invaginations occurred. Siamese-twin salamanders resulted. And Spemann in due course received a Nobel prize.

Spemann assumed the inducer was a group of specialized cells, secreting some subtle 'organizer' substance. But later Waddington discovered that a blue dye, methylene blue, would produce the same effect, and confusion reigned once more.

Spemann's second big contribution arose from an observation of 1891, that, when the eye is formed, an 'eye-cup' develops from underlying tissue and soon after, a lens develops opposite it in the skin-tissue. Spemann removed the eye-cup of a frog (*Rana fusca*) and showed that the lens failed to develop. Apparently the eye-cup *induced* the lens.

(In choosing *Rana fusca* he was lucky, for he subsequently found that in the edible frog, *Rana esculenta,* the lens forms anyway.)

Spemann also perceived the possibility of a somewhat different experimental approach. He cut out one part of an embryo and implanted it in another position to see what would become of it. Embryologists term that part of an embryo which will normally form brain 'presumptive brain', and that part which will normally form belly 'presumptive belly'. Spemann transposed presumptive brain with presumptive belly, and found that each became the kind of tissue which was required by its new environment.

It seemed, therefore, that the cell, before it became specialized, was completely open to any line of development, and that its future depended on some influence from surrounding cells. Further such experiments showed that a point in development is reached when such 'equipotentiality' is lost. Thus a limb-bud, transplanted elsewhere, remains a limb-bud. There is no going back.

This was not too hard to understand until a one-time student of Spemann's, Oscar Schotté, carried out an experiment which had a more surprising result. He managed to transfer presumptive belly from a frog embryo into the presumptive mouth area of a salamander. The result was that a mouth developed, but it was a frog's mouth, not a salamander's! (The two look quite different.) So now it seemed that when the environment ordered 'form a mouth' the supposed belly-cells hunted among their library of blueprints and found one marked 'plan for mouth' which they substituted for the 'plan for belly'.

Development thus seems to depend upon a delicate interplay between potentialities within the cell and influences on each cell from neighbouring cells. Subsequent advances in embryology and genetics were to show that this was plausible, but at the time it seemed difficult to credit the cell with such extraordinary potentialities.

Spemann himself, though he did so much to establish the idea that embryonic development is a physico-chemical process and not an inexplicable manifestation of entelechy, never ceased to wonder, when he constricted an egg and obtained two embryos, whether his thread had also separated two minds from each other.

From these groping attempts to study development arose a technique which was to prove of outstanding value in many other fields: tissue culture.

IN 1917 AN AMERICAN named Ross Harrison was recommended for the Nobel prize, but the committee eventually decided to award no prize for physiology that year. His name was again put forward in 1933, but was rejected on the strange ground that his discovery was now too old to qualify – strange in view of the long periods which have elapsed in the case of other Nobel awards.

The major biological discovery which put him in the running was that cells can be induced to grow outside the body. In 1907 he took fragments of nerve tissue from frog embryos and placed them in clotted lymph: they remained alive, and through the microscope he watched them gradually extend outgrowths. (He went on to do major work on nerve regeneration and the role of nerves in embryonic development.)

Alexis Carrel, a Frenchman who made major advances in the treatment of wounds, took up the method using blood plasma instead of lymph; by constantly removing the waste products excreted by the cells, he was able to keep a fragment of chicken's heart muscle alive for many years. All this time it continued to beat! Thus he proved also that the beating of the heart is inspired by the muscles and not by central nervous control, a question long debated. He received a Nobel prize in 1912.

Keeping a chicken's heart muscle alive *for many years in this apparatus, Alexis Carrel proved that heart-beats are initiated by muscle, not the central nervous system.*

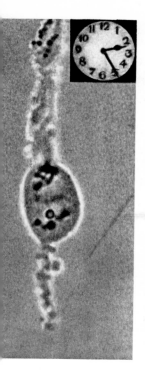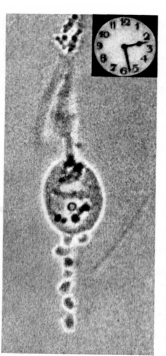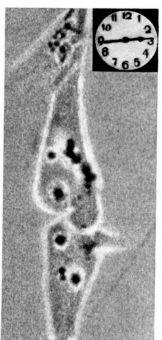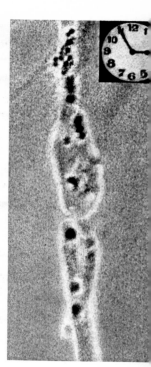

The first pictures by microcinematography to show the division of a cell, taken by R.G. Canti in the early 1930s. The clock shows how quickly the process is completed.

Thus biology acquired a tool of incalculable importance. Once tissues could be kept alive in 'tissue culture', experiments could be performed on them without the complications introduced by the rest of the animal.

F.S.P. Strangeways took up tissue culture in 1917 to further his work on arthritis, and joined forces with R.G. Canti, who took the first microcinematography pictures of cell division ever taken. At the Institute which he founded it was shown that not merely tissues, but whole organs, could be cultured.

But one refinement was still lacking. For many purposes biologists desired cells which would all have the same genetic constitution. Hence, they wanted to be able to culture a single cell, and thus to know that all the cells resulting from its division would be of one family. But isolated cells, placed in culture, refused to divide. Biologists varied the medium, the temperature, the acidity and constitution of the nutrient medium in vain. Finally Wilton Earle at the National Cancer Institute speculated that the cells might need a medium which had been conditioned in some way by themselves. So he enclosed single cells in finebore tubes, so that any substance they might emit would remain concentrated near them. As these pictures show, he soon produced a rich proliferation of identical cells.

The next problem was to grow cells in really large quantities. After another five years' work, Earle was growing several pounds at a time.

But beyond each advance lies a new problem. Biologists would like to grow cells on a completely artificial medium, instead of one containing blood plasma, in which there may be unknown components. Currently, a brief-lived success is being obtained with media containing eighty or more ingredients.

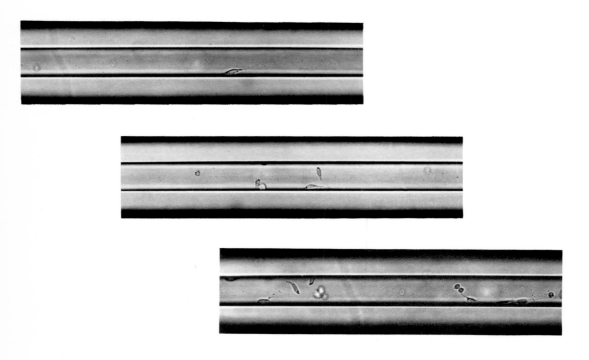

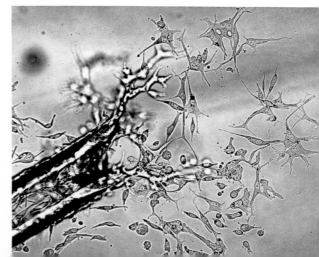

A single cell, *enclosed in plasma in a fine-bore tube (top), has multiplied after 65 hours to six cells, and 48 hours later to twelve (one on the left is dividing). On the 28th day of growth, countless cells migrate from the open end of the tube into a culture medium. (x 200)*

THE INVISIBLE DANCE

Fischer, Gowland Hopkins, Stanley

PERHAPS THE MOST surprising chemical discovery of the nineteenth century was made by the 28-year-old Friedrich Wöhler in 1828. He identified the substance which was formed on heating ammonium cyanate as urea – but urea was already known to be present in urine as a breakdown-product from food. This reaction synthesized an organic substance! Up to this time it had been firmly held that living substances were in some essential way different from non-living ('inorganic') substances. The latter could be made in the laboratory, but the synthesis of the former depended, it was held, on some mysterious vital property. Wöhler's discovery shattered this whole conception. Furthermore, four years previous to this discovery, Wöhler had found that if benzoic acid is given by mouth it reappears in the urine as the rather more complex hippuric acid – proving that the body can upon occasion synthesize more from less complex substances, which was also contrary to accepted ideas. (This period was Wöhler's heyday, for in 1827 and 1828 he isolated the previously unknown metals, aluminium and beryllium.)

There had always been 'vitalists' who held, in opposition to people like Descartes, that the body could never be wholly explained on a mechanical cause-and-effect basis. Now the controversy was re-animated: this was the central issue in nineteenth-century biological thinking. The idea that life-processes were open to explanation released a great wave of effort; and in the twentieth century the biochemical bases of physiology and genetics were to become the outstanding field of achievement.

Among the orthodox, however, the whole idea of a chemistry of life aroused suspicion, and nowhere more so than in America, where Liebig's book *Animal Chemistry* was published in 1845. As Charles Caldwell, the professor of natural sciences at the University of Philadelphia, declared: 'When the chemist declares that the same laws which direct the crystallisation of spars, nitre and Glauber's salts, direct also the *crystallisation* of man, he must pardon me if I neither understand him, nor believe him.' How one can disbelieve, or believe, what one does not understand, he did not explain. How short-sighted he was, we shall now see.

For the first time, *students of chemistry were able to gain*

'GOD HAS ORDERED all his Creation by Weight and Measure.' These words are written over the door of the laboratory seen above, the first chemical laboratory for students in the world. It was established, after a long and bitter struggle, by Justus von Liebig, the man who virtually created the science of

xperience of practical work, when Carl Justus von Liebig established this laboratory at Giessen in 1842.

biochemistry, the chemistry of living things. His many students established the tradition of eminence in chemistry for which Germany was famous until 1939. Wöhler, actually two years Liebig's senior, became his friend and pupil.

It was in 1838 that Liebig, after making important discoveries in inorganic chemistry (including that of chloroform), turned to the chemistry of life, and showed that the heat of animal bodies is due to the combustion of the food they eat and is not 'innate' – i. e. just something they mysteriously happen to have, as was strongly held by most doctors at the time. It was he who classified foods as carbohydrates (such as starch and sugar), fats, and proteins – the classification we still use. He taught, too, that plants derive their food from the carbon dioxide and ammonia in the air and that when they die and decay, these substances return to the air, so that there is an endless cycle. One practical result was that Liebig introduced artificial fertilizers into agriculture. (In 1888 it was found that plants obtain nitrogen from the soil, thanks to specialized bacteria which live in nodules on their roots, which explains why nitrogenous fertilizers are also effective).

Because of his success in analysing problems once supposed to be beyond the reach of chemistry, Liebig felt strongly that decay was a purely chemical process, and, as we have seen, it took Pasteur years to disprove this.

Liebig invented much new chemical apparatus, notably the condenser which can be seen in every chemical lab today. He was given a barony for his pains in 1845.

He introduced the important concept of metabolism – the chemical processes of building-up and breaking-down substances within the body. The notion of the body being composed simply of chemical bits and pieces, and manufacturing those it wants from those it doesn't want, was one which people found very difficult to accept. With the wisdom of hindsight, one can see that it was Spallanzani who laid the first brick, when he showed that digestion can be carried on outside the body, in a glass dish.

The problem which Liebig's followers chiefly attacked, therefore, was: what happens to the food one eats? The calorific, or energy-providing, value of a large number of foods was investigated. At the same time, the new biochemical approach was applied to a great range of other body substances. What were they basically made of? Chief among these investigators was Ernst Hoppé-Seyler, who explored the chemistry of blood, milk, pus, cartilage and other body materials. In 1862 he obtained the red colouring-matter of blood – haemoglobin – in pure, crystalline form for the first time, and showed that it links loosely with oxygen (which makes it an ideal vehicle for picking up oxygen in the lungs and surrendering it to the muscles) but that it binds firmly with carbon monoxide (which is what makes the latter so lethal to man).

There was a host of such investigations to be made, before the groundwork would have been laid for the great theoretical advances of the early twentieth century.

P. Zuber   Tönnies   Steiner   Hofart Ekstrand   Koenigs   Pauli   Burkhardt   Peder   Eisenberg   Stender   Niggl   Wislicenus
           O. Fischer   Prof. Volhard   Prof. Baeyer   E. Fischer   Voit   Sendtner

Winter-Semester 77/78.

Two great chemists, *one inorganic and one organic, sit next to one another in this group. Seated third from the left, with legs crossed, is Adolf von Baeyer, in whose Munich laboratory this photograph was taken. On his left Emil Fischer, who analysed and synthesized many of the proteins.*

SEATED third from the right in this group, taken in the winter of 1877, is Emil Fischer, the third great German biochemist of the nineteenth century. The scene is the *Verbrennungszimmer* of Baeyer's lab in Munich. Baeyer, one of the great inorganic chemists, was the first to synthesize indigo. Both men won Nobel prizes soon after the award was founded, in 1901.

Fischer's great contribution was to give precision to the concept of *proteins*. He showed that this great range of substances, so different in appear-ance and function, is constituted from some twenty building-blocks, known as amino-acids: these link into long chains. Fischer, whose forte was deter-mining the chemical structure of substances, also worked out the formula of a host of chemical compounds, from the caffeine which gives coffee its

267

punch, to veronal, the hypnotic, and managed to synthesize many of them in the laboratory.

But the precise structure of particular proteins continued to defy analysis. It seemed likely that the order in which the amino acids were assembled had something to do with it, for clearly the basic units could be grouped in many ways, just as the letters of the alphabet can be used to spell out many words. But, whatever the order, how could this account for the tremendous range of properties exhibited? Proteins can be rigid, like bone; tough yet flexible, like sinew; rubbery, like muscle; they can catalyse reactions as do enzymes; and so on. The answer did not emerge for another half century.

Their marked insolubility and resistance to melting suggested a huge molecule – today we know that even the smallest is relatively enormous, with a mass 5,000 times that of the hydrogen atom, while the largest is 50 times as big again – but at this date there was no way of measuring the molecular weight. Indeed it was hard even to get the proteins out of the living material of which they formed part. Usually they appeared as slimy messes which gummed up filters, while the oversize molecules were so fragile that chemical attack merely shattered them to fragments.

But in 1926 an enterprising Swede devised an incredible apparatus which broke this technical bottleneck – the ultracentrifuge.

This Brancusi-like object formed the core of Svedberg's invention. Here it is seen contrasted with the simpler version used in his first oil-

Small but massively strong, *these devices are the heart of the ultracentrifuge, for they hold the cells which contain the liquid to be treated. The one on the left is from an air-turbine machine, the other from an earlier version powered by an oil turbine.*

turbine centrifuge. The idea of the centrifuge was far from new. One still sees in many labs a simple crank with which a pair of test-tubes can be swung round in circles, so that centrifugal force will throw the heavy particles in a solution to the bottom of the tube, separating them from the liquid. Svedberg realized that if one could develop a sufficiently strong centrifugal force, one could separate particles differing only very slightly in mass. He succeeded in devising a turbine which would spin the rotor, in which the sample was placed, at speeds of up to 45,000 r.p.m., developing a force 100,000 times as strong as gravity. By 1934 the speed had been pushed up to 900,000 r.p.m. (Eventually two Americans, Beams and Pickels, achieved speeds of a million r.p.m. and forces of 1,200,000 times gravity. Beams's ambition is to reach one million revolutions a *second*.)

Here is the oil-turbine ultra-centrifuge lab at Uppsala, where Svedberg worked. As he devised more and more powerful equipment, the building became more and more crowded until even the lavatories and washrooms were encroached upon. Heavy walls had to be built for, at these fantastic speeds, the rotor was liable to burst like a bomb, after a few runs.

But to spin the rotor was not the only problem. Particles of molecular size diffuse among one another by heat energy. Svedberg realized that the various molecules present, depending on their mass, would take up positions within the rotor which represented a compromise between the two forces acting on them: the problem was to observe these strata in the liquid while it was

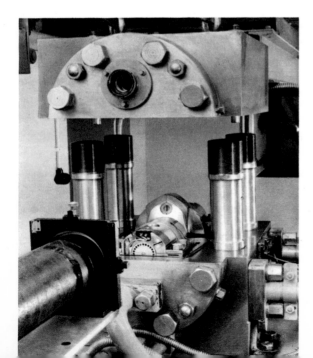

Secured by four thick steel bolts, *the head of this ultracentrifuge at Uppsala is raised to show the rotor. Creating centrifugal force over 100,000 times as strong as gravity, the apparatus must be very solidly built to minimize the danger of a burst.*

actually spinning at a fantastic speed. Some fancy mathematics was then called for to deduce the molecular weights.

Svedberg's first results with the ultracentrifuge caused great surprise. The protein molecules he was investigating turned out to be all of the same size. Like most people, Svedberg had supposed that proteins were colloids – glue-like substances in which a liquid is dispersed in droplets through a solid, or another liquid, or vice versa. One would therefore have expected to get out molecules of at least two different sizes.

By a stroke of luck, the substance which Svedberg chose for his first studies was haemoglobin, the red colouring-matter of blood. It turned out to have a molecular weight 16,700 times that of hydrogen, and four times as much in the blood of higher mammals. Had Svedberg chosen for his first investigations a substance like cellulose, which has long-chain molecules of varying lengths, his results would have been baffling and inconclusive. As it was, he went on to study other blood-pigments, such as the haemocyanins (the blue pigment in the blood of molluscs), and erythrins from lichens; then he looked at enzymes – the fermentative agents of cells. These had become a matter of intense interest, as I shall now relate.

Berzelius, the great Swedish chemist, forecast 'a new force producing chemical activity . . . which is undoubtedly more widely dispersed than we have imagined and whose nature is still concealed . . .' He called it catalytic force. This was in 1835: ninety years were to pass before the full truth of prophecy was realized.

The fact that certain substances would speed up specific inorganic chemical reactions had been noticed about 1812. And in 1830 a similar effect had been noticed in the biological field: starch will become converted to glucose without heating if fermented barley extract is added. Two years later the catalytic element in the barley had been isolated and named *diastase*, i.e. 'separating substance', because it separated dextrin from the envelopes of the starch-grains. This was in fact the first enzyme, though the word was not proposed until much later.

Enzymes, as we now realize, are more than agents which speed reactions. The kind of chemical reactions which take place within the cell will *only* take place when the enzyme is present, and the speed of reaction depends upon the amount of enzyme. Thus they are the taps by which intracellular reactions are turned on and off or regulated. The study of them is crucial for the understanding of cellular metabolism and other biochemical reactions.

The discovery of diastase was followed by the discovery of many other 'diastases' in plants, and of animal enzymes, such as pepsin and trypsin in the gastric juice. Today many hundreds are known and scores of groups of workers are studying their mode of action.

Jöns Jakob Berzelius, *professor of chemistry at the Caroline Institute, Stockholm. In 1835 he described and named, with prophetic insight, the force we know as catalysis — the force that regulates or speeds up certain chemical reactions.*

The usual nineteenth-century argument ensued as to whether fermentation was a 'vital' or a chemical process. Finally it became clear that though the enzymes are not themselves endowed with life, they are manufactured by living structures, viz. by the cells. The question, as usual, had proved to present a false choice. The point was finally proved in 1897, when Büchner showed that extracts from yeast cells would catalyse glucose, even though no actual cells were present.

Pure chance gave Büchner his niche in the hall of fame. He was supposed to be investigating ribose, a sugar which was the only constituent of any real value in the once-famous Liebig's meat extract. But he had conceived the idea that possibly proteins of medical value might be found in bacteria or yeast, and he gave up his vacation to investigate the point. Having squeezed a large quantity of yeast and obtained a brown, treacly liquid, the question arose, how to preserve it, for it rapidly went bad. A lab assistant, remembering how sugar preserves fruit, suggested adding a large quantity of sugar. This done, to their astonishment the brown liquid promptly started to convert the sugar into alcohol!

Not yet thirty, *Richard Willstaetter (seen above in his laboratory at Munich) had already determined the structure of atropine and cocaine. His Nobel prize was still fourteen years in the future.*

A casualty of war: *the laboratory of von Baeyer (shown also on p. 267), where much work on enzymes had been done under von Baeyer and his successors Willstaetter and Hans Fischer, was destroyed by bombing in 1945.*

IT WAS DINNER TIME. The 34-year-old chemist poured on to his young wife's plate a present: a cascade of coloured crystals, sparkling like jewels. He had succeeded in preparing pure crystals of the green colouring matter of plants, chlorophyll. Before long Hans Fischer had determined its structure. The year was 1906, nine years after Büchner's discovery. The young man, who was named Willstaetter, had already discovered novocaine and proved the structure of atropine. Now he was working on plant pigments. When, in 1911, he was made director of the Kaiser Wilhelm Chemical Institute, he investigated the colouring-matter of the flowers which bloomed in its decorative beds. Astonishingly, he found that the blue of cornflowers is due to the same substance which causes the red of cherries and poppies. Subtle variations in acidity regulate the colouring effect.

But it was in the field of enzyme research that he was to achieve his greatest fame. Until this time, enzymes had been thought of merely as agents of fermentation and digestion. Not until the '30s did their importance as cellular regulators become clear and work on them start in earnest. No satisfactory methods for purifying them existed, and without pure preparations their biological effect could not be accurately determined. Willstaetter was largely responsible for the change.

He published the results of ten years' work in 1928. The last four years had been carried out under extraordinary difficulties, for in 1924 he resigned his professorship in protest against a Jew being refused a university professorship on racial grounds. His successor, Wieland, kept his team of workers in being and they brought their results every night to Willstaetter's home.

With patient ingenuity, Willstaetter and his team chipped away at their impure enzyme preparations, removing first one substance, then another, by repeated solution in different substances and re-fractionation. They made best progress with peroxidase, an enzyme of common occurrence in plants. Finally they had so little substance left, that ordinary analyses showed neither protein nor carbohydrate present – yet the solution still catalysed the appropriate reaction. Willstaetter thought that he must have discovered some new class of substance unknown to chemistry. He began to wonder whether some new force was involved.

But, at precisely this moment, three thousand miles away, an American named Sumner was crystallizing another enzyme.

As Claude Bernard once said, much depends on whether one is lucky in choosing one's material. Sumner was lucky: he chose urease, which he obtained from the jack-bean. But he was also skilful and determined. Enzymes are fragile and elusive things, and break up if any but the mildest reagents and lowest temperatures are used. They will not crystallize unless the

James B. Sumner, *whose crystallization of the enzyme urease won him a Nobel prize.*

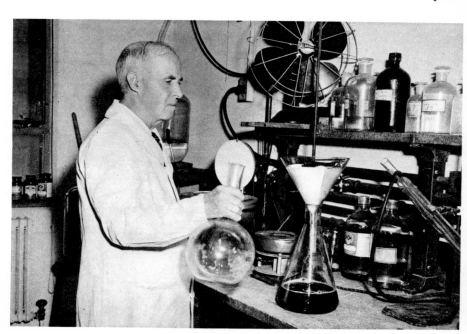

strength of the solution is just right. Sumner used to put his preparations on the window-sill to keep them cool, and then pray for cold weather. After various fruitless attempts, he had the idea of substituting acetic acid for the alcohol normally used as a solvent, and, after filtering, placed the filtered mixture in a newly-acquired ice-chest.

Next morning, he examined the liquid and was disappointed to see that it was quite clear. The usual precipitate was absent. However, he looked at it through the microscope, and was excited to see crystals of a shape he had never seen before. Redissolving these, he tested for urease activity. Yes, they were urease. Then he tested for proteins. Yes, they were proteins. 'I then telephoned my wife,' he relates, 'and said: "I have crystallized urease."' His announcement was greeted with frank disbelief: the thing was impossible.

Sumner had decided to tackle the supposedly impossible task of isolating an enzyme in 1917, when he was 30. He was told he was foolish, but he felt that he was getting nowhere and that his only hope was to gamble on a long shot. When he began to analyse the jack-bean he found so many substances in it he became discouraged, and several times abandoned his quest, which bore fruit in 1926. As a boy he had had his left arm amputated, which, as he was left-handed, was a severe handicap, but with immense determination he trained himself to use his right hand. (When he eventually received the Nobel prize, King Gustaf of Sweden was more interested in how he managed to serve at tennis than in his hormone.)

Sumner's methods were simpler than Willstaetter's and he was able to obtain large enough quantities of crystals to analyse and to show that urease was indeed a protein. Soon after, John H. Northrop crystallized pepsin, trypsin and chemotrypsin, which also seemed to be proteins. All enzymes which have been investigated since have also proved to be proteins.

Willstaetter would not accept this: he declared that the protein molecule was just a vehicle which carried the mysterious enzyme. The vitalists also took up arms again, saying it was 'unphysiological' to separate enzymes from cells: only work on undamaged cells was valuable. The matter remained open, despite attempts by Northrop to prove the purity of his extracts, and twenty years passed before the Nobel prize authorities felt confident enough to award Sumner and Northrop the prize which they richly deserved.

Driven from Germany by the Nazis, Willstaetter died during the war in exile, a broken man. In 1945 Fischer, broken-hearted at the destruction of his lab by the mass raids on Munich, committed suicide.

It was purification which revealed how highly specific enzymes are: with few exceptions, each will catalyse one reaction and one only. Between 1937, when only a handful of pure enzymes had been obtained, and 1957 upwards of 500 had been purified to some extent.

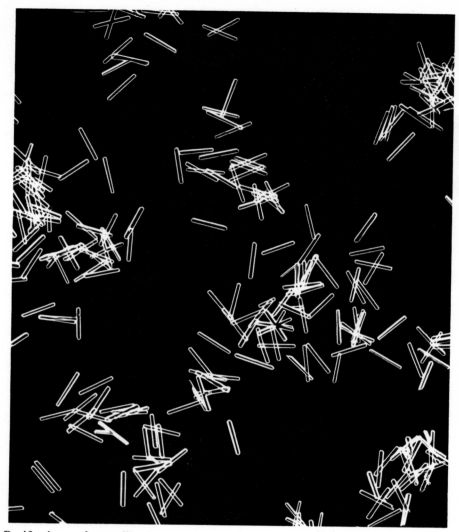

Purification and crystallization *are the essential first steps in the study of enzymes and in determining the reactions they catalyse. These are the crystals of trypsin, an enzyme in the pancreatic secretion which breaks down the food proteins; they were obtained by John H. Northrop.*

The real significance of these studies of enzymes was that they made it possible for the first time to trace the complex sequences of reactions which take place within the cell, and by which it maintains itself. Since each enzyme catalyses one reaction only, to identify the enzymes present in a structure is to identify the reactions occurring. Simple chemistry shows in which order they must occur, if the known raw materials are to be converted into the known end-product.

The father of cell chemistry,
*Otto Warburg, is here seen (left)
with K. Lohmann at a biochemical
conference in Berlin in 1959.*

THE STUDY OF CELL CHEMISTRY was put on its feet by the German chemist, Otto Warburg, whose discovery of the 'yellow enzymes' came just after his Nobel award in 1931, for investigations of other enzymes. (His best-known contribution was the discovery that cancer cells maintain themselves by a different sequence of reactions from normal cells, and can dispense with free oxygen, obtaining it instead from sugar. This held out the hope that some chemical substance could be found which would block the reactions of tumour cells without damaging normal cells – a hope not yet fulfilled, however.)

The key to cell-metabolism is the series of reactions by which sugar (glucose) is split into two molecules of lactic acid, and then converted to carbon dioxide and water. The sequence was uncertain until, in the 1930s, Hans Krebs, a pupil of Warburg's, solved the problem, showing that there is a continuous cycle of operations in twelve steps, the end-products of which provide the raw material for a repetition of the process.

The splitting of molecules, however, involves the expenditure of energy. The question which long baffled biochemists was: where did the energy for these reactions come from? Lohmann, in 1929, found that the splitting of sugar would not occur unless there was present an unstable, hitherto unknown substance, now known as ATP.

ATP has the unique property of storing energy in a form which the cell can utilize. As it gives it up, it changes to ADP. The 'Krebs cycle' stores the energy provided by the oxidizing of fats and carbohydrates in the form of ATP.

Since then, ATP has been found to be universally distributed in nature, being found in micro-organisms, as well as in plants and animals of every kind. The reactions into which ATP and the enzymes enter also generally require third parties, known as co-enzymes, and these are derived from vitamins. Thus the importance of vitamins is explained. They provide molecular groups which the body cannot synthesise, and which are needed because they complete the lock-and-key patterns on which the various cellular reactions depend. A. Szent-Györgi put this piece of the puzzle in place in 1940, when he showed that this was also the role of an odd substance which Miller had discovered in 1931, and had named Bios II (see p. 285).

In addition to making these reactions possible, ATP provides the energy for muscle contraction. The bundles of fibres which constitute muscle are made up of a complex protein called actomyosin. It can be shown in the test-tube that actomyosin contracts when ATP is added to it, the ATP being decomposed in the process.

A team headed by W. E. McElroy has shown yet a third role for ATP: it provides the energy for the glow of glow-worms and other bioluminescent creatures.

This brings us to the third great field of biochemical advance: vitamins.

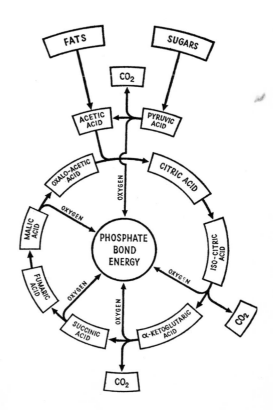

The energy for biological processes is derived from a sequence of chemical reactions discovered by Sir Hans Krebs, and known as the citric acid cycle. The diagram shows how a series of acids is converted from one to another in sequence, by the aid of oxygen and enzymes, the cycle constantly repeating. Carbon dioxide and water are given off. The 'fuel' which powers this 'engine' is acetic acid, derived from the fats and sugars ingested by the organism. In five of the reactions involved, energy-rich phosphate (PO_3) bonds are created — the process might be compared with compressing a spring — to the number of 15 in each cycle. The energy thus locked up is released in various biological processes.

Cats, dogs, rats – *twenty-five centimes the piece. Gustave Doré's drawing of besieged Paris in 1871 shows vividly the starvation that provided an early but not very fruitful stimulus to dietetic research.*

DURING THE SIEGE OF PARIS, in 1870–1, food ran desperately short and scientists were urged to reconstruct something edible from whatever was available – especially for infants and young children, who were dying in numbers from lack, it was thought, of fresh milk and eggs. A certain J. B. Dumas attempted to devise an artificial milk by emulsifying fat in a sweet-ened albuminous solution. The effects on the infants who consumed it were disastrous. From this sad experience Dumas concluded that something essential to life was lacking from his artificial milk. He seems to have been the earliest man to question the adequacy of a diet made up of protein, car-bohydrates, fat and salts.

Numerous experiments in feeding animals with restricted diets followed; the animals almost always deteriorated or died, but no one drew the logical conclusion that there must be substances, other than the four listed above, which were essential to life. Not till 1905 did anyone demonstrate the point: a Dutch professor of hygiene named Pekelharing fed mice a mixture he thought adequate, but after four weeks of it, all the mice were dead. Pekelharing then did what no one else had thought to do, he gave a second lot of mice the same diet plus a minute quantity of milk. They flourished. The food value of the milk was negligible: clearly it contained an unsuspected but essential something. However, his paper, published in Dutch, was neglected.

The word 'vitamine' was coined by a Pole, Casimir Funk, in 1912. The Lister Institute, where he was working, didn't like it, since it implied that all 'accessory food factors' were members of the chemical group known as amines. As it turned out, their doubts were justified – only one of the numerous vitamins so far discovered is an amine. But Funk slipped the word into an article in 1912, and the name stuck, though the final 'e' was eventually dropped.

Funk's own contribution was to isolate the substance involved in beri-beri. 'Beriberi' means 'I cannot': it is a disease which starts with weakness and ends in paralysis and death. About 1896 a Dutch military doctor in the East Indies, Eijkman, intending to carry out some research on fowls, had fed them with scraps from the army mess, consisting chiefly of cooked polished rice. His fowls soon developed a mysterious paralysis. Then a newly-appointed commander forbade Eijkman to use the scraps for this purpose; so he fed them the cheaper unhusked rice. Now the fowls recovered!

Eijkman had the intelligence to realize that what had attacked his fowls was beri-beri, but his conclusion was laughed to scorn. Confirming it by careful research, he concluded erroneously that there must be a toxin in the rice, and an antidote to it in the husk. By 1907, however, other workers had shown that it was the *lack* of something, present in the husk, from the polished rice which was the cause of the trouble.

Funk then showed that yeast was just as effective as the husk in curing beri-beri: in 1911 he isolated from it a substance so potent that one fifteen-thousandth of an ounce cured a pigeon of beri-beri within a few hours.

The cure which Funk's extract effected did not persist – owing, as we now know, to the fact that there are other vitamins lacking from polished rice – and his theories were scouted by doctors, many of whom were convinced that a bacterial cause for beri-beri would eventually be found. Funk himself thought there were two substances present, and later succeeded in isolating niacin (nicotinic acid) as well as thiamine (aneurin), i.e. Vitamin B-1.

But Funk saw that this might be just the opening of a door to something big, and suggested that not only beri-beri but also scurvy, pellagra and rickets might be diseases due to the deficiency of substances essential to health. He was absolutely right: the race to discover how far this break-through could be followed up began. At this point we must pause to consider a man who was not merely a pioneer of vitamin research, but one of the great figures in the history of biochemistry: Sir Frederick Gowland Hopkins.

The first specimen of tryptophane –
'a beautifully crystalline product' – was
prepared by Hopkins and Cole in 1901.
The two men are seen here in the
Physiological Laboratory, Cambridge;
Hopkins is holding a test-tube containing
the historic crystals.

'HOPKINS was small and slight in figure, his head was long and big for his frame, and his face was even and handsome. His hair and drooping moustache emphasised the distinction of the vertical lines of his face. He usually stood with his head slightly inclined forward, pondering . . . His courtesy was almost Chinese.' He was modest, humble, infinitely patient and understanding and described his work in a superb literary style. (Thus his admiring biographer, J. G. Crowther.)

An only child, whose father died while he was an infant, he had no friends of his own age, and recalls his sense of the world's cruelty when he encountered two bullies at school.

Hopkins, aged eighty,
*in the laboratory in 1941.
He continued to direct
the work here for another
two years before he
retired. With him is
Prof. E. F. Gale, who
afterwards discovered how
antibiotics achieve their
effect.*

When, as a young man, he told a famous chemist of his intention to
pursue biochemistry, the great man replied: 'The chemistry of the living –
that is super-chemistry. Seek, my young friend, for other ambitions!' The
idea was still prevalent that protoplasm did not obey the ordinary laws of
chemistry. Matter was built, many scientists thought, of a peculiar molecule
– 'biogen' – which was characteristic of life. Hopkins, however, was quite
clear in his mind that the chemistry of life consisted of 'simple substances
undergoing comprehensible reactions'. He even objected to the word biochemistry, as implying that it was somehow different from regular chemistry.
At the same time, he saw clearly that there might be molecules whose im-

281

portance to the body might be, not that they were structural units – bricks – but that they played a part in its working processes. Vitamins, and still more, hormones, were to prove how right he was.

When Hopkins appeared on the scene, biochemistry was a German science. He created British biochemistry from nothing. Not until 1914, when he was 53, was a professorship in biochemistry created for him, and not until 1924 did he get a decent lab, and then only through the charity of a hat manufacturer.

Hopkins' intellectual vigour was sustained into old age: he published some fifty scientific papers after his election to the Presidency of the Royal Society at the age of 68, and did not retire from the direction of his laboratory until he was 82.

At the bottom of a flight of steps lies the cellar in which British biochemistry was born. Here Gowland Hopkins conducted his experiments on dietary factors and founded the theory of muscle contraction, crammed in

Down a flight of worn stone steps *flanked by rubbish bins and stacked bicycles is this cellar where Hopkins worked on vitamins. One who knew him says, 'It reminds one of the Curies' shed, a triumph of determination over environment'.*

with Keith Lucas and E. D. Adrian, who were making their studies of the nervous impulse. Somehow A. V. Hill fitted himself in to carry out his work on muscles, and there was even a cave for the frogs. It was quite in the tradition of Purkinje.

Hopkins chose fundamental problems, devised brilliant technical methods of attack, and produced important results – yet, by an extraordinary irony, in every significant case his findings proved to have been wrong.

The undernourished girl typists whom Hopkins saw as a young man at the hospital gave him, he later recalled, an interest in nutrition, but his first work was on the colouring pigments in the wings of butterflies. Hopkins began to move towards his eventual field of work when he devised a reliable and easy way of crystallizing proteins. This led him to the discovery of the amino-acid tryptophane, one of the building blocks of protein: Claude Bernard had inferred its existence. (But Hopkins thought it was skatol-amido-acetic acid: it wasn't.)

Hopkins believed that the body required specific building blocks, in opposition to the vitalist view that it could make use of any raw material it liked. It occurred to him that tryptophane might well be one of the essential building bricks, since it was a constituent of protein, and in 1906 he therefore tried feeding rats on tryptophane-free diets. They sickened and died. Thus he was led to the belief that small qualitative variations in diet might prove crucially important, and pointed to the case of scurvy. His conclusion was right, although tryptophane was not a vitamin, and Hopkins never claimed to have discovered vitamins.

He spent the next six years pursuing this line of thought. As Pekelharing had shown the importance of milk, he fed rats on milk-free diets. Ironically, their recovery was due not to the vitamin but to refection, and at the age of 84 he attempted to disprove his own earlier conclusion.

Turning to look for vitamins among sulphur-containing substances, he ended up by discovering glutathione, an important enzyme, though he went wrong on its structure and also wrote a number of papers showing, what was not the case, that it stimulated oxidation (the removal of electrons from an atom).

Though he received the Nobel prize in 1929, he always felt himself to be an intellectual amateur. His real achievement was, however, not his actual discoveries, not even his brilliant improvements in technique, but the fact that he changed our conception of biochemistry into something more dynamic. I have taken the title of this chapter from a phrase of his. The biochemist, he said, 'strives to obtain a mental picture of that invisible dance and transformation of molecules which in every organ or tissue underlies its activities.'

IN 1916, AN HEROIC SCIENTIST named Goldberger found that some convicts who were being fed on a limited diet developed pellagra, a disease marked by skin inflammation, weakness, spinal pain, convulsions, melancholia and idiocy. To prove that the disease was due to the diet (as Funk had suggested) and not to a germ, as was generally supposed, he heroically injected himself with the blood of a pellagra sufferer. The next day, he swallowed the intestinal discharge of another sufferer.

All going well, he then ate the powdered skin rash of another, and his wife joined him in this horrifying demonstration. But if it was a deficiency disease, what was the vitamin involved? In 1937 it was found that nicotinic acid, a substance which had been prepared as far back as 1867, was in fact a vitamin, a member of the Vitamin B complex, and indeed the one associated with pellagra. Funk's prediction had proved correct! Funk was still alive to enjoy the victory; but Goldberger had died of cancer in 1929.

Why did it take the best part of half a century to exploit the original break-through? Because chemists had to learn to think like physiologists and physiologists like chemists. When E.V. McCollum, in the years before 1920, fed some 3,000 different experimental diets to rats, he actually produced (as he later realized with chagrin) several quite contrasting states of malnutrition. But as a chemist, he had not been trained to distinguish the different symptoms, nor to appreciate their medical significance. On the other hand, the physiologists were not equipped to design the kind of experiments which were needed; only a chemist could do that. But gradually the boundaries of two disciplines began to fuse. It was to become an increasingly common occurrence.

The whole vitamin field was mapped out in the half century which followed. Most of them were isolated in pure crystalline form, and many were synthesized. The task was not easy.

The anti-neuritic vitamin had been isolated in 1912 – but it was not until 1936 that the chemists were able to get enough to analyse: 5 grams of the vitamin from one ton of rice-polishings! Synthesis followed in 1937.

The outstanding figure in this phase of vitamin research was McCollum, an American who in 1913 discovered vitamin A, important to eye function, and in 1922 Vitamin D, the anti-rickets vitamin. Vitamins were turning out to be a very disparate group of substances. Vitamin A was found in the yellow colouring-matter of carrots and similar vegetables, but was absent from red and white ones. Vitamin D, in contrast, was produced in the body by the action of sunlight. Furthermore, while previous vitamins had been soluble in water, Vitamin A was soluble in fat, proving that fats provided something more than energy to the diet. Vitamin C, which prevents scurvy, is found only in citrus-fruits.

It also transpired that organisms – plants as well as animals – need minute amounts of certain elements, such as copper and zinc, and for much the same reason, that is to say, because they provide essential cogwheels for the biochemical machine. The occurrence of goitre as a result of lack of iodine was the first such deficiency to be recognized, but today we realize that many infertile areas of the earth's surface are 'trace-element deserts', where plants will not grow for lack of such elements.

Among the vitamins, one seems to be unique: biotin, which I mentioned earlier. Unlike other vitamins, biotin takes part in a wide range of biochemical reactions, and the current hunch is that it is needed for the synthesis of enzymes – it is a toolmaker rather than a tool.

The vitamin story is still far from a conclusion.

'WHEN I COMPARE our present knowledge of the workings of the body, and our powers of interfering with and controlling these workings for the benefit of humanity, with the ignorance and despairing impotence of my student days, I feel that I have had the good fortune to see the sun rise on a darkened world . . .' declared the great physiologist Ernest Starling in 1923. And he added that what he had lived through was not a renaissance, 'but a new birth of man's powers over his environment and his destinies unparalleled in the whole history of mankind'.

Starling himself made three important advances in physiology, and of these the most important was the discovery of hormones. The second was his Law of the Heart, which states that the amount of blood pumped by the heart does not in general depend on the resistance offered by the arteries, as would be the case with an ordinary pump, but on the amount of blood reaching it from the veins. The third was to show how the blood takes up fluids, and how lymph is separated from it. In addition to all this, he was one of the founders of the English school of physiology which arose at the beginning of the century, and included such men as Sherrington, whom we shall meet shortly, and Hopkins. Yet history has forgotten him.

'It must be a chemical reflex' were the exact words which Starling uttered on 16th January 1902, when, at his laboratory in University College, London, he made the crucial observation which was to open up the new world of hormones.

Stimulated by Pavlov's work, he had begun to study the functioning of the intestine. Having dissected away the nerves which supply the main absorptive part of the small intestine, he introduced a few drops of hydrochloric acid. Soon pancreatic juice began to ooze from the pancreatic duct. But what could have signalled to the pancreas that acid was present? Not the nerves, for they had been removed. Evidently, something had passed to the pancreas through the blood. It was a reflex, but a *chemical* reflex. The

Co-discoverer with Starling *of secretin, the hormone that excites the pancreas to secrete digestive juice, was Sir William Bayliss, here seen lecturing to his students. His 'Principles of General Physiology', published in 1914, had a world-wide influence.*

body had a second communication system, supplementing the nervous one. Such a thing had never been dreamed of.

Starling soon isolated the chemical messenger involved and named it *secretin,* because it was secreted. He at once realized that there were probably many more such messengers; Hardy named them *hormons.* (By some linguistic fluke, the word hormon subsequently acquired the 'e' which 'vitamine' had lost.) Starling was then 36.

The first reasonably pure hormone had been extracted from the adrenal glands five years before by J. J. Abel; and, when J. Takaminé had found how to produce it in pure crystalline form, had been marketed under the trade-name Adrenalin.

It proved the most powerful heart stimulant known. But it did not occur to these workers to generalize their discovery; for them, norepinephrine (to give it its correct name) was just a new drug.

IT WAS ON CHRISTMAS DAY, 1914, that the next hormone was isolated: twelve years had passed. Edward C. Kendall extracted thyroxin from the thyroid: from three tons of fresh cattle thyroid he obtained 35 grams of the hormone – just over an ounce. Another 13 years were to pass before it could be obtained in crystalline form. Thyroxin, it was found, could be used to treat the diseases which result from damage to the thyroid, notably cretinism. After a few injections, the whole appearance of the victims changed. 'Not the magic wand of Prospero, nor the brave kiss of the daughter of Hippocrates, ever effected such a change as that we are now enabled to make,' rejoiced the great physician, Sir William Osler.

By the twenties, discoveries were following thick and fast. On the 30th of October 1920 Banting, then a lecturer in physiology at the University of London, Ontario, read in a medical paper of an experiment in which tying-off the pancreatic duct led to the death of those cells in the pancreas which produce the digestive enzyme trypsin: furthermore sugar disappeared from the urine. The idea that there was something in the pancreas which could cure diabetes was not new: but attempts to cure patients by giving them pancreatic extracts had failed. Banting reasoned that the trypsin probably destroyed the curative substance – insulin, as we now know. He wrote in his notebook: 'Tie off pancreas ducts of dogs. Wait six or eight weeks. Remove and extract.'

Fired with excitement, he went to Prof. Macleod at Toronto and asked for ten dogs and facilities for testing his theory. Macleod told him to finish his work at London first, and it was not until July 1921 that he was able to make the crucial test. A young graduate named Best had been assigned to assist him by making the blood and urine tests. Would the sugar vanish from the urine of the treated dog? 'The intense exitement with which we watched the depth of colour in the sugar reagent fade as the blood sugar became reduced under the action of insulin is difficult to describe,' Best says.

The work had not been easy. Several of the dogs died from shock or infection, after having their pancreases removed. When those which had had the duct ligatured were inspected, it was found that the thread had not been tied tight enough, and the work had to be repeated. If the thread was tied too tight, trouble also resulted. The laboratory was 'a small inferno' and the sweat-soaked workers often retreated to the roof and continued working there. In a later phase, Banting tried to extract insulin from the pancreas of unborn calves – for no trypsin is yet secreted to damage it. The condenser of his equipment consumed two tons of ice a day, all of which had to be packed in by hand. Macleod, sceptical at first, now turned the whole force of his laboratory to bringing Banting's discovery to a reliable medical form, and shared with him the Nobel prize which followed.

288

Diabetics owe their lives *to two Canadian physiologists: Frederick Banting (right) and Charles H. Best. Between them stands a diabetic dog – the first patient to prove the efficacy of insulin.*

Hormone research now took the bit between its teeth, as research workers turned their attention to other organs in the body which looked as if they might contain something interesting.

First, Evans, the son of a diabetic surgeon who was saved by insulin, decided to discover whether the *pituitary gland* contained a hormone which controlled growth. He knew that O'Brien, the Irish giant, had had a pituitary as big as an egg, while Martina de la Cruz, who was 21 in. high, had a pituitary which had withered completely away. In 1922 he found it did: we now know that the pituitary contains more than a dozen hormones. One, *prolactin,* stimulates the maternal instinct, and has been described as 'mother love in bottles'. Even a tom-cat will give milk when injected with it.

Later, hormones important in controlling blood pressure (*vasopressin*) and the contractions of the uterus in childbirth (*oxytocin*) were found in the under-part of the pituitary by du Vigneaud in New York.

A STRANGE LAST REQUEST had been made by the dying Max Born, the great professor of embryology at Breslau, in 1902. Summoning to his deathbed one of the most able of his ex-students, he charged him to explore the yellowish body in the ovaries, known as the *corpus luteum* ('yellow body'). Born had a hunch that secretions from this body were crucial to the well-being of the embryo during pregnancy.

However, it was not his former student, but the American endocrinologist, George Corner, who, thirty years later, proved the truth of Born's intuition. After much chemical manipulation, he extracted from the corpus luteum a substance which, as he said, 'looked like a poor grade of automobile grease'. The test was to inject it into a pregnant animal which had been deprived of its corpus luteum. Without this structure, the pregnancy was likely to abort or end in premature delivery. Injection of the new extract, which was named *progesterone,* ensured a normal delivery.

'Can I forget the time when I went racing up the steps of the lab in Rochester, carrying a glass syringe that contained the world's entire supply of crude progesterone, stumbled and fell and lost it all? Or the day that Willard Allen showed me his first glittering crystals of the hormone, chemically pure at last?' exclaimed Corner, later, describing his achievement.

But progesterone was only one of the many hormones secreted by the reproductive organs and not, as it happened, the first to be isolated.

The outlines of the hormone picture now seemed clear. But two surprises were still in store. The first was the existence of 'local hormones' – physiologically active substances briefly created at a particular site and destroyed as soon as their job was done. They were christened *kinins.*

In 1937 Werle, a German, found that a mixture of blood plasma and saliva would cause smooth muscle to contract although each alone would not. He concluded that the mixture liberated an unknown substance, and after several more years' work, named it kallidin. But kallidin was only the first of a family whose size is still uncertain.

The next step came in 1949, when Rocha e Silva at Sao Paulo found something similar in snake venom, which he called bradykinin. Five years later, analogous substances were found in wasp and hornet venom by British workers. When it was discovered that bradykinin could be made from blood, it became possible to assemble enough to analyse. It proved to be a 'miniature protein' – a chain of nine amino-acids. Its function seemed to be to make capillaries more permeable, as a step towards wound repair, and the mechanism which forms it is interlocked with the process by which blood clots.

Meanwhile, a completely different aspect of the hormonal field had revealed itself – the fact that plants possess hormones.

There are three problems in plant physiology: how do plants nourish and reproduce themselves, and how do they move? Although progress had been made with the first two, the last was still a total mystery. Malpighi and Ray had observed how leaves turn athwart the sun's rays, how roots turn down towards water and the soil, but they attributed these movements to a 'vital force'. I have already mentioned (p. 92) the researches of Thomas Knight into this question, with the aid of his revolving wheel. He was 'unable to trace the existence of anything like sensation or intellect in plants', and thought that the bending of the roots might be accounted for by a redistribution of the sap, but could not think how to account for the way in which leaves place themselves across the sun. The matter was to remain a mystery, despite some experiments made by Darwin, until 1930. Darwin observed that the bending did not occur if the last one-tenth of an inch of root were cut off. Later it was found that inserting a fine mica barrier stopped the action, and biologists began to suspect the presence of a 'growth substance' diffusing down from the tip which would cause bending by stimulating more rapid growth on one side than the other of the root, and equally of the coleoptile, or sheath covering the stem.

The crucial experiment which proved that plants also possess 'growth hormones' was carried out in 1923 by a young botany student in Utrecht, named Frits Went. By day, Went was serving in the Dutch army, but at night he returned to his father's plant-physiology laboratory at the university to keep up his graduate studies in botany. The test which he thought up was to cut off the tip of an oat seedling, lay it on a small block of gelatine, and leave it for several hours, in the expectation that the supposed growth substance would seep out into the gelatine. Then he would take the block of gelatine and stick it on the side of a second decapitated seedling, in the hope that it would grow faster on the side where the block was stuck, thus causing the stem to bend.

This experiment was less easy than it sounds. It had to be done in only the dimmest red light, since roots also tend to curve away from a source of light; and in a very humid atmosphere, to prevent the cut tip drying out. At 3 a.m. on the morning of April 17, 1928, Went returned to the laboratory to see how his experiment was proceeding, and found that the tip had indeed curved as he had foreseen.

After a long and difficult research, Kögl, a chemist, extracted a few drops of the active agent from 100,000 maize seedlings, but there was not enough to analyse. Then came the discovery that human urine was rich in this growth substance: and soon Kögl had analysed it. In 1934 a substance 50,000 times more potent was discovered. It is now known as auxin A, while that which Went discovered is called hetero-auxin. Subsequently other

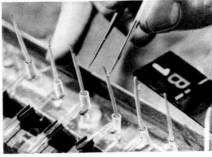
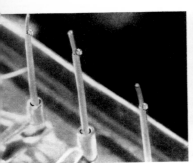
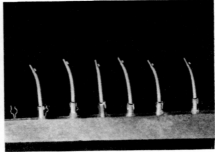

Went's classic experiment, repeated at his old university of Utrecht. Growing tips of oat seedlings are placed on gelatine, into which they diffuse their growth hormone. Cut into tiny squares, this gelatine is fixed to six more seedlings, which are soon observed to grow faster (hence the curve) on the side where the hormone-soaked gelatine is fixed.

growth substances, and finally a whole range of hormones controlling fruiting, root-development, leaf-fall and possibly flowering were found.

Later, Went made another and more astonishing discovery in the field of plant-hormones. He showed that certain plants produce poisons, or inhibitors, which enter plants of rival species and arrest their growth. The desert, particularly, is the scene of continuous chemical warfare between plants, for in the desert there is no water to dilute the substances.

English children sing a nursery rhyme which asks

> How can you or I or anyone know
> How oats and beans and barley grow?

It may not be strange that biologists have largely answered this question, but it is a very strange coincidence that it was precisely with work on oats and beans that the growth process was explored, and in barley that the flowering process was chiefly studied.

12

THE FLASHING SHUTTLES

Sherrington, Adrian, Huxley

THE MODERN PICTURE OF BRAIN ACTION was established in its broad principles by Charles Sherrington, a jovial pipe-smoking Scot, who wrote gritty poetry in his spare time (sample: *tongued turret and tongued stream, tracked pasture fenny*) and collected medical incunabula. It was he who told how, after leaving the chimpanzee's room, he put his eye to the keyhole to see what it was doing and found 'an eye, much like my own, looking through at me from the opposite side'.

Sherrington started his work with a prolonged study of the reflex arc, but soon realized that the idea of an isolated reflex is a pure abstraction. Any impulse from a sense receptor can stimulate any one of several muscles, and any muscle can be stimulated by many receptors. But these interlocking pathways never come into conflict. The brain integrates them into a coherent pattern. A given stimulus may cause flexion of a limb on one occasion, extension on another – the brain will determine which. Thus Sherrington arrived at his central concept of the 'integrative action of the central nervous system'. The brain is a 'gigantic combining mechanism' for sensory signals – it governs a system of interlocked reflexes.

He was led to this view when he observed that a muscle never pulls against an opposing muscle, and showed that this was due to the presence of sensory organs within the muscles which report its state.

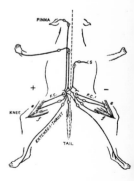

Sherrington made an important extension of this idea when he discovered that the brain can also inhibit, or block, an impulse. The inhibitory impulses travel by distinct pathways to nodal points where the excitatory and inhibitory impulses are combined, and the impulse either stops or goes forward, according to which is stronger. (Drugs, he found, may tip the balance.) Brain action, he summed up, is 'management of nerve by nerve', and added: 'It seems ludicrous to range such a paucity of nerve processes alongside the manifold variety of mind.' He drew a picture of the brain as an 'enchanted loom, where millions of flashing shuttles weave a dissolving pattern, always a meaningful pattern, though never an abiding one.'

The interlocking pathways *of reflex action, figured by Sherrington, using a dog's scratch reflex as example.*

Sir Charles Sherrington, *scientist and poet. Portrait by Augustus John.*

His *Integrative Action of the Central Nervous System* has been called the greatest landmark in the history of physiology since Harvey's *De Motu Cordis,* combining, as it did, a mass of original experimental observation with wide generalizations.

With Sherrington, the classical epoch of neurophysiology comes to an end. The modern phase starts with Lord Adrian: fittingly enough, the two men shared a Nobel prize in 1932. It was Adrian who showed how nerve and brain could be studied in unimagined detail by electrical means.

The thermionic valve, on which radio depends, was invented in 1904. The war of 1914–18 brought into common use amplifiers, employing these valves, which could multiply electrical signals thousands of times. The thirty-year-old Edgar Adrian realized that this device could revolutionize the study of nerve impulses. He realized, also, that it would not be enough to study whole nerves, which are bundles of hundreds of fibres, like the hundreds of circuits in a telephone cable. It would be necessary to isolate single fibres under the dissecting microscope without damaging or disconnecting them.

By a series of ingenious devices, he succeeded in doing this for a whole variety of different nerves, and then, using an old army amplifier, he measured the impulses in them. The result was quite unexpected. He found that fibres carry, when a nerve is functioning, a rapid fire of identical pulses – up to 400 a second. The frequency of the pulses reflects the strength of the sen-

Sherrington's successor *and fellow Nobel prizewinner was E. D. Adrian, now Lord Adrian, who studied the brain in detail by electrical means. Here he is seen (left) with his Swedish collaborator, Professor Yngve Zotterman, during the International Physiological Congress in Stockholm, 1926.*

sory stimulus. This pattern, he found, was the same in nerves of every type, visual, auditory, tactile, etc. It is the nerve itself which determines how the impulse is perceived. Nor could he detect any difference between excitatory and inhibitory impulses. These pulses each represent the 'firing' or discharge of a single nerve cell. When a nerve cell has fired, it cannot fire again for some thousandths of a second, and if a stimulus arrives in this 'dark period' it is ignored. By 1930 the general picture of nerve action was clear.

But how is the nerve impulse propagated along the axon? How, in fact, is an electric impulse transmitted through a structure which is largely water? A German, Julius Bernstein, had proposed a theory as long ago as 1902, but there seemed no way of testing it. Just before the second world war, a technique was evolved which brought about a break-through.

It consisted in the making of incredibly fine pipettes which could be introduced into the cut end of a living nerve fibre, so that the potential difference between inside and outside could be measured. At first these pipettes could only be introduced into certain unusually large fibres found in squids – so that the work had to be done at marine biological stations, such as Plymouth, and Woods Hole at Cape Cod. But in 1951 Ralph Gerard and Gilbert Ling, then at Chicago, devised a micropipette so fine that it could be slipped inside an ordinary nerve fibre. The tip tapered to a point no more than .0005 mm. across.

Soon these invisibly small tubes were being thrust into every conceivable type of nerve: Richard Keynes at Cambridge, for instance, used them to investigate how electric fish produce their 200-volt discharges.

Bernstein's suggestion was that the impulse depended on ions. Ions are electrically-charged fragments of molecules, and it is the passage of the charges which constitutes an electric current. Sodium and potassium ions were known to be present, both of them being positively charged. When the nerve is in a resting state, the sodium ions which enter are somehow pumped out again.

In 1938, A. L. Hodgkin and A. F. Huxley, working at Plymouth, applied the new technique to the giant axons of squids, as did Cole and Curtis at Woods Hole. The result surprised them. The interior of the nerve, normally negative, actually become positive during the passage of the current, by 40 millivolts or more, whereas, on Bernstein's theory, it should have fallen to zero.

The war interrupted these studies, but in 1947 Alan Hodgkin and Bernard Katz proposed an explanation of this phenomenon. They suggested that the outer membrane, or skin, of the nerve has the unusual property of momentarily letting sodium ions in (but not out) and then potassium ions out (but not in). It is thus a kind of double-action valve, capable of separating the two kinds of ion. Keynes and Lewis at Cambridge, and Nachmansohn at Woods Hole used isotope methods to measure the actual amounts of sodium and potassium exchanged. These proved big enough to account for the voltage difference actually observed. (Bernstein had been on the right track but he had suggested that the membrane simply lost its selectivity.)

But what provided the energy to run the pump? Keynes and Hodgkin, using radioactively-labelled sodium and potassium, showed that it was probably the same substance which powers the reactions of ordinary cells and the contraction of muscle – ATP.

Thus, though many difficulties remain, the broad character of the nature of the nerve impulse had been laid bare: it is a kind of electrical leak, propagated along the fibre and constantly repaired as soon as it has passed. To have identified the physico-chemical basis of the nerve impulse was a major advance.

But as Cajal had shown, one nerve cell does not quite touch another. Sherrington had christened the gap a *synapse*. What happens at the synapse? This problem meanwhile had also begun to yield. It had long been thought that some chemical 'transmitter substance' must be involved, and Sir Henry Dale had, in 1914, suggested acetylcholine, but no one could think how to test this idea.

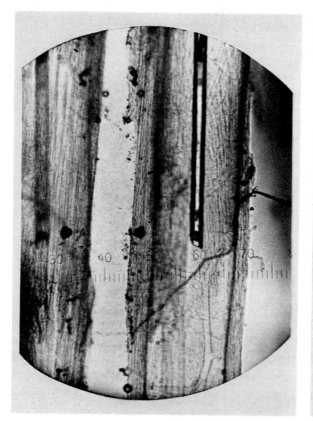

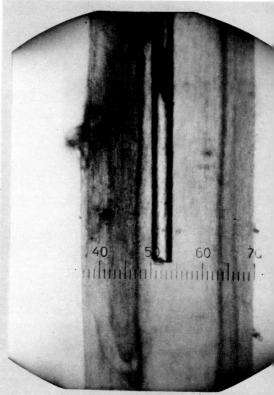

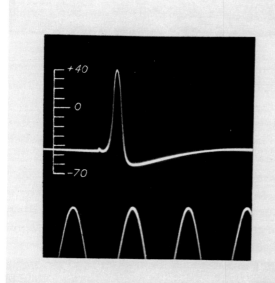

Inserting an incredibly fine needle *within the hollow tube of nerve, Hodgkin and Huxley were able to measure the electric potential of a single nerve fibre, using the giant axons of squids. The left-hand picture is formed directly by the microscope, the other being a side view in a mirror. The scale divisions are 33 μ, 1 μ being one thousandth of a millimetre. Left: a recording taken by this means of an action potential. Voltage swings from negative to positive and back as the signal passes.*

Otto Loewi, *who shared a Nobel prize in 1936 with Sir Henry Dale for his work on the chemistry of the nerve impulse.*

The night before Easter Sunday, 1920, Otto Loewi, an Austrian physiologist, awoke in the night with an idea which he jotted down on a tiny slip of paper and then went back to sleep. When he awoke again about six, he remembered that he had written down something of the greatest importance, but could not decipher his own scrawl. The next night, at three a. m., the idea returned. It was a way of determining whether there is any chemical substance involved in nerve transmission.

The nerve impulse was known to be electrical in nature, but it was a mystery why some nerves stimulate an organ, and others depress it. For instance, the vagus nerves slow down the rate of heartbeat, while the accelerator nerves increase it. Seventeen years before, it had struck Loewi that there might be a connection between this fact and the way in which some drugs stimulate while others depress.

The experiment which now occurred to Loewi, was to take a frog's heart, put it in Ringer's solution (a solution containing the salts which normally bathe cells, and which keep them alive for a while) and stimulate its vagus nerve repeatedly, in the expectation that some chemical substance would be liberated into the solution. Then to put a second frog's heart in the solution and see if it is slowed down. Loewi got out of bed, went to his lab, and did the experiment. It worked. Equally, if he stimulated the accelerator nerve, the solution would afterwards accelerate another heart.

Loewi commented afterwards that if he had thought of this experiment in the daytime, he would never have troubled to perform it. For he would have assumed that the amount of substance produced would be just enough to do the job, when released at the right spot. Diluted by a lot of Ringer's solution, it would, one would expect, be much too weak to exert any effect.

Loewi called the substance released by the vagus 'vagus-stuff' and soon it was identified as acetylcholine. Incidentally, it now became clear how alkaloid poisons work: for they block a substance, an enzyme, which destroys the acetylcholine, and so prepares the way for the nerve to act again. It took another sixteen years – that is, until 1936 – to identify the substance produced by accelerator nerves as epinephrine. As I mentioned in the last chapter, this is a substance secreted by the adrenal glands, on which the hor-mone chemists were working in quite another connection.

The nerves we have just discussed are efferent nerves, i.e. nerves which lead *from* the brain to an organ, to control it. But what about afferent nerves, the nerves which convey sensory messages *to* the brain? In 1938, Loewi had just done the last of a series of experiments designed to prove that they do not produce any acetylcholine, when the news came that the Nazis had taken over Austria. At three a.m. the following morning, storm-troopers broke into his house and carted him off to gaol, for he was a Jew. Loewi expected to be shot, and was obsessed by the idea that he must report the result of his experiments before this occurred. After some days, he induced a guard to allow him to write one postcard. On this he crammed the essential facts and addressed it to the German scientific periodical *Naturwissenschaft*.

Subsequently released, he escaped to England, and thence to America – though the Nazis compelled him to make over his Nobel prize money and declare himself a pauper before allowing him to leave.

During the twenty years which followed, attempts – mostly unsuccessful – were made to identify 'transmitter substances' at other types of nerve junc-tion. In particular, what happens in the brain is still obscure. Indeed, for a long time a strong party of opponents, who became known as the 'spark men', denied the whole proposition, claiming that the impulse was trans-mitted electrically across the gap. Those who claimed the process as chemical were known as the 'soup men'. Not until 1951, when electrical recording from single cells became possible, was victory conceded to the latter. (Oddly enough, a case where the transmission actually *was* electrical was discovered soon after.) Loewi and Dale, nevertheless, shared a Nobel prize for their work in 1936.

Recently, the electron microscope has made the picture clearer, by re-vealing – at enormous magnifications – a mass of tiny vesicles in the synaptic membrane from which the transmitter substance is released, though how this release is effected remains a matter of guesswork. These pictures also show the existence of a double membrane in the synapse, with a separation of about 20 millionths of a millimetre – just right for maximum efficiency.

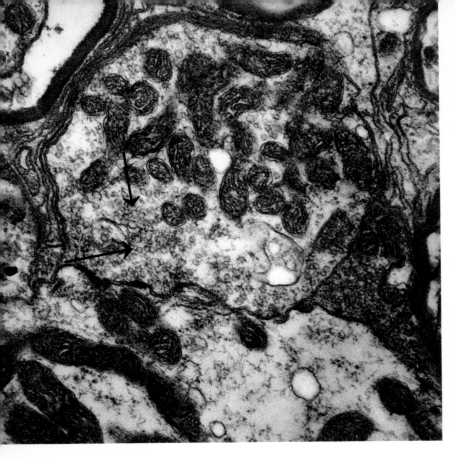

The gap between two nerve cells – *which Sherrington christened the synapse – is shown magnified 60,000 times in this electron micrograph of a section of lizard brain. The gap is bridged by the 'transmitter substance' released by the synaptic vesicles, some of which are arrowed.*

While the new techniques were clearing up the question of actual transmission, yet another electrical device was found to throw light on the immensely complex cellular networks of the brain.

Today we are accustomed to the idea of the brain as an electrical machine and the analogy between electronic computers and brains has become a cliché. But for centuries the brain was a total mystery, and to recognize its electrical activity was a turning point.

The idea was born in 1875. Richard Caton, a 33-year-old Liverpool doctor, specializing in heart disease, and a University lecturer, reasoned from the fact that nerve impulses were known to be electrical in nature, and from the discovery by Fritsch and Hitzig four years earlier that the brain could be stimulated electrically, that the brain might have an electrical response. To test his conclusion, he placed electrodes upon the exposed brains of dogs and rabbits: his galvanometer indicated the presence of weak electric currents. It was much too insensitive to show fluctuations, but Caton observed that when he shone a light in the animal's eye, or pinched its ears, the currents seemed to vary. Often the experiment failed to work, and soon after exposure the brain would swell and become congested, creating spontaneous variations. Caton hoped, nevertheless, to use the method to explore the question of localization: he thought he could identify visual and auditory areas.

Development of this discovery had to await the invention of more sensitive electronic apparatus. In 1913, Neminski, a Russian, recorded rhythmic waves from the exposed brains of dogs, and just over half a century was to pass before the discovery was confirmed in man.

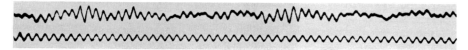

The first human electroencephalogram. *The lower line is a time marker, at 10 cycles a second.*

In 1925, a German psychiatrist, Hans Berger, who was then director of the Psychiatric Clinic in Jena, succeeded in recording this, the first human electroencephalogram, from the scalp of his young son. At first he used platinum wires pushed into the scalp. Later he found that metal plates strapped to the scalp and forehead would serve. The waves changed, he

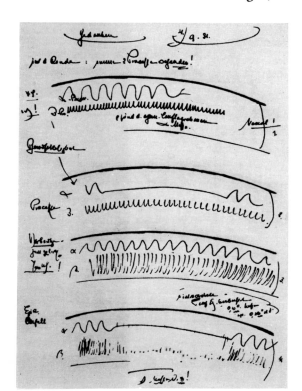

A page from Berger's notebooks, *in which some of his classic experiments in electroencephalography are noted. He was withdrawn and secretive, publishing none of his results until four years after his great breakthrough.*

found, when the eyes opened – Caton had thought he noticed a change when his animals awoke. They changed too on mental effort, and on painful stimuli or loud noises. Brain activity, it seemed, was not merely electrical: it had a complex, variable pattern. Before long, epilepsy was recognized as a stormlike disturbance of these patterns. Cybulski, a Pole, had demonstrated in 1914 that epilepsy could be induced in dogs by electrical stimulation.

Berger was a man of rigid and severe character, very difficult to work for. He ran his life to a time-table, worked out to the minute, and his staff were expected to do the same. He had attempted to repeat Caton's experiment as early as 1902, but had failed to find any connection between the currents he detected and sensory stimuli. After further attempts over the next ten years he abandoned the problem, and concentrated on evolving a theory to account for telepathy. The physical basis of psychic activity was his ruling interest. Only in 1924 did he resume his experiments.

Ever more withdrawn in manner, Berger kept his discovery to himself for four years, publishing only in 1929. His findings were ridiculed at first: the idea that the brain was in constant activity was thought absurd. But in 1937 he was welcomed to a symposium in Paris on the electrical activity of the brain, as its most distinguished visitor; his eyes filled with tears as he replied, 'In Germany I am not so famous.'

Adrian at once realized the importance of Berger's work, invited him to Cambridge, and was soon exploring the electrical activity of the brain with this new tool. The brain, it became clear, was in constant action, whether anything was being perceived or not. Until now, it had been imagined as lying idle, waiting until some stimulus should arrive and demand to be dealt with. But the new tool could report only on the outer layers of the brain. About 1951, methods were devised of implanting electrodes in the brain, through holes in the skull, so that recordings could be made from specific structures deep within the brain, or these could be stimulated. The technique was refined until recordings could be made from a single nerve-cell in the central nervous system. Today, the detailed study of brain action by these methods is the central task of neurophysiology.

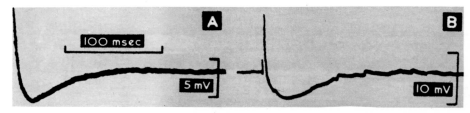

Recordings taken *from a single nerve cell in the brain – a refinement of eletroencephalography first perfected in the early nineteen-fifties.*

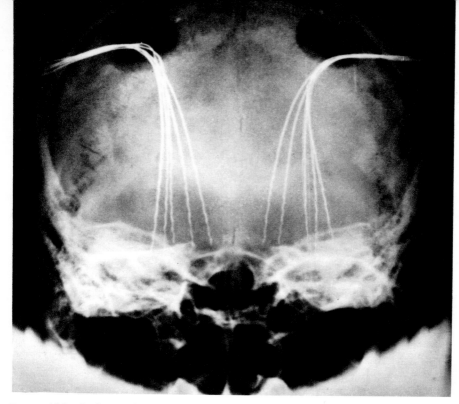

Deep within the brain, *fine electrodes of gold wire are inserted through holes made in the skull –*
sometimes as many as 60 – and can be left in for months. Recordings from the tips aid diagnosis of
brain disorders and throw light on brain function.

Four main areas had long been recognized in the brain. The outer layers,
or cortex, responsible for perception and thought; the inner brain, concerned
(as the new techniques made clear) with feelings, and maintaining the
physiological state of the body; the cerebellum, responsible for co-ordi-
nating movement and balance; and the brain stem. An American, Magoun,
and an Italian, Moruzzi, by these and other methods, revealed the purpose
of the brain stem: it regulates awareness, spraying the cortex with alerting
impulses when work is to be done, letting it subside when it is time to sleep.

But the question still remained: how do the impulses from the brain
make the muscle contract? Electron micrographs of muscle, at magnifications of 100,000 times or more, made possible by elaborate mounting and
staining techniques, finally revealed the answer to the problem. Muscle is
remarkable stuff: it can shorten at a rate equivalent to ten times its own length
in a second. It can exert a pressure of more than forty pounds per square
inch. It comes in two forms, striped and unstriped. Striped muscle is that
which is under voluntary control (e.g. leg muscles) and it was work on
striped muscle which led to the new concept.

303

When a muscle contracts, *heat is produced. And when A.V. Hill gained a Nobel prize in 1922 for his work on muscle, his students at University College, London, produced considerable muscular heat in chairing him round the quad.*

Moreover, when A.V. Hill at University College measured the heat produced when a muscle contracts, he found that – unlike the mechanisms we know in daily life – the amount did not depend on the load lifted or the work done. It depended only on the distance which the muscle shortened. This seemed odd.

The generally-held idea was that muscle fibres were coiled, like springs. Many coiled structures were known, such as wool fibres, which could be pulled out straight, but which would coil up again when released. But the micrographs seen here revealed quite a different picture: bundles of fibres of two kinds, thick and thin, lying parallel, with a thin one between every three thick ones. At magnifications of about 600,000 times a system of bridges between thick and thin can be seen. H.E. Huxley and Jean Hanson threw the first rays of light on how such a system might function when they showed that the thick fibres were composed of myosin, the thin of actin (and probably of a third protein, tropomyosin). As I have told in Chapter 11, it had been shown by Szent-Györgyi that when actin and myosin are brought together in the presence of ATP, the artificial fibres thus formed will con-tract.

The probability is that the thick fibres haul on the thin ones, in a kind of ratchet action, much as a gang of sailors haul hand-over-hand on an anchor rope. Each sailor must be imagined to change his grip several hundred times a second, and at each pull of each hand, a molecule of ATP is consumed.

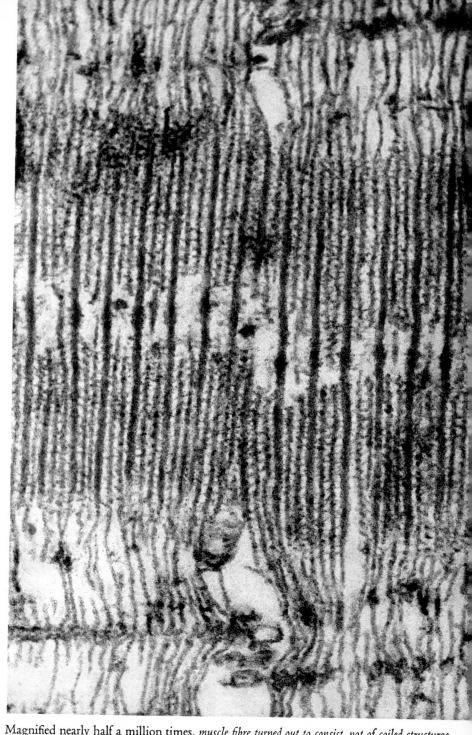

Magnified nearly half a million times, *muscle fibre turned out to consist, not of coiled structures like springs, as had been expected, but of thick and thin fibres lying parallel, with numerous 'bridges' between them. Hodgkin and Huxley took this picture, and the one overleaf, in 1958.*

Such a picture neatly explains A. V. Hill's observations, for clearly the number of molecules of A T P consumed will depend on the length of rope hauled in, and not on the weight of the anchor. It also explains the remarkable power of muscle, for several hundred molecules of A T P can be consumed at each site every second, instead of only one as would be the case in a more rigidly-linked system.

In this analogy, the bridges seen in the micrographs are represented by the sailors' arms, and if we suppose that the number of arms put to the rope varies with the weight of the anchor, we can see how the energy provided will be adjusted to the work to be done.

Repeating patterns of dark and light are caused by overlapping of thick and thin fibres. The broad dark band (A band), which is composed of the thick fibres, is about 1.5 microns (thousandths of a millimetre) in length.

Nerve and muscle had thus by 1960 yielded their essential secrets. The brain, however, remained mysterious. Hopes were rising that electronic computers would prove to be the tools which would be capable of analysing its intricate activity.

Yet the pendulum seems to be swinging away from a primarily electrical explanation. The brain is being increasingly seen as a complex chemical system. Chief among the discoveries which have caused this reorientation were the hallucination-causing drugs.

The drawings overleaf were made under the influence of a hallucinogen, LSD 25, by a Hungarian artist, L. Matéfi.

The drug, analogous to mescal, but much more powerful, had been discovered in 1943 by a Swiss chemist, Albert Hofmann. Hofmann had been investigating substances analogous to mescal one day, when he began to feel sensations of unreality; on getting back home, he lay down and proceeded to experience a series of extraordinary hallucinations. Next day, he woke, feeling tired but otherwise normal. Back at the lab, he looked at the substances he had been synthesizing and decided he must have absorbed through his skin a small amount of a substance entered in his lab-book as LSD 25, an abbreviation for lysergic acid diethylamide, plus the date. He therefore took by mouth what he supposed to be a minimally small dose. He did not know that the substance was a thousand times stronger than mescal, and he had actually taken several times the maximum dose. Before long, he felt extreme sensations of unease and depersonalization, disruption of the time-sense, and so forth. He was driven home, where a series of fantastic hallucinations beset him, with some nausea. He felt sure that he had gone out of his mind, and that he would never be able to report his discovery. Next day, however, he was all right again.

Subsequently he extracted a similar drug from mushrooms used by Mexican Indians in religious ceremonies, analysed and synthesized it: it was named Psilocybin.

Hallucinatory experiences like Hofman's rather resemble certain forms of schizophrenia – hence the name psychotomimetic for such drugs – and raised the hope that this form of insanity might be understandable in chemical terms.

The discovery of these drugs dramatized the importance of the chemical aspect of brain function, which had been neglected in the excitement of pursuing the electrical methods of investigation, and intensive work on the chemical aspect is now developing. So much so, that one research chief – bearing in mind that the chemical state of the brain depends primarily on the chemical composition of the blood – was moved to exclaim: 'The future of brain research lies in the liver.'

Drawn under the influence of LSD 25

1. 20 min. after first dose (50 μg.). Charcoal drawing.

2. 85 min. after first dose, 20 min. after another 50 μg.

1. *Condition normal. No effect from the drug yet.*

2. *Euphoria. The subject sees the model correctly but finds difficulty in controlling the wide, sweeping movements of his hand.*

3. *Outlines of the model seen normally, but very vividly and in changed colours, The subject states: 'My hand must follow the bold sweep of the lines. I feel as if my consciousness is situated in the part of my body that is now active.'*

4. *'The outlines of the model are normal but those of my drawing are not (Fig.3). I pull myself together and try again: it's no good. I give up trying and let myself go at the third attempt (Fig.4).'*

5. *'I try again and produce this drawing with one flourish.'*

6. *Agitated. 'The perspective of the room has changed, everything is moving ... everything is interwoven in a network of colour ... The model's face is distorted to a diabolic mask.'*

7. *Euphoric mood, intoxication less marked. The subject attempts to draw a portrait similar to his first one. 'If I am not careful, I lose control of my movements.'*

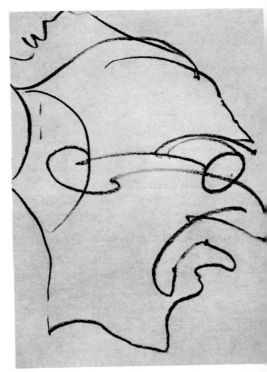

5. Shortly after third and fourth drawings.

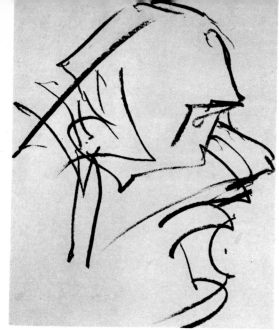

3. 2½ hours after first dose. Charcoal sketch.

4. Shortly after third drawing.

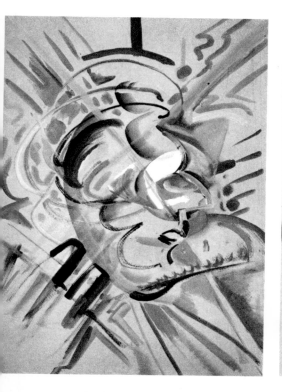

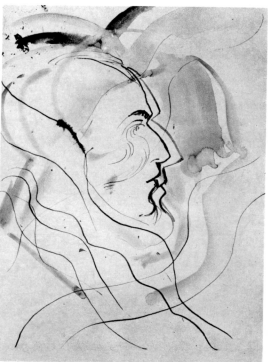

6. 2¾ hours after first dose. Tempera.

7. 4 hours 25 min. Pen and water-colour drawing.

8. 5 hours 45 min. Crayon drawing.

'It is probably because my movements are still too un-steady that I am unable to draw as I normally do . . . The intoxication is wearing off, but I can both feel and see it ebbing and flowing about me (now it only reaches to my knees); finally, only an eddying motion remains.'

9. 8 hours. Charcoal drawing.

The intoxication has now worn off, apart from a few small waves (for example, sudden distortions of faces from time to time). The subject feels bewildered and tired. 'I have nothing to say about the last drawing; it is bad and uninteresting.'

13

THE GREAT SYNTHESIS

Mendel, Morgan, Avery

WHEN DARWIN'S THEORY of natural selection was published, the question of how characters were inherited became of burning interest – for if the mechanism were understood, it might be possible to see how the variation of species occurred. The problem had been examined earlier in the century by plant-breeders, in the light of the discovery of the sexual nature of plants. But the facts observed seemed only to make the mystery more baffling. Thus John Goss bred green and white peas together about 1824 and found to his puzzlement that, when green offspring were bred on, they produced only green peas; whereas if the white offspring were bred on both green and white were produced. Soon afterwards, a German biologist pointed out that, when a cross is made, the offspring are often not of an intermediate type but resemble either one parent or the other. He cited the case of a cross between a black pointer and a wolf bitch: of the three offspring, two were typically wolves, one a typical pointer.

When Darwin's paper renewed interest in the field, the man who decided to tackle the problem in a big way was the famous German biologist Karl Nägeli, whom we have already met in connection with the discovery of the cell. He had already done six years' work on the hawkweed, and he now returned to the breeding of this plant.

However it was the obscure Moravian monk whose portrait is seen overleaf who was to reveal the mechanism, while Nägeli wasted his time. The monk was, of course, Gregor Mendel. Born in very poor circumstances, he had realized that his one chance of escaping from peasant poverty into comparative ease and security was to enter the Church. He was ordained at 25 and summoned to be a teacher. But he proved a disappointment to the examiners: in 1850 he was ploughed for the triviality of his replies to a science examination, and in 1856 withdrew or failed in his third attempt to qualify as a High School teacher in natural history.

As a teacher in schools of lower rank, however, he was much liked by his pupils. One of them recalled him as 'a rather stocky, healthy-looking,

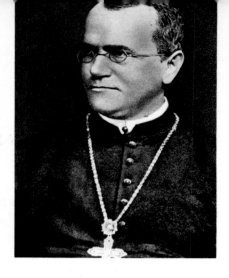

An obscure Moravian monk, *Gregor*
Mendel, laid the foundations of the science
of genetics, and died as obscure as he had lived.

cheerful sort of cleric, contemplating the world and life through his gold-
rimmed spectacles, and never disposed to give anyone the cold shoulder . . .
his goodness won all hearts.'

Mendel started his experiments in 1858 and worked for eight years before
he published his epoch-making paper. With remarkable penetration, he
selected the precise method needed to provide the required information.
He confined himself to breeding together two varieties, between which the
differences were small and well-marked. He chose, for this series of observations, two varieties of peas, which can be tall or dwarf, green or yellow,
smooth or wrinkled. He sowed each seed separately, cross-fertilized the
resulting plants by hand, and then – what no one else had done – kept the
hybrids themselves apart, in different plots. Lastly, he adopted a statistical
approach (at a time when statistics had not been established as a method)
and studied the numerical ratios in which the characters were transmitted,
instead of trying to trace individual lineages.

In the limerick about the young woman who had an affair with a
coloured man,

> The result of her sins
> Was quadruplets, not twins —
> One black and one white and two khaki.

The poem correctly formulates the expected ratios for the expression of a
single hereditary characteristic. These are explicable on the assumption that
each parent donates a factor, or predisposition, for blackness or whiteness of
skin to the offspring. There are then four possible combinations of such
factors: black + black (i.e. black tendency is received from both parents),
black + white, white + black, and white + white. If it is true that posses-
sion of two contrasting factors manifests as 'khaki' skin-colour, the 1 : 2 : 1
ratio is explained.

312

But, as Mendel succeeded in showing, the situation is frequently made more complex by the fact that, when contrasting factors come together, one dominates the other. Thus a person who has received both blue and brown factors for eye-colour will have blue eyes, and will be indistinguishable from a person carrying two blue factors. The difference will only emerge in subsequent generations. Thus if two blue-eyed persons, each carrying only blue factors, breed offspring, all their eyes must be blue; whereas if two blue-eyed persons each carrying mixed factors breed, the offspring will be both blue and brown in the proportion of 3:1.

In his main experimental series, Mendel obtained 8,023 peas from 258 plants: of these, 6,022 were yellow, 2,001 were green – a ratio of 3 to 1. Yellow was dominant to green, as he had already begun to suspect from earlier runs. The same 3:1 ratio was found for each of the seven factors he was studying – form of pod, wrinkling in skin, and so on. In the next season, Mendel crossed round yellow peas with wrinkled green ones, obtaining 315 round and yellow, 101 wrinkled and yellow, 108 round and green, 32 wrinkled and green – that is, in the proportion of 9:3:3:1. On the assumption of dominance, this was precisely the ratio to be expected. Darwin had also experimented with peas and had noticed the 3:1 ratio for a single

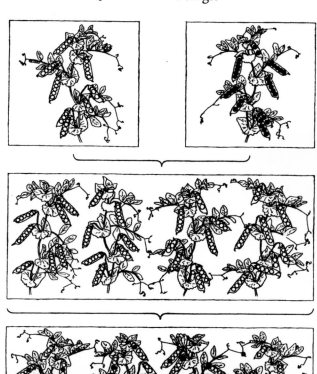

Crossing round yellow peas (left) with wrinkled green ones, Mendel showed that the first generation had only the dominant characteristics (round, yellow). After that, the recessive characteristics creep in, in all possible combinations (bottom line) and in the proportions that Mendel discovered – 9:3:3:1

character. It took Mendel to extend the method and to deduce from it the principle of dominance.

However, Mendel did not immediately publish his conclusion. He persisted in the still more laborious task of studying the interplay of three factors, giving twenty-seven possible combinations. Again, the ratios predictable on the assumptions just described were found. Mendel, who had now been working on the problem for eight years, then generalized his findings into three classic principles. The essential feature of these was that living things are a mosaic of independent hereditary factors, and, as he said, 'in each successive generation, the two primal characters issue distinct and unadulterated out of the hybridized pair . . .'

Mendel announced his results in two lectures to the local scientific society, and his monograph appeared in its *Proceedings* in 1866. The paper remained unnoticed by the scientific world. Darwin's book on Variation appeared two years later, and did not mention Mendel. Perhaps it was because people were absorbed by the origin of differences between species that they could take no interest in the differences within a species.

Mendel now wrote to Nägeli, asking for help and offering to work on hawkweed. After a lapse of two months Nägeli replied, in a supercilious tone, and it is obvious that he thought Mendel's idea of the endless recombination of independent factors impossible. He thought that the pure strains, if bred long enough, would eventually vary, and urged Mendel to grow more peas. As Mendel had already recorded observations on 12,980 specimens this must have been irritating advice.

Nägeli offered however to grow some of Mendel's seeds at the Botanic Gardens at Munich. Mendel promptly sent him 140 packets, but Nägeli never planted them, and in his great work of 1884, did not even refer to Mendel. Mendel's further letters were briefly acknowledged or ignored.

Mendel, for his part, attempt to repeat Nägeli's work with hawkweed. Hawkweed was, in fact, totally unsuitable. Being small, it is hopelessly difficult to fertilize by hand, and in 1869 Mendel began to develop eye-trouble. More serious still, it has a number of remarkably constant intermediate forms and sometimes even produces seeds without fertilization, as was later discovered. Mendel who at one stage thought he had discovered self-fertilization, was frustrated by the inexplicable results he obtained. Eventually, he gave up hawkweed and took to keeping bees.

Mendel was made prelate of his foundation in 1868. In 1875 the monastery became embroiled in a tax dispute, and he had no more time for research. He died, a scientific nonentity, in 1884, the year in which Nägeli's findings were published amid paeans of praise. A fuchsia was, however, named, after him by a grower, in gratitude for his adjudication at flower shows.

Evening primrose mutants, *found growing on waste land, intrigued de Vries, who developed from this basis his theory of 'mutations'. Mutant forms bred true, he found, and concluded that the species was splitting up into several new species.*

THESE UNUSUAL dwarf and broad-leaved forms of the evening prim-rose, *Oenothera lamarckiana*, were found growing, together with the normal form, on a piece of waste land near Amsterdam in 1886, by a Dutch professor of botany, Hugo de Vries. The plant, an importation from America, had escaped from a nearby garden. De Vries took a house near the meadow, and proceeded to breed several of the abnormal varieties by self-fertilization. In the next few generations, he found, many variants arose, and these seemed to breed true. To de Vries it seemed as if the species was disintegrating into a number of forms so distinct as to constitute new species. During the next ten years, in pursuit of this promising clue, he raised 53,509 plants and found among them what he considered to be eight new species.

De Vries, even before this discovery, had become suspicious of the Darwinian view that species are modified gradually by the piling-up of many slight variations, and he had begun to look for evidence of sudden jumps ('saltations', Huxley had speculatively called them) in the manner already suggested by Koelliker and Nägeli. Here seemed to be the evidence he needed. Then in 1894, while he was still investigating the question, William Bateson published his great work *Materials for the study of Variation*, citing many other instances.

In 1900, de Vries finally brought out the book in which he put forward his 'mutation theory'. In addition to asserting the occurrence of jumps, or mutations, he asserted, to the annoyance of the Darwinists, that one ought not to ask: what is the origin of a species, but rather, what is the origin of a species character?

315

The irony in this is that, as was afterwards proved by a Dane who repeated his experiments, what de Vries had painstakingly garnered were not new species at all, but simply stable intermediate types.

Nevertheless, the idea of mutation proved sound: many experiments confirmed that sudden jumps do occur.

De Vries performed one other service for biology. In preparing his book, he read widely and, in so doing, came across a monograph in an obscure scientific publication by an unknown Moravian monk – the now dead Mendel's paper of 1866. He at once realized its importance, as did two other biologists about the same time. So, just half a century after it was written, this epoch-making paper was finally recognized by the world. Recognized, but not generally accepted: to many, the idea that factors could join forces within the cell, and yet remain quite unaffected by each other, seemed too improbable to credit. It was an American, T. H. Morgan, who eventually proved the validity of Mendel's claim, but before he could do so, the structure of the nucleus had to be established.

Two technical advances combined, while Mendel's paper was accumulating dust unrecognized, to open up the nucleus of the cell to inspection, and thus, as it proved, paved the way towards understanding the cellular processes underlying the phenomena which Mendel had so conscientiously recorded.

The first was the invention of improved microscopes, with lenses still less affected by differences in the colour of light; the second was improved means of staining. Dr H. Sorby of Sheffield stained specimens with such primitive dyes as port and carmine. The discovery of the selective character of dyes derived from logwood, which pick out some tissues and leave others clear, was vital to the advance of biology.

These dyes made clear that the nucleus was not a transitory phenomenon but a permanent feature of the cell. What was its function? Much work was devoted to it after about 1875. Soon new structures were seen within the cell: for instance, the Golgi apparatus (the function of which is still obscure), seen in 1867, was first described in 1885. But above all the new methods revealed the evanescent appearance of clusters of rods within the nucleus: the chromosomes. These rods, it was found, appeared shortly before cell-division. They split in two lengthwise and the two sets resulting were pulled (apparently) into opposite ends of the cell, which then divided in two. After which the chromosomes wound up into a ball and again vanished from view.

From the historical point of view, what is interesting is how slowly the facts were uncovered and what a large number of biologists were required to discover them.

It was the Liège cytologist Eduard van Beneden who in 1875 gave the first detailed account of how the nucleus divided, based on a study of rabbit cells: he showed how the nuclear material forms a disk across the middle of the cell, prior to the separation of the split chromosomes. In the same year Eduard Strasburger described the process in a classic book. The following year a Frenchman, E. G. Balbiani, observed the formation of chromosomes from the nuclear mass, and their subsequent division into pairs: the secret of his method was to use cells from the skin of grasshoppers, in which the process is unusually clear. He made one error: he thought the chromosomes split into two segments. It was the German cytologist Walther Flemming who, using the newly developed oil-immersion lens, showed that the division was longitudinal. By this time microscopic technique had advanced to the point where the process of division could be followed continuously in living material. Hitherto, it had been necessary to use stained (and therefore dead) material, and the sequence of events was a matter of inference.

These pictures, the first clear delineation of the sequence of nuclear division, were drawn in 1882 by Flemming, using cells from a salamander larva, in which the process was also found to be clearly visible. Flemming had been one of those who believed that the nucleus vanished at cell-division.

Flemming named many features of the nucleus, calling the dark thread which appeared at cell-division *chromatin.* Balbiani, showing that it resolved into rods, called them *bâtonnets,* or staves. In 1888 they were renamed chromosomes. By an ironical chance, Balbiani had drawn a pretty good picture of the chromatin as much as sixteen years previously, without realizing what he was seeing. He was studying the one-celled organisms known as *Paramoecia,* which occasionally come together and fuse their nuclear material, in a primitive version of sexual conjugation; he drew a sketch of this, in the detail of which the chromatin can be seen. But Balbiani thought, like others at that time, that the protozoa (of which *Paramoecium* is an example) were complete animals, with mouth, stomach, sexual organs, etc. He therefore interpreted the nuclei as ovaries and spermatozoa-forming organs, and the chromatin threads as clusters of sperm.

But what happened to the chromosomes when the nucleus grew invisible? Did they persist, somehow, unaltered until the next division? In 1885, van Beneden, using the horseworm *Ascaris megalocephala,* which has large, clear chromosomes, proved they did. Soon it was shown that the number of chromosomes is the same in every cell of a given plant or animal, and indeed in every specimen of any one species, but that it varies widely from one species to another. In the normal form of *Ascaris* there are 4; in man, 46.

Here, then, was a plausible mechanism, by which the blueprints in one cell could be transmitted to the next: a substance which duplicated itself

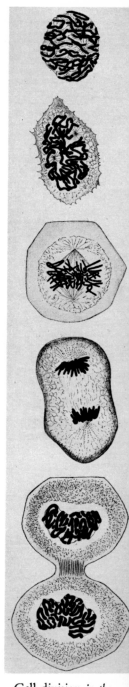

Cell division *in the Salamander larva, drawn by Flemming.*

and passed the twin copies to the daughter cells. But before it could be proved to meet the requirements of a genetic mechanism, it was also necessary to know what happened when the organism reproduced itself.

First the fact had to be established that all multicellular creatures bear some form of egg which is fertilized by a sperm. It was Pringsheim who first saw a sperm enter a female cell, in 1856. In 1873 Bütschli saw two nuclei within a fertilized egg, and three years later, O. Hertwig realized that one of these had come from the sperm. Thus it was seen that the genetic material is contributed to the offspring from both parents. But when it was understood that the number of chromosomes was constant, it was evident that somewhere along the line the number must be reduced, or else the offspring would have twice as many as each parent. It was an obvious guess that a special cell-division must occur in which the number was halved, in the case of both egg and sperm, for in this way the offspring would receive a selection of characters from each parent.

In 1883 van Beneden, using a variety of his horseworm, *Ascaris,* which has only two chromosomes, was able to see that each parent contributed only one to the offspring. This discovery sounds simple, but was complicated by the fact that in many species the division follows a more complex course, small cells being formed which are abandoned: at first these 'polar bodies' were not even recognized as cells. A few years afterwards, Boveri and Hertwig corrected van Beneden's errors in this respect. The process was soon shown to occur in plants also, and the fact that there are differences of detail in many species emerged. The term *maiosis* (later corrupted to meiosis) for this reduction-division was proposed in 1905.

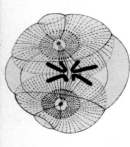

The machinery of the cell: centrosomes and asters in the horseworm, Ascaris.

This Naum Gabo-like construction shows the mysterious centrosomes, or central bodies, which seem to pull the divided chromosomes apart. The drawing is from van Beneden and Neyt's book of 1887, and shows a cell from *Ascaris megalocephala.* It was identified as a permanent feature of the cell-nucleus, and soon it was discovered that it derived from the middle segment of the sperm, and that it was this structure which provided the stimulus to the egg to divide on fertilization. The system of rays springing from it is called the aster. (This system is absent from higher plants.)

Thus was established the fact that the nucleus of the cell contains minutely ingenious machinery for controlling the development of the cell, and the form of the organism of which it is part; and that the blueprints for this are transmitted from one cell to another and finally to the offspring. This was

The moment of fertilization, *magnified by the electron microscope about 60,000 diameters. Sperm of the sea-urchin (top) sends out a filament from the acrosome at the tip; this penetrates the egg, and from that moment no other sperm can fertilize the egg.*

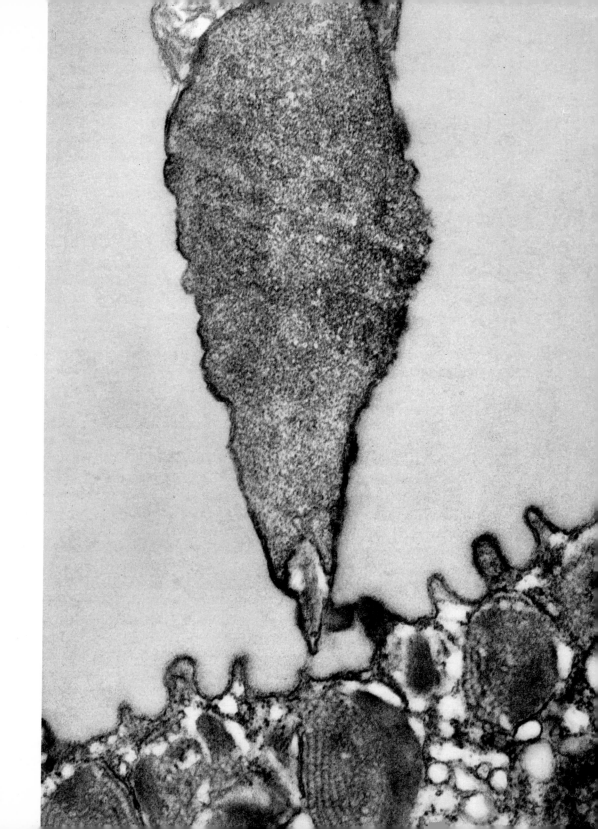

the great achievement of the latter part of the nineteenth century. Establishing the nature of these blueprints and their mechanism of action was to prove the major achievement of the twentieth century.

IN 1904 DE VRIES, accompanied by the great Swedish chemist Arrhenius and the great German-American biologist Jacques Loeb, went to California to visit a man who was already world-famous as a plant breeder: Luther Burbank. They were disappointed to find that all his crosses were uncontrolled: often he let whole fields of specimens cross-pollinate each other in a wholly random way, on the off-chance that something saleable would emerge. Moreover, he did not look for specific mutations, but merely selected for superficial characters, which might or might not breed true.

Burbank's own vast claims, and those of the nurserymen to whom he sold his varieties outright, had made him a national figure. His hard work and non-smoking teetotalism made it possible to bill him as a model of Americanism – his divorce was tactfully suppressed. Burbank himself had a conviction he was a Messiah, and believed his head was steadily growing larger.

Actually Burbank denied the existence of mutation, rejected Mendel's findings and claimed to have produced all de Vries' varieties of *Oenothera* himself. How the Carnegie foundation was hypnotized by this American success-story into giving him a grant of $50,000 to put his 'scientific work' on record is one of the more amusing stories in the history of biology. Naturally, no report was ever published.

An ignorant populace believed his claim to have 'created new flavours' and thought his powers almost magical. When the famous earthquake spared his nurseries, though damaging his house, this was thought a miraculous intervention. By a final irony, this reputed Christian was suddenly revealed as an infidel, and two months later died and was given, as he had previously arranged, a freethinker's funeral.

The Burbank myth still persists in the USA: one of his books is still in use in schools, and in 1940 this commemorative stamp was issued.

In the 1930's, a Russian plant breeder, Trofim Lysenko, assailed Mendelism and claimed to have caused plants to adapt to special environments, such as unusually dry or cold climates. Lysenko had to his credit some successes in the 'vernalization' of wheat, but he was not a scientist, and his 'experiments', conducted without controls or scientific precautions, aroused only ridicule in the west. The Russian government, always anxious for both practical and ideological reasons to stress that man can overcome his environment and that he is not limited by the past, and anxious in particular to stimulate agricultural progress, erected Lysenkoism into an orthodoxy and banished or penalized orthodox geneticists.

Portrait of a myth.
Three-cent stamp (1940)
commemorating
Luther Burbank.

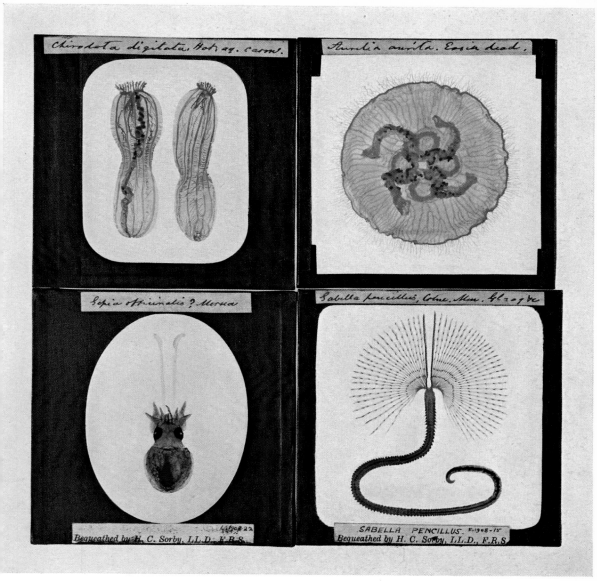

The invention of staining *helped to open up the cell nucleus to microscopic inspection. Henry Sorby of Sheffield made these slides of marine animals in the middle of the 19th century, using carmine, port wine and other primitive dyes.*

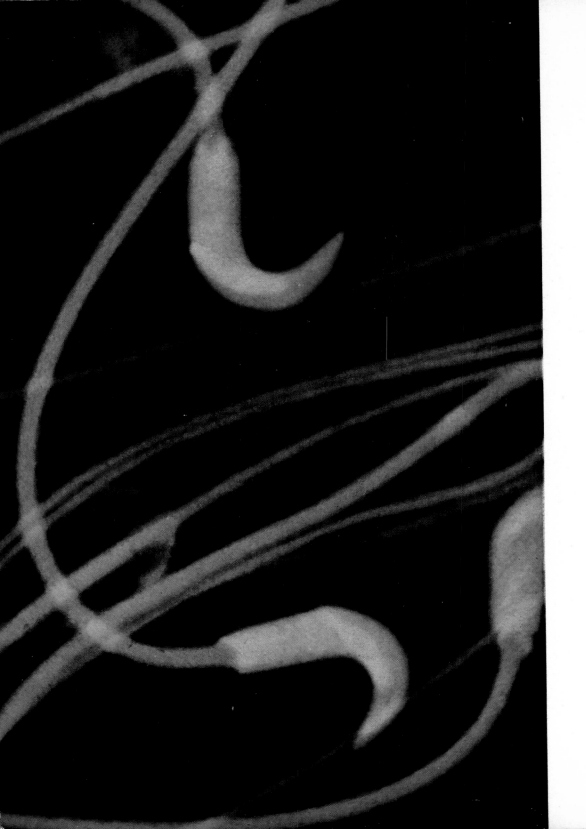

'A motley throng' was the comment of H. J. Muller, Morgan's pupil, on the numerous mutant forms of fruit-fly produced when the parents were subjected to irradiation. Stunted wings, changes in colour, etc. provided geneticists with useful markers for studying the location of different genes on the chromosomes.

IT WAS WITH THE SMALL FRUIT-FLY seen here that the American biologist T. H. Morgan explored, in incredible detail, the subject of mutation and laid the basis of genetics as it was understood in the first half of the twentieth century.

Morgan, who had started life as an embryologist, was 43 when he suddenly perceived that mutation, as established by de Vries, provided a brand-new means of investigating genetics. Ironically enough, he had at first been sceptical of the Mendelian interpretation and agreed with Pearson's comment in 1908: 'There is no definite proof of Mendelism applying to any living form at present.'

But, seized with the idea of making a thorough study of mutation, he cast around for suitable experimental material. He tried mice, rats, pigeons and

Miscroscopic staining has advanced enormously since Sorby's day. These hamster spermatozoa have been treated with acridine orange and photographed, still living, by ultra-violet light. The acrosome – the cap-like structure at the head, which probably plays a vital part in penetrating the egg – shows up in a brilliant fluorescent red, and the nucleus in bright green. Where the two overlap, a yellow or yellowish-green image results.

even the plant-louse or aphid. Then he heard of some work on the fruit-fly, *Drosophila,* and decided that this was what he needed. The fruit-fly breeds rapidly, attaining maturity in twelve days: 30 generations can be bred in a year. It thrives on a simple mash of bananas. It has clearly marked mutations. Soon Morgan's room at Columbia University was filled with milk-bottles containing fruit-flies.

Morgan subjected them to high and low temperatures, to acids and alkalis, to radioactivity and unusual diets, in an attempt to produce mutant forms – in vain. After about a year, however, in April 1910, there suddenly appeared a fly with white eyes – normally the eyes of *Drosophila* are red. This was what he needed. Breeding the solitary abnormal specimen with normal females, he soon had 1,237 offspring – all red-eyed, for the red was dominant to white. But in the following generation of 4,252 flies, 782 were white-eyed.

By the end of 1910 Morgan had forty mutants, to which, in Disneyesque style, he gave such names as Humpy, Dumpy, Chubby, Pink-eye, Crumpled and Speck. He had wingless flies, hairless flies, eyeless flies, flies of unusual colours and flies with abnormal veins in their wings. Most of these variations were disadvantageous. But the finding which intrigued him most was that the white-eyed variation appeared only in males. Breeding more and more flies, Morgan found that *white eye* never occurred in conjunction with *grey wing,* only with *yellow wing.* Similarly, *ebony body* appeared only with *pink eye, black body* appeared only with *vestigial wing.* There seemed to be three groups of characters which went together – which could be explained if *Drosophila* had three chromosomes. But unfortunately it had four, three big and one small.

Then, in 1914, *bent wing* was found; it did not link with any of the other groups – so it must be controlled by a factor on the small chromosome. Soon after, *eyeless* was found, and after another five years' effort, *shaven.* These linked with *bent wing.* The chromosomal basis of heredity was now proven. But what of the so called sex-linkage – the fact that some features appeared only in the male sex?

The next picture gives the answer. In *Drosophila* one of the male chromo-somes is slightly bigger than the corresponding chromosome in the female: it has a hooked end. This additional material carries the sex-determining factor and a number of other factors which accordingly are only found in con-junction with it.

Chromosomes *of fruit-fly larva:*
X and X, female; X and Y, male.

SCALE

10 μ

Thomas Hunt Morgan, *whose classic studies of heredity in the fruit-fly may cause him to be ranked even higher than Darwin and called forth the quip, 'God must have created the fruit-fly especially for Morgan'.*

One more major discovery was to come. One day, *white eye* and *yellow wing* were found *not* linked together. Morgan made the bold postulate that a chromosome had broken and that at the time of nuclear division, each half had rejoined with the wrong bit of the reduplicated chromosome. If this were the case, one would expect a whole block of characters to remain linked, in all subsequent generations, with a block from which it had formerly been unlinked. So it proved. The phenomenon was termed 'crossing over'. Thus mutation was seen to take two forms: the changing of a single characteristic, due to damage to a single gene, and a major reshuffling of characters.

At first Morgan's results were greeted with the customary incredulity. It all seemed too neat. In 1922, the British biologist William Bateson visited Morgan's lab. He arrived sceptical, but left conceding, 'I can see no escape from capitulation on the main point. The chromosomes must in some way be connected with our transferable characters.' His report convinced people, and soon Institutes of Genetics were being set up all over the world.

Morgan brought in able men to help him, notably Sturtevant, the son of a racehorse breeder: it was he who first postulated that the genetic factors, which were christened *genes,* were arranged linearly, like beads on a necklace. The third of the trio was Bridges, who discovered *shaven* and built the incubators in which it was necessary to keep the flies in cold weather. By 1936 Bridges was propagating no fewer than 900 distinct stocks of *Drosophila,* and supplying specimens to scientists all over the world. He died of a heart attack aged 49. One of Morgan's ablest co-workers was his wife, Lilian who, having inferred the possibility of hermaphroditism in *Drosophila,* found the first hermaphrodite in 1922.

It is difficult to convey the titanic impulse which Morgan's work gave to biology for the next thirty years. It was his method as much as his actual discoveries which was significant. In *Drosophila* he found a tool which has become classic. But it was above all the unprecedented scale on which he tackled the problem which sounded the death-knell of the old pattern of a single devoted scientist working alone, and introduced the new era of teams of varied specialists tackling problems previously thought too complex to investigate. In the view of Lancelot Hogben, Morgan's name will be mentioned more often than Darwin's two hundred years hence.

The defect of Morgan's method was the rareness of natural mutation. Millions of flies had to be bred before any occurred. One of Morgan's former students, H. J. Muller, who had worked in the 'fly squad', decided to renew the attack on producing mutations artificially. He started in 1918; his first task was to establish normal mutation rates with which the effects of treatment could be compared. Then he subjected flies to various temperatures, without significant effect. Next he tried more drastic methods. Many other scientists were also seeking to cause mutation. 'In the course of this work,' Muller said, 'animals and plants have been drugged, poisoned, intoxicated, illuminated, kept in darkness, half smothered, painted inside and out, whirled round and round, shaken violently, vaccinated, mutilated, educated, and treated with everything except affection from generation to generation.' None of this had any effect except to give Muller a nervous breakdown from overwork. Obviously, since most mutations are disadvantageous, nature has taken care to protect the gene from every conceivable risk.

Then Muller did some thinking. Mutations, he reasoned, concern only a single gene, a single point on the chromosome. The cause of mutation must therefore be something which strikes at a single point, not something which influences the whole chromosome. It must be due to a 'microscopic accident'. Radiation was the only thing which seemed to fill the bill.

He therefore exposed a batch of flies to a dose of X-radiation so strong as to produce sterility in some. These flies were then bred with untreated flies. Ten days later, he had a great mass of mutant flies. 'They were a motley throng,' he commented; some were even hermaphrodite. A count revealed that he had increased the mutation rate 150 times. Microscopic inspection showed that chromosomes had even broken in pieces. 'Here indeed was the promised land. The results in these experiments were startling and unequivocal. The roots of life – the genes – had indeed been struck and they had yielded.' This was a form of attack with which evolution had not developed methods of coping, since it scarcely existed in nature.

Soon other scientists were irradiating a wide range of other organisms, from wasps to wheat, with like effect.

In the years which followed, one theme was dominant: the attempt to 'map' the chromosomes, i.e. to establish the order of the genes. By studying which factors are found together in a large number of cases of 'crossing over' it is possible to calculate the relative position of different factors. For factors remote from one another on the chromosome will become separated relatively often; those adjacent to each other only seldom. This work received a big impetus in 1933, when Painter published a paper on a new method of staining which, in the case of the large chromosomes found in the salivary glands of *Drosophila*, revealed the cross-banding seen below. Painter showed that this banding appeared to correspond to the genes themselves.

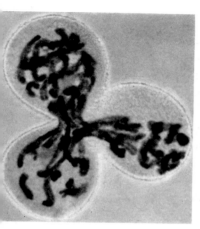

Damaged chromosomes, *as a result of being subjected to radiation, are seen here. Breakage, failure of the parts to separate during cell-division, or even – as here – splitting three ways, commonly ensue.*

'Beads on the chromosome necklace.' *Cross-bands were revealed by the electron microscope when it was applied to the giant chromosomes found in the salivary glands of the fruit-fly. Do they correspond to the genes – the units of heredity?*

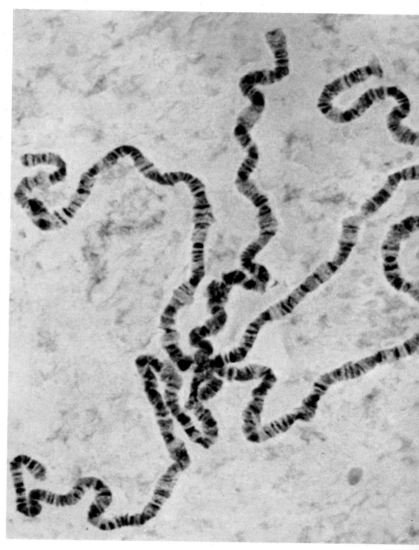

How genes produce their effect remained a mystery. It was George Beadle who first found a means of investigating the problem.

In 1932, feeling that purely genetic work on *Drosophila* was yielding diminishing returns, he cast about for new methods of approach. During a year's leave from the California Institute of Technology, where he was a National Research Fellow, he worked in Paris with Boris Ephrussi; together they set out to transplant the eye of one *Drosophila* embryo into another of different eye-colour, to see what would happen then. When they had eventually succeeded in performing this incredibly delicate operation, they found the colour of the implanted eye was altered. This caused Beadle to speculate how genes might regulate formation of the pigments determining eye-colour. Chemistry, he decided, was the key to future work in genetics.

Back in the USA, at Stanford University, he teamed up with a chemist, Edward Tatum. In 1940 they decided to abandon *Drosophila* for some organism of which the chemistry was simple and well understood. They selected the red bread-mould *Neurospora crassa*. It was known that this would grow readily on a jelly containing a mixture of mineral salts, sugar and biotin. (Biotin had only recently been discovered.) Furthermore, it would reproduce either sexually – that is by the fusion of the branches of two specimens leading to the formation of spores – or asexually, by simple division. They therefore exposed some 2,000 test-tubes containing the mould to X-rays to induce mutations, and awaited results. To their intense satisfaction, two of the specimens – in tubes number 299 and 1,090 – failed to grow. Other spores from the same stock also failed to grow: the inference was that a mutation had occurred, as a result of which they were now unable to make some needed substance from the raw materials provided.

They therefore divided the mutant forms into a number of batches and added a different vitamin to each. In the tubes to which vitamin B-6 had been added, the mould soon began to grow. This seemed to prove that the mutation involved an inability to manufacture B-6.

To test this, the mutant form was crossed with the normal, and the cross was bred on. Of the many spores it produced, half should be defective, half normal, if the defect was being transmitted in a Mendelian manner. This proved to be the case.

With this series of experiments, Beadle established the validity of a basic principle: one gene, one enzyme. His theory was that the genes act as a pattern or template on which enzymes are formed: each enzyme makes possible a given chemical process within the cell – in this case the formation of B-6. Damage a gene, and the enzyme fails to be formed.

By this advance, a link was forged between two major fields of enquiry: genetics and the study of the metabolic processes by which cells maintain

The red bread-mould, *Neurospora crassa, was the choice of G. W. Beadle for his investigations into the chemistry of genetics. Here he is seen (centre) examining some of the thousands of test-tubes containing the various strains of the mould.*

themselves and grow. But what *were* genes, actually, and how did they control the formation of enzymes? In the twenty years which followed, a great part of this question was answered.

In the next few years Beadle and Tatum grew some 80,000 spores, among which were found some 400 mutants. A few of these were potentially advantageous: thus one enabled the mould to accept as food a material which had previously been poisonous to it. In the course of detailed study of the varying nutritional requirements of the mutants, much light was thrown on the metabolic processes themselves. Again, the fact that some rats, fed on a diet containing tryptophane, did not need the vitamin niacin, was found to be true of *Neurospora* also, and revealed that it made its niacin from tryptophane. Since human sufferers from pellagra were cured by niacin, it was a logical inference that their diet was deficient in tryptophane.

Beadle's choice of *Neurospora* was a brilliant stroke: it has been used by many another investigator. Beadle decided that he was unlikely ever to make another discovery of such value, and that he would become a scientific administrator. Returning to Caltech, he built up the biology department into one of the world's leading centres of research.

In 1932 a bombshell exploded in the field of immunology. Fred Griffith, an English bacteriologist, injected a virulent strain of pneumococcus (the bacterium which causes pneumonia) into mice, and then transferred it from the first batch of mice to a second, and on through 36 generations. In its passage through their bodies, the virus lost its virulence and become attenuated. This is a standard method of preparing vaccines discovered originally by Pasteur. Then, one day, Griffith injected into some mice both the attenuated Type I strain, and also bacteria of a virulent strain, Type III, which had been killed by exposure to heat – another standard method of preparing a vaccine.

To his surprise the mice, which should have been doubly protected, developed acute pneumonia. Examining the blood cells, he found them alive with Type III bacteria, identifiable by their gummy coats or capsules. He wondered whether he had failed to kill the Type III with the heat treatment, but a check on the rest of the batch eliminated this possibility. The only possible conclusion was that the living Type I had somehow acquired both virulence and the characteristic gummy coat from the dead Type III!

It seemed totally incredible. One of those who refused to accept Griffith's claim, which appeared to upset the whole basis of immunology, was a melancholy, brooding American immunochemist, named Oswald Avery. Avery, who was suffering from Graves's disease, was obliged to take six months' sick leave. When he returned, Griffith's results had been duplicated at the Rockefeller Institute and also in Germany. Indeed, the experiment was repeated in a test-tube. Avery now accepted the facts and immediately perceived the far-reaching implications, not merely for bacteriology and genetics, but for medicine and for biology as a whole.

Avery combined a respect for facts with a sense of classical purity. He despised verbal confusion. Conversation with him was apt to degenerate into a monologue, in which (according to a colleague) 'each statement, each word, indeed each hesitation, was carefully weighed and staged. The marvellous precision of the performance was not achieved by accident. Endless rehearsals assured the perfection of conversation pieces that most of us came to know by heart and referred to as "the Red Seal Records".'

Avery lectured but rarely in public: he shunned publicity and felt that a scientist should be judged by his achievement, not by the trivia of his daily life. He was somewhat cut off from the main stream of scientific development, but he had an uncanny sense of what was truly important, and spent long hours formulating and reformulating a problem in the most precise terms possible. The final experiment had to be one which required no statistical analysis, covered all significant variables, and never failed – an *experimentum crucis*.

This Avery achieved, and why he did not receive a Nobel prize is one of the mysteries of that somewhat arbitrary award.

He had shown that virulent pneumococci are those which have a coat or capsule, and that this enables them to resist phagocytosis. Moreover, antibodies act by neutralizing this property of the capsule. Furthermore, there are a number of types of capsule, and specific antibodies are formed against each one.

But it was not until 1944 that Avery, working at the Rockefeller Institute, performed his crucial experiment – one which launched a tide of experimentation unequalled in the history of biology. The discovery to which it led was as radical as the discovery of the cell; the experiment itself was unusually decisive and convincing. The discovery was that the genetic information carried by the chromosomes is expressed in the structure of a molecule of an obscure acid, known to chemists since 1869. This molecule is known as deoxyribose nucleic acid, or DNA for short.

Essentially, what Avery now did was to take two strains of pneumococci, one of which had a smooth coat, the other a rough one. With the enthusiastic aid of younger collaborators, he separated from the coated variety a substance into which he placed the uncoated bacteria. When these in due course divided, some were found to have acquired smooth coats, and this feature persisted in all subsequent generations. A hereditary factor for smooth coat had been conveyed from one strain of bacterium to the other. The process could also be carried out with other factors, such as the ability to dispense with certain vitamins. Avery then purified the substance until it could be crystallized, showing that it was still effective as a genetic determinant, and proved that it was DNA.

Let us pause a moment to recognize the epoch-making nature of this advance. It was immediately clear that DNA is the blueprint which determines the way in which every organism develops. Hence it offered a key not only to understanding the metabolic processes of cell life but to the great mystery of how the embryo develops into a complex organism. Obviously there were many DNAs, differing from each other in some subtle respect; these differences must be responsible not only for the differing structure of the many species of plants and animals, but for the differences within species. Like a blueprint, it carries the information which determines the appearance of the final product. If the 'code' in which this information was expressed could be cracked, an extraordinary control of living processes might be achieved. Perhaps – though no one liked to hint at such a bizarre idea – living material could be synthesized in the test-tube. To the exploring of the nucleic acids, and to the cracking of the code, a cataract of effort was soon devoted.

The story of DNA had started in 1869, with a young Swiss biochemist, Friedrich Miescher, who was studying under the famous Hoppé-Seyler, in Tübingen. Assigned to make analyses of pus cells, he sought a way to extract the nuclei in bulk. It occurred to him that pepsin, the enzyme which digests proteins in the stomach, might also digest cell proteins. It did so very nicely. When he analysed the solution, he found it contained a hitherto unknown substance, which he named nuclein.

Hoppé-Seyler, surprised and always anxious to be in on a new discovery, repeated the experiment and published his own account simultaneously with Miescher's, which was delayed two years for the purpose. When the substance was shown to be an acid, the name was modified to nucleic acid.

Miescher, on returning to his home-town, Basle, continued to explore this new substance, and found a rich source in the sperm of the salmon which swam up the Rhine every spring: the nuclei are particularly large. He required a low temperature for many of his analyses and therefore had to work with blue and trembling hands in the early morning hours and in unheated rooms in mid-winter. He showed that the sperm contained carbon, oxygen, hydrogen, nitrogen, and – this was the surprise – phosphorus. Hitherto the only substance found in animal tissues observed to contain phosphorus was the lecithin in egg-yolk.

Then interest waned. In the twentieth century, sporadic work was done towards establishing the structure of the nucleic acid molecule. It was obviously a big one, and it became clear that it contained four of the building bricks known as amino-acids – adenine, cytosine, guanine and thymine – but the exact structure eluded analysis. In the 1930's it became clear that there were in fact two nucleic acids. The second, known as RNA, for ribose nucleic acid, proved to contain uracil in place of the thymine of DNA, and ribose sugar instead of deoxyribose. It was thought at first that DNA was peculiar to animals, RNA to plants, but in the early 1940's it was proved that both occur in the nucleus, while RNA alone is found in the cytoplasm. Such was the state of knowledge about this crucial molecule at the time of Avery's experiment. But upon his revelation of its importance, a new wave of attacks on its structure was launched.

WITH THIS APPARATUS, Michael Tswett, a Russian botanist, succeeded in 1906 in separating the plant pigments known as carotenes – responsible for the red colour of carrots, among other things. The tube

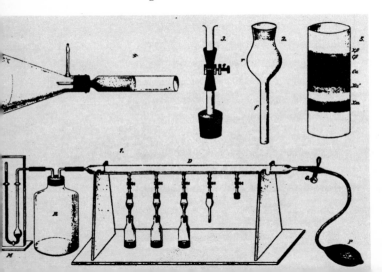

First crude version *of Michael Tswett's apparatus for analysis by chromatography. Several small samples could be analysed at once, the constituents showing up as bands of different colours in the columns.*

contained salt or sugar, and the mixture of pigments was dissolved in petrol and was poured on the top of the column. More petrol was added. In half an hour or so the material had sorted itself out into at least six different layers – green ones due to chlorophylls, yellow ones due to xanthophylls, and red and orange ones to carotenes.

Thus was invented the delicate method of separation known as column chromatography. Later it was realized that it could be used for any materials which would be washed down the column at different speeds or picked up by the absorbent material with different degres of readiness, and many improvements of method were evolved, notably by Martin and Synge.

Chromatography has become the universal tool of the biochemist, making possible separation of large molecules too fragile to be isolated in any other way. It was by this method that, in 1949, Chargaff and Davidson reopened the attack on the structure of DNA, and succeeded in showing that the amount of adenine found in any one specimen was always equal to the amount of thymine, while the amount of cytosine was always equal to the amount of guanine. The significance of this discovery was not immediately obvious.

The chemical formula of DNA, already known in general terms, could now be accurately worked out. It consisted of a series of similar groups, which came to be called nucleotides. Each consisted of a sugar (of the sort known as deoxyribose) with one of four possible groupings attached to it. These groupings were adenine, cytosine, guanine and thymine. The nucleotides were linked into chains by phosphorus atoms, with three oxygens on the side ('phosphate groups'), thus:

The chain thus made was extremely long, consisting of many thousands of nucleotides. It was obvious that variations in the order of these nucleotides might well provide a 'language' in which the instructions controlling cell growth could be written; what remained mysterious was how the blueprints were copied at the time of cell division. Before this question could be answered, it was necessary to prove how these chemical groups were ordered in three-dimensional space.

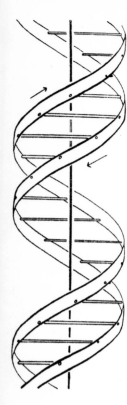

One of the earliest models ever made of the structure of DNA stands to-day on top of a bookcase in Edinburgh. Like an early aeroplane, it displays all the main features of the fully-fledged modern version in a crude form.

In 1952 a group at King's College, London, led by Maurice Wilkins, set out to examine the DNA molecule by X-ray crystallography.

Wilkins is seen (opposite) by his X-ray diffraction apparatus. The X-rays, having wavelengths of the same order as the distances between atoms, are deflected in a complex manner, and produce, on a photographic plate, the sort of pattern seen here. He found that the molecule must repeat at regular intervals, the size of which could be measured. Interestingly, DNA from many different sources proved to have the same kind of diffraction pattern; this suggested that the differences in its genetic role must lie in the order of the units, not in the structure as such. It was in in fact a helix, and the helix completed one turn for every ten nucleotides.

It was in 1953 that Francis Crick, working at Cambridge, together with James Watson, on a visit from Harvard, put forward, in a short but now classic note in *Nature,* 'A Structure for Deoxyribose Nucleic Acid'.

Shortly before, two American workers, Pauling and Corey, had proposed that it might consist of three intertwined threads, with the phosphates near the axis, the bases on the outside. Crick and Watson felt that the phosphates, which are negatively charged, would repel each other, and could not see what would hold it together.

Crick, who had trained originally as a physicist and had worked on sea-mines during the war, felt that it must be possible to make a model which would account for the known behaviour of the molecule – that is, it must be capable of being copied or of reproducing itself, and it must carry in-formation.

So, while Crick worked on his doctoral thesis, Watson built models of wire and tin, to see how the rules governing the bonding of atoms could be observed. They found a clue in Chargaff's discovery of the equivalence of the amounts of adenine and thymine, guanine and cytosine. This suggested some kind of pairing.

Crick and Watson proposed that DNA consists of a double spiral, with the bases on the inside, opposed in pairs, and linked by the weak inter-atomic force known as a hydrogen bond. Then, since thymine can only pair with adenine, and guanine with cytosine, if one chain is known, the other is determined. That is, each chain can build another complementary one. Here was a model which would account for the copying process. And since the order of bases can vary, it constitutes a sort of four-letter alphabet, in which a series of words can be written. (Thus, if we denote the bases by A, C, G and T, one can write such combinations as AGC, ATA, CGT, etc.) Later,

The Crick-Watson model *for the structure of DNA. Compare this, the first hypothesis, with the colour plate facing p. 320.*

Crick showed that such three-letter combinations would be sufficient to provide twenty clear alternatives, even when run on continuously after one another. Thus one could conceive them dictating sequences of amino-acids in enzymes or other proteins.

The proposal roused phenomenal interest, and was important because it made possible a great range of new experiments. For instance, Stahl and Meselson in America succeeded a few years later in showing that the two threads in the DNA helix retain their integrity between cell divisions, as one would expect if they were to convey genetic information into the daughter cells. This model, as one biologist commented, 'captured the imagination of geneticists as few other ideas ever did.'

After so big an advance, a period of digestion and consolidation might have been expected. But in fact the discovery was even more radical than people at first realized: soon the whole field of virus research, and then that of bacteriology, were to be linked to that of chemical genetics. The term 'molecular biology' was coined (over the mutterings of physicists) to describe the new field, and before long many physicists were asking to be given lectures in biology.

Little as Twort and d'Hérelle foresaw, their discovery of 'bacteria-eating' viruses during the First World War was to contribute the next piece of the jigsaw. (In 1933, these bacteriophages had been discovered to contain DNA.)

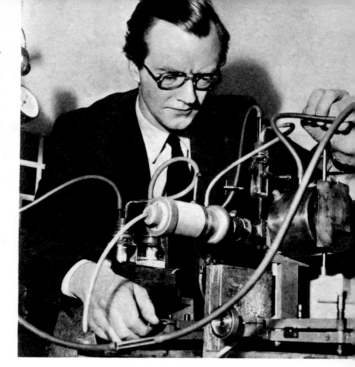

With this apparatus, *Maurice Wilkins projected a beam of X-rays through crystals of DNA, at various angles, and obtained photographs such as that below.*

From this pattern *of dots, produced by the X-rays after being deflected by the atoms in the crystal, the way in which these atoms must be arranged was inferred by mathematical procedures. Hence the main structural features were deduced.*

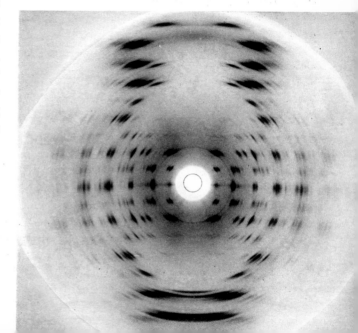

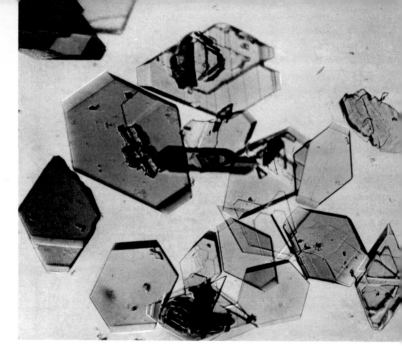

Crystals of myoglobin, *a substance related to haemoglobin, which has the power of holding oxygen until needed. This was the first protein to yield the secret of its molecular structure.*

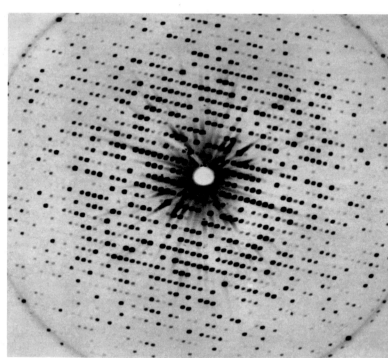

This was the first model *Kendrew produced, from a relatively coarse analysis based on 400 spots, with the aid of a computer. The long, sausage-like protein molecule is seen to be intricately folded. The dark mass is the 'haem' group which has the ability to hold oxygen. But how was the 'sausage' made up?*

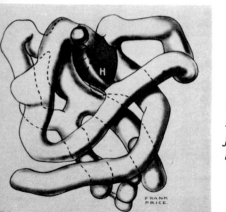

Diffraction pictures *of myoglobin were made by methods similar to those used for studying DNA (see p.333). From them, J.C.Kendrew was able to deduce, for the first time in biological history, the complex structure of a protein molecule. On the various kinds of folding the widely varying properties of diffrent proteins are believed to depend.*

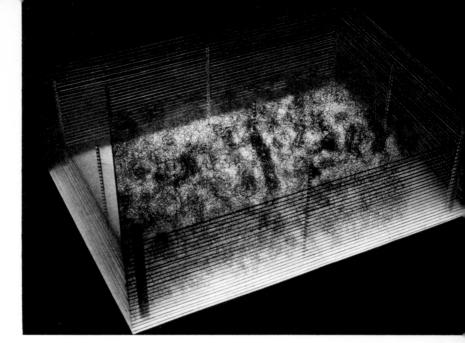

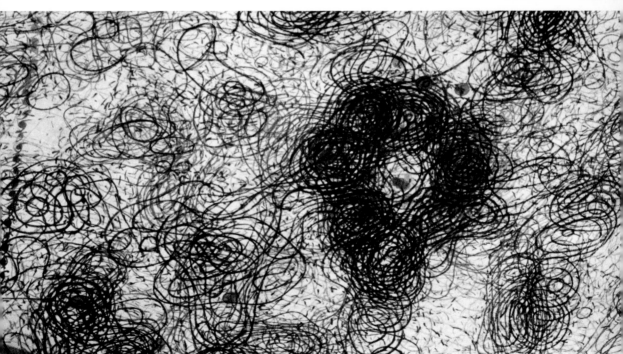

Analysis of the spots *was translated into electron-density maps. These contours, drawn on lucite sheets and stacked up in series, depicted the shape of the protein molecule, just as contours on a map depict the three-dimensional surface of the landscape. But this time, using 9,600 spots, the position of individual atoms began to emerge.*

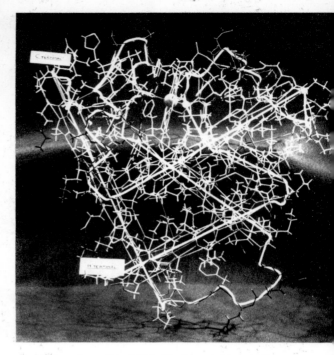

As the position of each atom *was identified, a col/oured marker was clipped to a metal rod at the appro/priate point in space. When as many as possible had been identified, neighbouring atoms were linked with wire, in accordance with their known physico/chemical affinities. Kendrew (left) and Max Perutz are seen discussing the growing model.*

Removing the rods *yielded this fantastically complicated picture. The sausage was revealed as a 'coiled coil'. Thus the structure had three orders: the basic chemical pattern (a long chain); the coiling of this chain into a sausage; and the folding of the sausage. Work continues, on the basis of analysing 25,000 spots with the fastest available computers, to fill in a number of doubtful points.*

While Kendrew was analysing myoglobin, *Max Perutz was attempting to do the same for haemo/globin, the red colouring/matter in blood, which also has an affinity for oxygen. Haemoglobin turned out to consist of four myoglobin molecules, fitted to/gether like a Chinese puzzle. Here is a wooden model, in which the myoglobin units are painted in contrasting colours, to show how they interlock.*

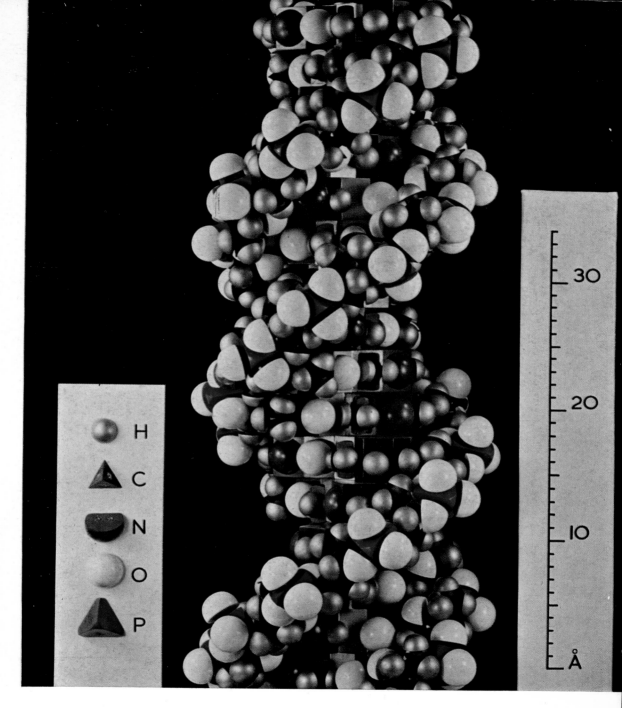

Portrait of a molecule. *Intricately and logically arranged in a double spiral, this DNA model sets out in visual form the construction of the complex long-chain molecule which carries the 'blueprint' of inheritance within the cell nucleus. This is only a short section of a chain which can be many thousand times its thickness in length. The scale is in Ångström units, ten million to the millimetre.*

Something never seen before *was depicted in this colour-plate, when it was first published in 1953 – a successful graft of skin from one mouse to another of a completely different strain (heterograft). Medawar (who received a Nobel prize eight years later) achieved this feat by injecting the recipient mouse, while still in the embryo stage, with antibodies from the future donor. By varying the timing of such injections he showed that there is a point in development at which the range of cells which will in future be recognized as 'own cells' is determined. Cells introduced after this stage are rejected. This proved that the organism is not formed equipped with an unique label of individuality and narrowed the research problem in immunology, as well as opening the way to achieving heterografts of kidneys and other organs in man.*

'FEW BIOLOGICAL phenomena are as dramatic as this,' said Evans in 1952. 'When one adds a small amount of bacterial virus to a vigorously-growing bacterial culture, nothing occurs immediately. Then, suddenly the suspension begins to foam, as materials inside the bacterial cell are liberated into the medium, and within a short time the heavy mass of growing bacteria has been replaced by floating shreds of debris that settle slowly to the bottom of the containing vessel. The clear, bluish supernatant liquid now contains a hundred-fold multiplication of the original virus inoculum.'

The lysis or dissolution of bacteria by phage was first observed in 1921. Then in 1929 Burnet and McKie in Australia discovered that phage could persist in a non-infective form. Here was a mystery. Was phage, as some thought, an enzyme which dissolved the bacterium? What stimulated lysis to take place? Was it a bodily defence mechanism? But the arrival of chemo-therapeutic drugs in the 1930s virtually killed research on phage.

In 1940, a group headed by Max Delbrück of the California Institute of Technology (generally known as 'The Pope') decided to make a new onslaught on the problem. It was found that phage attaches itself to the outside of the bacterium, and squirts its contents into it. Empty shells of phage, known as 'ghosts', are left sticking to the outside. The turning point came in 1946 when it was shown that what the phage squirts in is its DNA. By 1952 it was clear, thanks to Hershey and Chase, that it is this which disorganizes the bacterium. From this moment phage became for the molecular biologists what the fruitfly had been for genetics at the chromosomal level.

Life cycle of the bacteriophage. *The whole process, from the first injection of phage DNA to the break-up of the host bacterium and the discharge of hundreds of new virus particles, takes only about twenty minutes.*

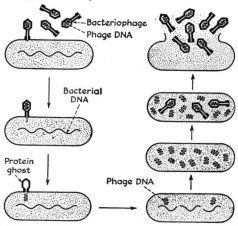

UNDER THE TITLE 'The T2 Mystery', Salvador Luria, a physicist turned bacteriologist, described how he investigated the phenomenon of 'latency' already observed by Burnet. 'T2' is the identification of the strain of phage with which Luria had been experimenting in 1946. He found that occasionally the infected bacterium dissolved, but no new virus appeared. This was the mystery. Could it be that the juice from the dissolved bacteria contained some kind of unassembled phage or 'phage precursor' – a sort of arrested virus? He determined to examine it and see. Chance then intervened: wishing to use a bacterium resistant to streptomycin, and having none of the colon bacteria with this feature which she normally used, his colleague Mary Human substituted the dysentery bacillus, on which T2 acts equally well.

'The next day,' says Luria, 'the T2 mystery was solved, or rather, as often happens in science, it had been transformed into a bigger one.' The juice from the dissolved colon bacteria, supposedly virus-free, played havoc with the dysentery bacillus. In other words, it contained viruses which were fatal to the latter but harmless to the former. But the big surprise was that after a single cycle of reproduction in the dysentery bacillus, it reverted to the original type, and could infect colon bacilli again!

In other words, the virus had not mutated, as Luria had thought at first. Instead the host had imposed a modification on it. This was something quite new. Soon other workers found more 'host-induced modifications': in each case the virus had no 'memory' of any host but the last. Just how the viral nucleic acid is modified by the host – whether by its nucleic acid or by factors in the cytoplasm – remains unknown.

How far this may happen in the disease viruses which affect man and animals is still a matter of study, but it seems probable. Viruses, in fact, began from this time to be thought of less as foreign invaders of the cell, and more as genes which had somehow escaped. As Luria put it, they seem to be 'bits of heredity in search of chromosomes'.

ONE OF THE YOUNGEST biologists ever to receive the award, Joshua Lederberg, at the age of 33, shared the Nobel prize with Beadle and Tatum in 1958. In 1946, when only 21, he and Tatum had proved that the colon bacterium – a favourite experimental object – sometimes reproduces by mating with another of its kind. Normally, of course, bacteria increase by simple division, like cells. By bringing together two strains of bacteria, and showing that some of the offspring possessed characters derived from both types, he proved that a mixing of genetic material – 'genetic recombination' – must occasionally have occurred. (Thus he reversed the method of Mendel, who discovered recombination, knowing that sexual conjunction occurred.) In this way was proved, what was previously uncertain, that bacteria have a genetic system not wholly unlike that of ordinary cells.

But Lederberg's greater achievement, made when he was 28, with the aid of Norton Zinder who was then 23, went much further than this, and revealed a fact so startling that its full implications are still by no means worked out. It was the fact that viruses are capable of conveying genetic information from one organism to another; that is, they can endow one organism with an inheritable characteristic derived from another. This is as if one should convey from a coloured man to a white man the characteristic of having dark-skinned offspring, or vice versa. Obviously, if genes are going to migrate on the backs of viruses the consistency of Mendelian heredity is undermined. The extent to which such transfers may actually occur is of intense interest to evolutionists as well as to geneticists.

Lederberg and Zinder were trying to see if the mating experiment would work with a bacterium of another kind, to wit, *Salmonella,* which causes typhoid fever in mice. They used two strains, each of which lacked the capacity to synthesize a particular amino-acid; as before, they found that some of the progeny were able to live on media which lacked both these amino-acids. 'Genetic recombination' had evidently taken place.

But, with due scientific caution, they did confirmatory experiments to see if a similar recombination would occur with other traits. Each time, no recombination occurred. Puzzled, they put the two strains of bacteria in the two arms of a glass U-tube, separated by a filter which would pass neither

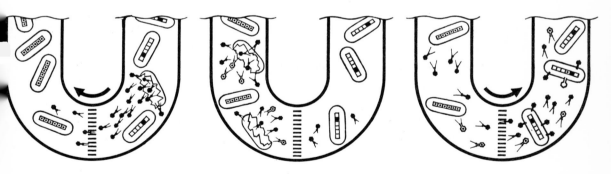

The fact that genetic material *can be transferred from bacteria of one species to another by viruses (bacteriophage) was discovered in 1953 by placing bacteria of two kinds in the two arms of a U-tube, separated by a filter. The central rod represents a chromosome; the black square, 'latent' virus genetic material which has become incorporated with it.*

Occasionally, one of the bacteria in the right arm bursts, releasing live viruses, which pass through the filter and inject their genetic material into bacteria in the left arm. Here they multiply at the expense of the bacterium; some of the viruses thus produced incorporate genetic material from the bacteria on the left.

Some of these pass back through the filter and inject their genetic material into the bacteria on the right, where it becomes incorporated with the bacterium's own genetic material, and remains 'latent'. These bacteria now contain genetic material derived from those on the left, and when they multiply, show features characteristic of the latter.

cells nor bacteria. Recombination in respect of the amino-acid requirements still took place, yet clearly the bacteria were *not* in contact – how then was the genetic information passing from one strain to another?

If one asks, what can pass through a porcelain filter carrying information, 'a virus' is the only answer. And in fact they found that bacterial viruses were present, and were passing through, and entering the bacteria in the second arm. Normally, the phage did not lyse the bacteria, but remained latent. However, when occasionally lysis did take place, some of the resulting viruses were found to have cores of phage-type DNA, and some cores incorporating particles of *Salmonella*-type DNA.

In passing from one bacterium to the next, the phage would pick up one or two genetic units from the first bacterial host and convey them to the new host. This phenomenon was named *transduction*.

This was indeed a discovery of Nobel-award calibre. But only the fortunate chance of using unwittingly a type of phage which does not usually lyse led to the confusion which eventually revealed what was occurring.

By this stage, the classic conception of inheritance had become – as you can see – severely dented. The whole vast edifice of Darwinian thinking was based on the assumption of a systematic transfer of determining factors from parent to offspring. The suggestion that an individual's physical characteristics could be modified by the actual transfer of 'gemmules' or 'pangens' from one to another was an idea Darwinians had never entertained. But here — if only in the specialized world of bacteria – this arbitrary muddling of the hereditary accounts was occurring. Could it be possible that such falsifications could take place in higher organisms? Almost shamefacedly, and in secret, experiments were initiated to test the idea. While experiments with ducks and rabbits are still felt to be inconclusive, the power of tampering with the heredity of viruses has been clearly demonstrated.

IN 1956, HEINZ FRAENKEL-CONRAT, a Prussian who left Germany in the year Hitler came to power, and who has worked in California since 1942, succeeded in the reconstitution of a virus. He chose for the purpose the rodlike virus of tobacco-mosaic. It was already known that it contained RNA and not DNA, and that it had a protein coat comprising all twenty amino-acids. His intention was to try to remove the coat from the nucleic acid and put it together again.

A German, Gerhard Schramm, had shown some years before, when the role of the nucleic acids was not understood, that the protein coat could be broken down into disk-like units and that these could be re-assembled. He also found that the reconstituted rods were no longer infective to tobacco-plants. As we now know, this was because they no longer contained any nucleic acid. By 1955, when Fraenkel-Conrat decided to attempt his experiment, though the infectivity of DNA was clear from the phage-story, many people still thought it was the virus protein which was the infective part. RNA was supposed to have some role in protein-building, but was not recognized as genetic material.

By various ticklish manoeuvres, Fraenkel-Conrat managed to separate the two components. The electron microscope showed only hollow protein rods and nucleic acid strands: no whole viruses were left. He tested each on tobacco plants for infectivity, without result. Then, predicting that nothing would happen, he mixed the two solutions together. Within a few minutes the appearance of the mixture began to alter, and under the microscope were seen perfect TMV viruses. These proved infective. The press burst out in headlines: 'MAN-MADE VIRUS' and 'LIFE CREATED IN THE TEST TUBE'.

This was hardly what Fraenkel-Conrat had done. But further experiment showed that the RNA thus extracted *was* indeed infective to tobacco-plants – it was fragile without its coat, and lost infectivity easily or broke up as it attempted to enter the plant. 'Our conclusion,' reported Fraenkel-Conrat, 'is that infectivity is a property of nucleic acid *per se*.' Meanwhile Schramm, by a different experiment, had arrived at an identical conclusion.

This experiment confirmed the idea that viruses act by modifying the hereditary mechanism of their hapless host. They substitute some of their own blueprints for those of the cell they invade. And, since tobacco-mosaic virus contains only RNA, it showed that RNA carried information as effectively as DNA.

Later, Fraenkel-Conrat found he could take the coats from one strain of TMV and the nucleic acid from another and reconstitute them, thus creating a virus unknown in nature. In such experiments, the new virus always behaved in the same manner as the virus which had donated the RNA – proving the master-role of the nucleic acid as against the protein.

As I write, work is continuing on the mechanism by which DNA controls protein-synthesis in the cell; and on the role of RNA, which seems to have various guises, appearing as working drawing, conveyor-belt and jig on which the protein is assembled. Attempts are being made to determine the base order in specific DNAs, and to ascertain how this code is interpreted. Simultaneously, the structure of the many enzymes involved is under attack. Above all the attempt is being made to duplicate these processes in the test-tube.

In the mid-fifties 'nonsense' DNAs and RNAs were made in the test-tube. The enzymes had been found which would assemble the nucleotides, but the order was meaningless. (Kornberg and Ochoa received Nobel awards for these achievements.) Finally, in 1961, Marshall Nirenberg, in the USA, using one of these artificial RNAs, achieved the synthesis of a protein mole-cule in a test-tube: man had duplicated one primary activity of the living cell! Even before this last fantastic achievement, an eminent biologist had summed up the position in these words:

'Clearly these advances not only bring within reach the artificial synthesis of hereditary material, but open up breath-taking vistas down which one may glimpse the controlled synthesis of proteins and a full understanding of the mechanisms of genetic and enzymatic control over metabolism and growth . . . A major break-through has undoubtedly been achieved, perhaps the greatest in biochemistry since Eduard Buchner established the nature of enzymes.'

THE GREAT SYNTHESIS was emerging. The virus was linked with the cell; the mechanism of heredity was clear, and the relationship of here-dity and evolution had been illuminated by the understanding of mutation. The functioning of the cell had been clarified by the discovery of mito-chondria and the role of ATP. And ATP had thrown light on muscle contraction. But at least one major step remained: to fit into the picture the proteins which compose such a large part of living material.

Proteins were already known to be large molecules, composed of chains of amino-acids. But their varied properties were almost certainly due to the way in which this chain was folded or coiled. No one had managed to work out the chemical structure of these complex molecules – the exact order in which the amino-acid units were arranged – still less to study their arrange-ment in space.

It was Linus Pauling who, with Howard Corey, in 1937 addressed himself to this problem. Pauling was a physical chemist, who had made his name studying the nature of the chemical bonds between atoms, and his work found application in the drug and plastics industries. When he discov-ered that haemoglobin, the red colouring matter of blood, was attracted by a magnet in venous blood and repelled in arterial blood, he became fascina-ted by the biological aspects of his work. With the aid of a team of assist-ants he was able to establish the exact angles at which the bond between two given atoms in a protein must lie, and the spacing between the atoms. Given these limitations, the chain can only take a certain form, and Pauling realized that it must be a coil or helix.

FREDERICK SANGER'S professor told him he was mad, when he an-nounced that he proposed to try to establish the chemical structure of a pro-tein, and that he would work on insulin. He forbade him to work on the subject in his official time.

Sanger's aim was limited to determining which groups of atoms (amino-acids) were involved and in what order: he did not undertake to show how

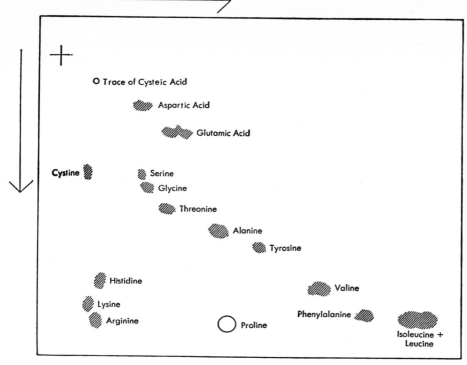

O Trace of Cysteic Acid

Aspartic Acid

Glutamic Acid

Cystine

Serine

Glycine

Threonine

Alanine

Tyrosine

Histidine

Valine

Lysine

Arginine

Proline

Phenylalanine

Isoleucine + Leucine

Paper chromatography *was one of the methods used to establish the complex structure of the insulin molecule. A sample of insulin, broken down by hydrolysis, was placed at the cross in the top left corner. A solvent was allowed to run down the paper, carrying each of the sample's 17 amino-acids with it for a certain distance before depositing it. This distance of travel is known for each amino-acid, so that once they had been 'developed' by a chemical spray, they could be identified.*

these were arranged in three dimensions, whether they formed a coil or not. But this was hard enough; it took him ten years to achieve. His success depended on two developments, paper chromatography, and a method which he found of labelling the end group of a chain of amino-acids, with a substance called DNP.

He soon found that the molecule must consist of two chains: these he was able to separate and analyse separately. One proved to contain 21 amino-acids, the other 30. By shattering the chain many times, establishing the order of the units in each bit, he was finally able to deduce the order in the whole chain. An almost equal effort was required to show how the two chains were joined together. Not until 1955 did success come. The Nobel prize followed in 1958.

Since then, the amino-acid order in many proteins has been established. But how are protein molecules arranged in space?

Max Perutz, working at Cambridge, decided to devote himself to finding a method of elucidating the *spatial* structure of a protein, about the same time that Pauling was speculating, and chose, as being of special interest, haemo-globin, the colouring matter of blood and the substance which is respon-sible for oxygen transport. He hoped the structure might reveal why it takes up oxygen when in the lungs and releases it when in the muscles. He made studies by the X-ray diffraction method which suggested that the structure was a coil. Indeed, certain features of the pictures led Crick to suggest that it was a 'coiled coil'.

After the war Perutz was joined by John C. Kendrew, who felt that there were unrealized possibilities in the application of physical methods in biolo-gy. Some ten years passed without noticeable progress. 'People told me I was wasting my life', he said afterwards, 'and I began to think it might be true.' The central problem was to work a heavy atom into the protein structure, without distorting the molecule in any way.

Kendrew chose to study myoglobin, which acts as a store for oxygen, and is plentiful in deep-swimming creatures such as whales. He rightly inferred from its light molecular weight that it might prove simpler to analyse.

The enormously detailed X-ray patterns were analysed by the new Cambridge computer, EDSAC, and late in 1959 the first results began to come through. Soon the picture was revealed. Haemoglobin consists of four myoglobin molecules fitted together. The work of the two men proved complementary. The four units were indeed coiled coils. Not all the atoms could be assigned a place, however. More detailed studies, involving cal-culations so vast as to be beyond the range of EDSAC, were launched, for eventual computation on STRETCH or ATLAS, the world's most advanced computers, due for delivery in 1962.

Thus, for the first time in the history of biology, the conformation in space of the long, convoluted thread of a protein molecule had been estab-lished. To study the convolutions of the many thousands of other kinds of protein molecule will certainly be a major preoccupation of the next half-century. The victory was achieved by applying the techniques of physics to biology.

To sum up this long chapter: the last fifty years have seen the gradual pushing of analysis down the scale of size from the microscopic to the sub-microscopic and finally to the molecular level. Biology, which in the last century coalesced with chemistry, in this one has coalesced with physics. The three great areas of scientific knowledge have ceased to be separate continents. This is an historic phase, and a major step towards the final unification of all knowledge.

14

WHAT IS LIFE?

FROM A BLIND GROPING with apparently insoluble problems, biology has become a full-fledged science, now in the floodtide of discovery. As far as one can judge, the broad character of all the problems it faces has become clear, and all are seen to be susceptible of solution, even if much time and effort may be required.

Of the six major problems which I listed at the start of the book, we may say that four have been solved in broad outline, though many details remain to be filled in; one is in process of solution; and one remains obscure, with just enough of a break in the clouds to convince one that a solution will be found. The four which, perhaps rashly, I describe as solved in outline are: 1, What accounts for the variety of species of creatures? (The answer being, of course, the process of evolution by natural selection.) 2, What accounts for the resemblances and differences between parents and offspring? (The answer being, the mechanisms of genetics.) 3, How do the bodies of animals and plants function? (This is the whole system of ideas based on chemical processes mediated by enzymes.) 4, How are organisms stimulated to reproduce themselves? (By the mechanisms of fertilization.)

To be sure, there remains, in these fields, a mass of problems to be solved. In physiology, particularly, there are numerous special mechanisms, of which blood-clotting may be taken as an example, which require lifetimes of work. Some of them, including many disease processes (e.g. multiple disseminated sclerosis) are still totally mysterious. Nevertheless, the broad character of these processes is confidently expected to follow familiar physico-chemical lines. Blood-clotting, for instance, involves a score of interrelated chemical reactions, in which many substances unknown a few years ago are produced. But these reactions are all orthodox biochemical reactions. We are rather in the position of a man who knows how a petrol engine works, without knowing how the various engines of different manufacturers vary, and still a bit puzzled by specific bits of equipment, such as the petrol-pump.

The problem which is in process of solution is that of how the body is controlled. We have established that this is by two mechanisms, the nervous system and the hormonal system, the two being tied together in the mid-brain. The way in which nerve impulses act on muscles, and the way hormones regulate cells, are being steadily clarified. What remains baffling is the brain – the most intricate device of which we know. Nevertheless, the last thirty years have seen enormous progress, and the problem no longer seems beyond solution. We can imagine several ways in which the brain *could* perform its tasks, and we can simulate its action on computers. The brain contains about ten thousand million nerve cells, and an equal number of supporting (glial) cells. It may be a very long time before the fine details of its operation are known, but the nature of the task now seems clear enough.

The problem which remains very intractable is that of how an organism develops from a seed or egg. Such work as has been done has tended only to deepen the mystery; but it is becoming clear that complex recognition processes are at work, and new light may be expected as immunology progresses. Still more important, a whole new avenue of approach has been opened up by the latest advances in genetics. Now that artificial D N A can be made in the test-tube, we can hope to explore the effect of inserting it in cells, in place of the natural D N A.

One is struck by the extreme slowness of the growth of knowledge. Only a few minds seem capable of rejecting the popularly accepted false explanations and formulating experiments which will decide the issue. Genius, Albert Szent-Györgyi once said, consists in seeing what everyone has seen and thinking what no one else has thought.

Many of the important steps in biology could have been taken at any time. Technically, there was nothing in Mendel's work which was beyond the reach of the Greeks, and certainly any of the plant-breeders of the eighteenth century could have done what he did, had they been alert enough. Others, such as the discovery of the mechanism of cell division, depended upon technical advances – in this case, the invention of really good microscopes. Yet others, such as the explanation of hormonal action, depended upon the prior growth of chemical knowledge. These physical and chemical advances would have come slowly, if at all, without the stimulus of the industrial revolution.

It seems clear that, at any stage of development, only certain problems are ripe for solution. No one could hope to make significant progress in understanding nerve action or brain function until electrical phenomena were well understood. Early attempts to explain how the embryo developed could never do more than accumulate a stock of observed facts.

Above all, advance takes place by the undermining of established pseudo-theories which all accept. Chief of the pseudo-explanations which has bedevilled biology has been *vitalism* – the attempt to explain the mysterious by postulating some ill-defined force capable, by definition, of doing whatever was seen to be done. The healing of wounds was thus attributed to a *vis medicatrix naturae* or healing force of nature. Today we know it to be based on lymphocytes, antibodies and other explicable mechanisms. The history of biology is the story of the gradual abandonment of such question-begging explanations.

What is striking is how persistent they have been. That Aristotle appealed to such principles is not surprising; we may look indulgently on mediaeval scientists such as Paracelsus, and even excuse sixteenth and seventeenth century scientists such as van Helmont and von Stahl. But when we find von Haller and John Hunter to be vitalists, we begin to raise our eyebrows. Lamarck too was wholly vitalist, and when the philosopher Richerand described life as a succession of phenomena in organized bodies, Lamarck exclaimed: '... it is not these phenomena which constitute life, but they themselves are caused by life.' In the nineteenth century, vitalism, driven out of its main bastions, fights on in the obscurer corners of biology. Bütschli is mocked for making physical models of cells. To Driesch, regeneration seems incompatible with a mechanical explanation, and the vitalist Radl, delighted by Driesch's findings, boldly declared: 'Driesch marks the end of Darwinism!'

Today it is the brain which is the last stronghold of vitalism: the workings of this organ are referred to an ill-defined entity known as 'mind'. Most neurophysiologists, however, are reasonably confident that human behaviour can and will prove wholly explicable in terms of the physicochemical interaction of brain cells. The presence of certain random elements, plus the uniqueness of every individual pattern of neuronal interconnection, derived from the uniqueness of individual experience, suffice to account for individuality and free will.

One major question remains: how did life originate? It no longer seems necessary to refer its origin to the miraculous fiat of a Creator.

A young student, Stan Miller, at the suggestion of his professor, Harold Urey, mixed methane, hydrogen, ammonia and water vapour – the gases which, Urey estimated, comprised the atmosphere of the primitive earth, before ever plants appeared to give off oxygen – and irradiated the mixture briefly with a weak source of ultra-violet light (see p. 348). He found that a number of amino-acids had been created. Later, it was shown that proteins could arise spontaneously, by the linking of these amino-acids. The idea that living organisms might have arisen spontaneously began to

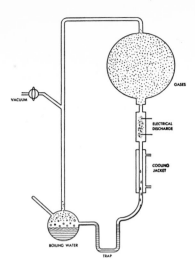

The primeval atmosphere *of the earth, imitated in this apparatus, gave rise to amino-acids when exposed to weak ultraviolet radiation. By spontaneous linking, amino-acids could form proteins – themselves the basic material of life. Thus was recreated in the laboratory a path by which life, over countless millions of years, could have arisen.*

be taken seriously. It was pointed out that living forms could not arise spontaneously today, for the atmosphere is different, and in any case existing forms, more highly specialized, would promptly destroy them.

The Russian biologist A. I. Oparin drew attention to the existence of droplets, known as co-acervates, which had the property of concentrating certain substances within themselves, and rejecting others. Here was something which might have been the forerunner of the living cell. Oparin argued strongly for the spontaneous emergence of life on earth, in a book, *The Origin of Life*, which was widely read by biologists.

Later, in an experiment in which the conditions ruling in outer space were duplicated, it was shown that amino-acids were again produced, widening the area of speculation. In 1959 examination of meteorites by new analytical techniques revealed hydrocarbons of the sort associated with organic substances such as butter. Then, in 1961, Nagy, a Hungarian working in America, found these suggestive objects in a meteorite which had fallen a century before in France. They resemble algae well-known on earth. Other meteorites also proved to contain them, and one of them contained a series of objects never seen on earth. Was it some form of life unknown to man?

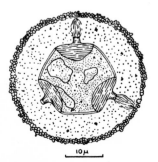

Found in a meteorite, *minute forms like this, resembling algae well-known on earth, are cautiously called by their discoverer 'organized elements'. Are they an indication of life outside our planet?*

CHRONOLOGICAL TABLE

of the History of Biology

DATE	SPECIES	GENETICS	CELL	EMBRYOLOGY	FERTILIZATION
	Aristotle postulates cosmic order			First observation of formation of embryo	Belief in spontaneo[us] generation
1000					
	Observation and classification Plants from New World and Orient compared			*Fabricius* studies development of egg	*Harvey* studies fertilization of deer
1650					
	Revision of classificatory schemes		Cells seen	Preformation epigenesis controversy	Spermatozoa seen
	Conception of 'the ladder of Nature'			Regeneration of hydra seen	
		Maupertuis foresees mutation		Parthenogenesis shown	*Redi* attacks spont[a]neous generation
1700					
	Linnaean system of classification adopted			Epigenesis proved	*Spallanzani* attacks spontaneous genera[ti]on
	E. Darwin foresees evolution by selection				
1800					
	Lamark's evolutionary theory: inheritance of acquired characteristics	Plant and animal breeders	Enzymes discovered Universality of cells asserted *(Schwann)*		Mammalian egg se[en] by *von Baer*
1850					
	Darwin announces theory of natural selection	*Mendel* discovers basic laws	Process of cell division established	First attempt to study embryo experimentally	*Pasteur* demolishes spontaneous genera[ti]on
		Miescher discovers nucleic acid	Chromosomes recognized		
	Much work checking theory of natural selection				Spermatozoa seen entering egg
1900					
		Existence of mutations proved		Concepts of induction and the organizer	
		Fruitfly as genetic tool: mechanism of inheritance established	Intensive work on enzymes		
1940					
		Avery shows nucleic acid carries genetic information	ATP fuel of cell	Cell aggregation studied	Structure of sperm revealed
		Structure of nucleic acids established	How cells make proteins investigated		Method of entry in[to] egg studied
	Natural selection seen in action	Artificial protein synthesized by artificial nucleic acid	Nature of cell membrane established		

FUNCTION	CONTROL	PLANTS	DISEASE			DATE
alen's theory of al spirits	*Galen* cuts pig nerve	Plants as medicines	*Varro:* disease due to invisible organisms			
natomists examine imal and human dy			*Fracastoro* revives this idea			**1000**
irculation of blood	First atlas of brain	Plants studied anatomically	First bacteria seen			**1650**
ea of man as achine	Notion of irritability	Sexual nature suspected				
ymphatics scovered						**1700**
éaumur and allanzani study gestion *ales:* blood pressure *voisier-Priestley* dy respiration *Haller's* first com-hensive textbook physiology	Irritability distingui-shed from nerve force	Root pressure studied by *Hales*	First scientifically based germ theory			
		Sexual nature of plants proved	Inoculation (*Jenner*)			**1800**
ueller's 'Hand-ch': a resynthesis	*Gall:* anatomical studies of brain *Bell-Magendie* law Animal electricity Nerve paths traced Brain chemistry starts	Plants and climate studied	Fungal cause of a disease shown (*Bassi*)			
rnard studies nction of liver	Speed of nerve impulse measured		Nature of anthrax suspected (*Davaine*)			**1850**
	Detailed study of nerve cells	Alternation of genera-tions discovered	*Pasteur* shows decay and fermentation due to micro-organisms			
	Pavlov studies reflexes	Role of chlorophyll studied	*Koch* discovers nature of anthrax	First virus seen		
vlov studies gestion	Integrating role of brain (*Sherrington*)		Chemotherapy	Virus de-monstrated	Phagocytic theory	**1900**
le of vitamins covered	First hormone shown Transmitter substances First electrical studies of nerve impulse Electrical action of brain shown Intensive work on hormones	Plant communities studied Plant growth substances studied by *Went*	Intensive work on bacterial diseases	Bacteriophage discovered Virus crystallized	Antibodies discovered Blood groups distinguished Anaphylaxis demonstrated	**1940**
uscle contraction plained	First kinin isolated	Phytochrome discovered	Antibiotics: bacterial cell wall studied	Virus re-constituted Transduc-tion and latency shown	Immunology emerges as a branch of science Tolerance to grafts conferred	
etabolic role of vita-ins begins to emerge	First studies of inner part of brain Chemical studies of brain	Nature of photosyn-thesis clarified				

1 THE VARIETY OF SPECIES

B.C.

287 Theophrastos dies after writing two treatises on botany.

50 Crateuas makes drawings of plants.
Pliny, *Natural History*.

A.D.

c. 77 Dioscorides, *Materia Medica,* describes 600
plants etc. Standard work for 1500 years.

c. 1300 Albertus Magnus, *On Plants:* best work
on natural history in Middle Ages.

1530 Herbal of Otto Brunfels.

1554 Cordus dies: his *Historiae Plantarum* not
published for another 20 years.

1551–1621 Gesner, *Historia Animalium*.

1555 Belon, *Histoire des Oyseaux*.

1569 Monardes, *Joyfull Newes out of the New
Founde Worlde*.

1576 L'Obel's work on classification.
Rondelet, a friend of Rabelais, publishes
illustrated work on marine animals.

1583 Cesalpino, *De Plantis*.

1599 Aldrovandus publishes 3 vols. on birds.

1602 Aldrovandus, illustrated book on insects.

1619 Bauhin devises binomial system.

1634 Moufet, *Theatre of Insects*.

1660 Ray's catalogue of the flowers of Cam-
bridgeshire: first local flora.

1667 Ray's Flora of the British Isles ('Catalo-
gus'): standard work, foundation of systematic biology.

1676 Ray's book on birds, based on Willughby's work.

1679 Jung's *Isagoge phytoscopica:* ideas which
influenced Linné.

1682 Ray's *Methodus* divides plants into monocotyledons and dicotyledons. Other
major works by Ray, 1686, 1691, 1693:
declares true nature of fossils.

1700 Tournefort's *Institutiones* develops binomial system and prepares way for Linné.

1732 Linné visits Lapps.

1735 Linné, *Systema Naturae*.

1749–1804 Buffon's *Histoire Naturelle* in 44 vols.

1768 Cook circumnavigates New Zealand.

1772 Cook's second circumnavigation.

1796 Erasmus Darwin, *Zoonomia*.
Cuvier founds comparative zoology.

1799–1804 Von Humboldt's explorations in
S. America.

1801–1805 Flinders expedition to Australia.

1803 Lamarck, *Recherches*.

1809 Lamarck introduces term 'invertebrates'
in his best-known work, *Philosophie zoo-
logique*.

1813 Papers by Wells, Prichard and Lawrence
put forward theories of natural selection
and repudiate Lamarckism.

1831 Lyell, *Principles of Geology*.

1831 Patrick Matthew, *On Naval Timber:* an-
ticipates Darwin's views.

1831–1836 Voyage of the 'Beagle'.

1840 L. Agassiz, *Etudes sur les Glaciers*.

1840–1844 Audubon, *Birds of America*.

1841–1865 Sir W. Hooker enlarges Kew Gardens.

1844 Chambers, *Vestiges of the Natural History
of Creation*.

1856 Neanderthal skull found.

1858 Papers on variation of species, by Darwin
and Wallace, read to the Linnean Society, London.

1859 Darwin, *Origin of Species*.

1862–1883 Sir J. D. Hooker and Bentham,
Genera Plantarum.

1868 Marsh lays foundations of American pa-
laeontology.

1871 Darwin, *Descent of Man*.

1872–1876 'Challenger': the first oceanographic voyage.

1900 De Vries propounds idea of mutations.

1931 Wright presents first useful picture of evo-
lution-cum-genetics.

1953–1959 Kettlewell on industrial melanism in
moths: first case of evolution seen to occur.

2 HOW IS THE BODY CONTROLLED?

c. 180 Galen cuts recurrent laryngeal nerve of
pig: discovers that nerves control muscles.

1664 Willis, *Cerebri Anatome*.

1672 Francis Glisson, doctor, surgeon, physiologist, introduces concept of irritability
in his *Tractatus,* when aged 75.

1680 Descartes puts forward idea of reflex action.

1759–1766 Von Haller, *Elementa Physiologiae:*
distinguishes inherent muscular force (or
irritability) from nerve force.

1771 Galvani discovers electric nature of nervous impulse.

1808–1819 Gall, *Anatomie et physiologie du sys-
tème nerveux* (4 vols.).

1811 Legallois first locates a physiological centre in the brain.
Bell, *New Idea of the Anatomy of the Brain:*
differentiates between sensory and motor
nerves.
1822 Magendie's paper on 'functions of the
roots of the spinal nerves'. Bell-Magendie
law.
1833 Mueller's law of specific nerve energies.
1848 Du Bois-Reymond publishes first vol. of
his *Investigations into Animal Electricity.*
1850 Von Helmholtz establishes speed of nerve
impulse (90 f.p.s.).
1861 Broca locates the centre controlling speech.
1863 Sechenov, *Reflexes of the Brain.*
1874 Thudichum publishes his first paper on
brain chemistry.
1875 Caton's first experiments on electrical
response of the brain.
1888 Ramon y Cajal begins to study embryo
nerves, using Golgi staining.
1897 Abel isolates adrenalin.
1902 Starling and Bayliss discover first hormone.
1906 Sherrington, *Integrative Action of the Nervous System.*
Cushing and Lashley in localization controversy.

1907 Pavlov turns to conditioned reflex.
1914 Kendall extracts thyroxin from the thyroid.
1920 Loewi demonstrates importance of acetylcholine in triggering nerve impulse.
Adrian isolates single nerve fibres and
measures their impulses.
1921 Banting and Best discover insulin.
1925 Berger records first human electroencephalogram.
1937 Werle demonstrates existence of a 'local
hormone' (kallidin).
1938 Hodgkin and Huxley show that nerve
impulse consists of a wave of depolari-
zation.
1938-1951 Controversy over nature of transmission at nerve junction: chemical or
electrical? 'soup' or 'spark'?
1949 Roche e Silva discovers bradykinin in
snake venom.
1951 Electrical recording from single cells
achieved, thus proving 'soup' theory.
1951-1952 Technique of electrode implantation developed, leading to discovery of
'pleasure centres'.
1960 Structure of bradykinin established.
1955 Magoun and Maruzzi's work on brain
stem.

3 HOW ORGANISMS FUNCTION

B.C.
500 First known dissection of the human
body.
357 Death of Hippocrates, father of medicine.
350 Aristotle, first marine biologist.
A.D.
164 Galen settles in Rome.
1543 Vesalius, *De Humani Corporis Fabrica.*
1553 Servetus describes pulmonary circulation.
1554 Fernel gives 'physiology' its modern meaning.
1612 Santorio refers to thermometer (describes
it, 1625).
1614 Santorio describes first physiological investigations (metabolism).
1627 Aselli discovers lacteals.
1628 Harvey, *De Motu Cordis et Circulatione
Sanguinis.*
1653 Rudbeck discovers lymphatics.
1661 Malpighi describes capillaries.
1662 Descartes, *Tractatus de Homine:* man a machine.

1669 Lower shows that vagus nerve controls
the heart; discovers nature of respiration.
1674 Mayow on 'nitro-aerial spirits', without
which animals die.
1680-1681 Borelli's posthumous *De Motu* declares physiology to be a branch of physics.
1697 Stahl propounds phlogiston theory.
1718 Hale measures blood pressure of mare.
1737-1738 Swammerdam, *Biblia Naturae.*
1752 Réaumur's experiments on digestion,
with the aid of a kite.
1757 Von Haller's experiments on irritability.
1757-1766 Von Haller, *Elementa physiologiae
corporis humani.*
1774 Lavoisier discovers that oxygen is consumed by respiration.
1774-1775 Priestley destroys phlogiston theory.
1780 Lavoisier and Laplace conclude that respiration is a form of combustion.
1783 Spallanzani's experiments on digestion.
1789 Séguin and Lavoisier make first measurement of human metabolism rate.

1822 Alexis St Martin shot in the stomach; beginning of Beaumont's study of digestion.
1828 Wöhler synthesizes urea.
1832 'Diastase' separated from barley: first enzyme.
1833 J. P. Mueller, *Handbuch der Physiologie des Menschen*.
1838 Liebig establishes biochemistry.
1843 Bernard's first physiological paper.
1850 Bernard shows role of curare.
1850–1855 Bernard shows glycogenic function of the liver.
1857 Pasteur demonstrates that lactic acid fermentation is due to a living organism.
1858 Bernard's work on vasomotors finished.

1878 Kühne introduces the word 'enzyme'.
1894 Fischer establishes nature of enzyme specificity.
1897 Buchner demonstrates that cell-free yeast extract will catalyse glucose.
1904 Pavlov's Nobel prize for work on physiology of digestion.
1911 Funk demonstrates cause of beriberi.
1912 Funk coins the word 'vitamine'.
1913 McCollum isolates Vitamin A.
1922 Evans and Scott isolate Vitamin E. McCollum isolates Vitamin D.
1925 Keilin discovers cytochrome.
1926 Sumner crystallizes urease.

4 WHY DO OFFSPRING RESEMBLE PARENTS?

c. 1750 Maupertuis foresees the chromosomal basis of heredity.
1866–1869 Mendel's papers on heredity (rediscovered by de Vries, 1900).
1869 Miescher discovers nucleic acid.
1876 Hertwig establishes that genetic material is contributed to the offspring from both parents.
1900 De Vries, *Die Mutationstheorie*.
1909 Morgan chooses Drosophila as a means of investigating genetics with the aid of mutations. Postulates 'crossing over' (demonstrated by Sturtevant in 1913).
1918 Muller exposes flies to X-rays.
1940 Beadle and Tatum establish 'one gene one enzyme' theory.

1944 Avery discovers 'blueprint' function of DNA.
1952 Hershey and Chase prove that DNA injected by bacteriophage is what disorganizes bacterium. Phage becomes the fruit fly of the molecular biologists.
1953 Lederberg and Zinder discover transduction.
Crick and Watson propose 'A Structure for Deoxyribonucleic Acid' – a double spiral.
1959 Kornberg and Ochoa awarded Nobel prize for discovery of enzymes that produce artificial DNA and RNA.
1961 Nirenberg, using artificial DNA, synthesizes a protein molecule.

5 UNITS OF LIFE: CELLS AND CELL DIVISION

1665 First drawing of the cell (Hooke).
1765 First drawing of cell division (Trembley).
1818 Bichat founds histology, distinguishing 21 kinds of tissue and relating disease to them.
1830 Purkinje describes the 'germinal vesicle' (nucleus) in the hen's egg.
1831 Brown recognizes the cell nucleus as regular feature of all plant cells.
1838–1839 Schwann and Schleiden found modern cell theory: plants and animals composed of basically identical units.
1840 Koelliker points out that spermatozoa are cells.
1845 Siebold recognizes protozoa as single-celled organisms.

1858 Virchow's Doctrine '*Omnis cellula e cellula*': says that all disease is disease of cells.
1861 Gegenbaur shows that all vertebrate eggs are cells, as Schwann had suggested.

Cell division story
1844 Nägeli sees 'bâtonnets'.
1875 Van Beneden describes division of the nucleus.
1876 Balbiani sees formation of chromosomes.
1882 Fleming sees longitudinal division of chromosomes.
1885 Van Beneden proves that chromosomes persist between cell divisions.
1887 Centrosomes identified and explained.
1888 Chromosomes named.

1898 Benda discovers and names the mitochondria, previously seen by Altmann.

Cell metabolism story
1897 Buchner discovers that cell-free yeast converts sugar to carbon dioxide and alcohol.
1905 Harden and Young show inorganic phosphate responsible for fermentative ability of yeast juice.
1929 Lohmann identifies adenosine triphosphate (ATP) as necessary for the phosphorylation of sugar.

1932 Sir Hans Krebs describes and names the citric acid cycle.
c. 1945 Role of mitochondria revealed.
1956 Tijo and Lavan report that number of chromosomes in human cell is 46, not 48 as believed from early 1920s.
1959 Mongols found to have 47 by Lejeune, Turpin and Gautier.
1962 Cell wall structure revealed.

c. 400 BC Hippocrates, *On Generation* (attrib.): development is from male and female seed.
c. 320 BC Aristotle's coagulum theory.
1280 Albertus Magnus dies.
1554 Rueff, *De conceptu et generatione hominis,* shows development from coagulum.
1573 Coiter the Friesian gives best account of development of hen's egg since Aristotle.
1600 Fabricius, *De formato foetu,* shows stages in development of chicken embryo.
1620 Fienus argues that the soul organizes the foetus.
c. 1640 Sir Thomas Browne tries to test curd theory.
1644 Digby observes development of egg; his *Two Treatises* gives determinist account of development.
1651 Highmore replies; studies embryonic development under microscope.
Harvey's experiments with eggs.
1653 Harvey starts experiments with deer at Hampton Court.
1657 Gassendi, contradicting Harvey, argues that development can be explained atomistically: a brave attempt to tie embryology to physics.
1669 Swammerdam describes metamorphosis.
1672 Malpighi, *De ovo incubato:* traces first hours of development of egg. The first micro-iconographer. Concludes for preformation and launches controversy.
Swammerdam finds butterfly in chrysalis and takes this as confirming preformation.
1677 Leeuwenhoek discovers spermatozoa. Spermism replaces ovism.
1684 Zypaeus reports seeing embryo in unfertilized eggs.

1708 Boerhaave, *Institutiones:* the first chemical embryologist.
1722 Maitre-Jan sees Malpighi's error but is ignored.
c. 1745 Bonnet, on strength of parthenogenesis, becomes preformationist; proposes 'emboîtement'.
1746 Maupertuis, *Vénus physique:* rejects alternatives of ovism and spermism on grounds that children often resemble both parents.
1758 Von Haller studies development of the heart, but turns from epigenesis to preformationism.
1759 Wolff, in *Theoria generationis,* argues that if one sees parts at all, one should, on preformationist view, see them fully formed – which one does not.
1768 Wolff, *De formatione intestinorum:* reply to v. Haller's criticisms; wrecks preformationism. Formulates 'recapitulation' theory.
1802 Lamarck publishes his researches. Much work done on amniotic fluid, chalaza, foetal urine, meconium, egg and shell, membranes, white, yolk.
1828–1837 Von Baer, *Ueber Entwicklungsgeschichte der Thiere* (first book of comparative embryology), proposes germ-layer theory and law of corresponding stages. Discovers notochord.
1840 Reichert introduces cell theory into embryology, showing that egg-segments develop into cells, and organs develop from them.
1840–1860 Rathke (Baer's successor), J. P. Mueller, Huxley *et al.* pursue germ-layer theory, after publication of *Origin of Species.*

Haeckel, Mueller, Kölliker, Virchow, Gegenbaur pursue implications of Darwinism: 'systematic evolutionary embryologists'.

1874 W. His attempts mechanical account of development.

1881 Roux produces a further mechanical theory, and (1888) launches experimental embryology.

1891 Driesch starts to experiment with sea urchins' eggs, and (1900 onwards) rears complete larvae from 2-cell stage.

1903 Roux shows that sperm's point of entry determines planes of first cleavage.

1904 Harrison obtains induction of lens by optic cup.

1907 Wilson demonstrates reaggregation in sponges.

1918 Spemann invents grafting techniques.

1921 Spemann describes 'organizer' effect.

1931 Needham, *Chemical Embryology*.

1940 Waddington, *Organisers and Genes*.

c. 1940 Holtfreter shows that dissociated amphibian cells will re-associate.
Moscona's re-aggregation experiments.

1952 Weiss and Andres inject pigment-forming cells into blood of unpigmented chick embryos.

7 FERTILIZATION

1625 Aromatari says that plants arise from the seed, likewise all animals are born from the egg.

1651 Harvey, *De generatione* ('all things from the egg').

1653 Harvey starts his experiments on the deer at Hampton Court.

1667 Stensen demonstrates follicles in dogfish, and says that roe corresponds to ovary in woman.

1668 Graaf writes treatise on sex organs in man; describes Graafian follicles, which he takes to be eggs.
Redi brings first experimental evidence against spontaneous generation.

1677 Spermatozoa observed.

1694 Camerarius, *Letter on the Sex of Plants*. Grew guesses flowers to be sex organs.

1700 Vallisneri demonstrates that gall insects are not spontaneously generated.

1740 Trembley demonstrates regeneration.
Bonnet shows parthenogenesis in plant lice.

1745 Bonnet, *Traité d'Insectologie*.

c. 1763 Koelreuter's first account of his experiments on artificial fertilization of plants.

1765–1766 Spallanzani seeks to disprove spontaneous generation.
Buffon and Needham seek to show neither sperm nor eggs essential.

1778 Cruikshank finds blastocysts in Fallopian tube of rabbit.

1779 Spallanzani shows seminal fluid necessary to fertilization.

1793 Sprengel puts forward general theory of fertilization in his *Entdeckte Geheimnis*, and (1794) loses his rectorial post.

1823 Amici sees pollen tube approach ovary of plant.

1824 Prevost and Dumas report that sperm are essential to fertilization.

1827 Von Baer discovers the mammalian egg.

1841 Koelliker proves that sperm are derived from tissue cells: egg also a cell.

1846 Amici definitely establishes sexuality in flowering plants; sexuality in Cryptogams established soon after by de Bary *et al*.

1851 Hofmeister erases the distinction between flowering and non-flowering plants, demonstrating alternation of sexual and non-sexual generations – 'the greatest discovery that has ever been made in the realm of plant morphology and taxonomy'.

1856 Pringsheim sees sperm enter female cell.

1861 Pasteur demolishes spontaneous generation.

1873 Bütschli sees two nuclei within one egg.

8 DISEASE AND DEFENCES

1st cent. B.C. Varro suggests diseases due to invisible organisms.

1546 Fracastoro's *De contagione* makes first scientific statement of how infections are transmitted.

1658 Kircher sees 'innumerable worms' under microscope.

1720 Bradley's germ theory.

c. 1740 Buffon's 'organic molecules' as infective agents floating in the air.

1765 Spallanzani shows that Buffon's 'organic molecules' are distinct organisms.

1796 Jenner inoculates James Phipps with cowpox.

1835 Bassi's theory of 'living contagion' in silkworm disease.

1844 Bassi asserts smallpox, bubonic plague, syphilis, spotted fever due to living parasites.

1850 Davaine asserts that anthrax is due to 'bacterides' which he sees in the blood of dead sheep, and (1854) sees 'monads' in stools of cholera patients.

1864 Pasteur invents pasteurization (for wine).

1876 Koch gives three-day demonstration of his work on anthrax, in which he had discovered the sequence of development.

1877 Koch describes techniques of fixing, staining and photographing bacteria.

1880 Laveran sees malarial parasite but is disbelieved; typhoid bacillus and leprosy agent discovered same year.

1881 Koch works out method of culturing bacteria on gelatine.
Pasteur, spurred by Koch's work, turns to anthrax; publicly inoculates sheep at Melun with his 'attenuated culture'.

1882 Koch discovers tubercle bacillus, and enunciates 'Koch's postulates'.
Metchnikov launches phagocytic theory: 'cellular theory of immunity'.

1885 Pasteur inoculates Joseph Meister for rabies.

1887 Buist, Edinburgh infirmary superintendent, sees pox virus; thinks it a form of bacteria.

1888 Richet confers immunity on rabbits, accidentally, with serum from an infected dog.

1898 Beijerinck discovers and names tobacco mosaic virus; viral cause of foot-and-mouth disease demonstrated.

1902 Richet discovers anaphylaxis.
Landsteiner investigates agglutination when blood from different human donors is mixed.

1903 Sir Almroth Wright and others discover 'opsonins' (i. e. antibodies) in blood of immunized animals.

1915 D'Hérelle and Twort, independently, show existence of bacteriophage, viruses which destroy bacteria.

1923 Landsteiner shows M and N factors in blood.

1928 Elford demonstrates size of viruses (from 10 to 3,000 mμ).

1935 Stanley crystallizes virus.

1952 Sexuality discovered in bacteria.

1953 Medawar shows tolerance to grafts can be conferred by inoculating new-born animal or embryo with antibodies from future donor.

1957 Virus structures determined.
Interferon discovered.

1962 Role of thymus established.

9 HOW PLANTS FUNCTION

1648 Van Helmont experiments on plant nutrition.

1672 Grew anatomizes vegetables.

1727 Hales measure root pressure and concludes that plants are nourished in part from the atmosphere.

1772 Priestley discovers that plants give off oxygen.

1779 Ingenhousz's *Experiments on Vegetables:* shows that light is necessary for plants to produce oxygen.

1788 Senebier shows that it is light not heat which is needed.
Knight investigates plant movements.

1796 Ingenhousz concludes plants utilize carbon dioxide.

1804 De Saussure: first quantitative experiments.

1832 Diastase separated from barley: first enzyme.

1837 Dutrochet recognizes that chlorophyll is necessary to photosynthesis.

1840 Liebig shows that plants synthesize organic compounds from carbon dioxide in the air, but nitrogenous compounds from precursors in the soil.

1851–1855 Boussingault demonstrates that plants cannot use atmospheric nitrogen.

1862 Sachs proves starch is a product of photosynthesis and (1865) finds that chlorophyll is contained in the chloroplasts.

1880 Darwin and his son publish *The Power of Movement in Plants,* showing it to be due to 'some influence'.

1883–1888 Engelmann discovers photosynthesis in certain bacteria.

1898 Barnes proposes the term 'photosynthesis'.

1906–1926 Willstaetter and co-workers discover chemical constitution of the chlorophylls.

1910 Boysen-Jensen shows the influence causing plant movements is material.

1923 Frits Went demonstrates plant growth hormones.

1925 Molisch shows that dried leaves will photosynthesize.

1933 Kögl isolates auxins and determines their chemical constitution.

1937 Hill shows carbon dioxide *not* essential to photosynthesis; van Niel suggests water is starting point.

1938 Hill shows that chloroplasts isolated from the cell will photosynthesize in the presence of ferric salts.

1939 Rubid, Hassid and Kamen apply radioactive tracers to study of photosynthesis.

1940 First electron micrographs of chloroplasts (Kausche and Ruska).

1954 Arnon *et al.* discover that chloroplasts alone can photosynthesize. Mechanism of photosynthesis begins to become clearer.

1959 Hendricks *et al.* discover phytochrome, a key enzyme in plant flowering mechanisms, etc.

1961 Calvin awarded Nobel prize for tracing sequence of reactions in photosynthesis.

10 TOOLS AND TECHNIQUES

1545 First botanic garden (Padua).

1555 First use of word 'physiology' in modern sense (Jean Fernel).

c. 1590 First compound microscopes.

c. 1610 Accademia dei Lincei (Lynx-eyed Academy).

1645 The Invisible College founded.

1657 Air pump devised (Boyle, Hooke).

1660 Royal Society founded.

1661 Académie des Sciences founded.

1665 *Philosophical Transactions* of the Royal Society first published.
Hooke's *Micrographia*.

1681 First use of term 'comparative anatomy' (Grew).

1691 Catalogue of Ruysch's museum published (most important prior to Hunter's).

1770 Hill introduces new methods of staining and preserving specimens for microscopic study.

1777 *Botanical Magazine,* first journal in botany, begins publication.

1778 Banks elected President of the Royal Society.

1780 Adams *et al.* devise first microtome.

1785 Hunter's museum established in own building. Finally bought by Government, 1799.

1802 First use of word 'biology' (Treveranus).

1807 First achromatic microscope.

1821 First international congress of biology (organized by Oken).

1828 First electrical stimulation of the brain (Rolando).

c. 1860 First selective biological staining.

c. 1870 First good microtome (His).

1880 First neurone stains (Golgi).

1883 First apochromatic microscopes.

1895 X-rays used by Cannon.

1906 Column chromatography (Tswett).

1907 Tissue culture (Ross Harrison).

1912 X-ray crystallography.

1919 Valve amplifier and cathode ray tube used to study nerve impulse (Adrian).

1925 Electroencephalography (Berger).

1926 Ultracentrifuge (Svedberg).

1933 First electron microscope (Ruska).

1934 L'Héritier and Teissier devise 'population cage' method of studying evolution.

1935 Radioactive tracers used to study metabolic processes (Schoenheimer).

1948 Electrophoretic methods (Tiselius).

1951 Electrode implantation in the brain.

1952 Partition chromatography (Synge and Martin).

1953 Phase-contrast microscope.

SOURCES AND ACKNOWLEDGMENTS

The illustrations on p. 23 are reproduced by gracious permission of Her Majesty the Queen. The sources of other illustrations are listed below, followed by the number of the page on which the illustrations occur. Author and publishers gratefully acknowledge the necessary permissions.

Messrs Abelard-Schuman Ltd: 13

Dr Björn Afzelius: 319

L. Agassiz, *Etudes sur les glaciers*, 1840: 146

American Museum of Natural History: 169

G. Aselli, *De lactibus*, 1627: 65

Ashmolean Museum, Oxford: 22

J. J. Audubon, *Birds of America*, 1827–38: facing p. 121

Dr C. R. Austin: facing p. 321

C. E. von Baer, *De ovi mammalium et hominis genesi*, 1827: 120

C. Bauhinus, *Prodromus theatri botanici*, 1620: 34 (above)

W. Beaumont, *Experiments on the Gastric Juice*, 1838: 250

Sir C. Bell, *Anatomy and Philosophy of Expression*, 1844: 205

P. Belon, *L'histoire des oyseaux*, 1555: 36

P. Belon, *L'histoire naturelle des estranges poissons marins*, 1551: 14

Johannes Beringer, *Lithographiae Wirceburgensis*, 1726: 100

C. Bernard, *Leçons de physiologie expérimentale*, 1855–56: 252

C. Bernard, *Mémoires sur le pancréas*, 1856: facing p. 193

Prof. Marcel Bessis: 195

Prof. Charles H. Best: 289

E. du Bois-Reymond, *Untersuchungen über tierische Elektrizität*, 1848: 212

C. Bonnet, *Oeuvres*, 1779–83: 112

G. A. Borelli, *De motu animalium*, 1680–81: 61

The Editor of *Brain*: 203

Dr Mary A. B. Brazier: 215 (both), 301 (both)

British Empire Cancer Campaign: 261

Brookhaven National Laboratory: 321, 325 (left)

O. Brunfels, *Herbarum uiuae eicones*, 1530–40: 33

Comte de Buffon, *Histoire Naturelle*, 1749: 108, 109

Comte de Buffon, *Histoire naturelle des oiseaux: Les planches enluminées*, 1786: facing p. 80

Bulletin de l'Académie Royale des Sciences de Belgique, 1887: 318

Dr Dean Burk: 276

California Institute of Technology: 323, 327

Central Office of Information: 333 (above)

J. C. Spurzheim, *Physiognomical System,* 1816: 198

Städelsches Kunstinstitut, Frankfurt a/M: 139

W. Stirling, *Some Apostles of Physiology,* 1902: 188–9 (Müller, Schleiden, Schwann)

Prof. Theodor Svedberg: 268 (both), 269

Svenska Linné-sällskapet, Upsala: 75

Svenska Porträttarkivet, Stockholm: 271

J. Swammerdam, *Bibel der Natur,* 1752: 58

J. Swammerdam, *Ephemeri vita,* 1675: 59

Swedish Institute for Cultural Relations: 72

The Syndics of the Cambridge University Press: 293

G. Taliacotius, *De curtorum chirurgia per insitionem,* 1597: 231

Technische Hogeschool, Delft: 237

Thames and Hudson archive: 21, 37, facing p. 64

Sir C. Wyville Thomson, *Report on the Scientific Results of the Voyage of HMS 'Challenger',* 1873–76: 167, 172–6

A. Trembley, *Mémoires pour l'histoire des Polypes,* 1744: 115–17

Triangle, the Sandoz Journal of Medical Science: 308–310

The Trustees of the British Museum: 87, 119, 126 (below), 127 (below), 128, 154, 200–01, 232

The Trustees of the Tate Gallery: facing p. 64

E. Tyson, *Oran Outang, sive Homo Sylvestris,* 1699: 98

University of California: 243, 244

University of Nottingham (Dept. of Manuscripts): 70 (both)

University of Paris (Faculté des Sciences): 253

University of Pennsylvania (Edgar Fahs Smith Memorial Library): 267, 272 (below), 330

University of Upsala: 71

University Zoological Museum, Copenhagen: facing p. 176

U.S. Geological Survey, 1895: 170

Brig. C. H. V. Vaughan, DSO (photograph by courtesy of the National Museum of Wales): 126 (above)

A. Vesalius, *De humani corporis fabrica,* 1543: 25, 27

L. Vincent, *Elenchus tabularum,* 1719: 67 (below)

H. de Vries, *Die Mutationstheorie,* 1901–03: 315

Prof. E. W. Walls: 209

A. Weese, *Die Bildnisse Albrecht von Hallers,* 1909: 86

Wellcome Historical Medical Library: 20, 42, 210

Wellcome Historical Medical Museum: facing p. 81

Dr M. H. F. Wilkins, FRS: 333 (both), facing p. 336

Robert Willis, *Cerebri Anatome,* 1664: 69

Richard Willstaetter, *Aus meinem Leben,* 1949 (by courtesy of the publishers, Verlag Chemie GmbH): 272

Douglas Wolfe Esq.: 336 (top left)

Prof. G. Wolf-Heidegger: 26, 194

Ole Worm, *Museum Wormianum,* 1657: 66

Yale University Press: 258

Prof. Yngve Zotterman: 295

INDEX